$12.50

MORE GHOSTS IN IRISH HOUSES

by JAMES REYNOLDS

In 1947 James Reynolds' *Ghosts in Irish Houses* was published. It was the first of Mr. Reynolds' ghostly collections, and the demand for it was so great that all copies were soon in the hands of private collectors. Today the book commands a very respectable price in the rare book field.

More Ghosts in Irish Houses is a companion volume to this first much-sought-after collection. Identical in format, lavishly illustrated in both full-color and black-and-white, it contains a near double dozen of lilting, chilling, enchanting tales. A glance at the table of contents will suggest the color and wit of the collection. There is such a profusion of tempting stories that it is hard to decide which to read first. Start where you will—with "Potatoes and Babies," "Lilylight of the Blasket Isles," or "The Beautiful Mrs. Oranmore is Dead"—you will be quickly caught in the kind of delight that only James Reynolds and the Irish can give. This is ghostly lore with a silvery glint of difference—a collection for connoisseurs of the fine things of the book world.

ghost stories, told with drama, wit, and the feel for legend and tradition which have made the author's *Ghost in Irish Houses* a collector's item. James Reynolds' haunting apparitions are found from Maine to Florida, from Manhattan's Central Park to the bayous of Louisiana, and he reports on several notorious ghosts of the far West.

$12.50

More Ghosts in Irish Houses

Also by James Reynolds

MORE GHOSTS

IN IRISH HOUSES

James Reynolds

NEW YORK

FARRAR, STRAUS AND CUDAHY

17501

TO
HAL VURSELL

Contents

Foreword ix

The Dandy Gambler and The Sporting Buck 1

Jocko the Monk Dances Finnegan's Jig 19

The Beautiful Mrs. Oranmore is Dead 25

Lira from the Sea 51

Sulphur Burns a Blue Flame 63

God Forbid I Bear a Pooka 71

The Ossary Legend 83

Slippers that Waltz till Dawn 99

Potatoes and Babies 109

Ten Peculiar Apparitions and Ghostly Manifestations 117

    The Black Abbess of Carlingford Castle 117

    The Winged Dagger of Braghee 124

    The Shriek of Slaney 129

    The Dreamer in the Tower 131

    Fatal Foxgloves at Skreen Castle 134

    The Lament of Brian Healy 138

    The Old Rock Creature 141

    White Horse Shod with Silver 146

    Conflagration on Christmas Eve 147

    Dunmahon Castle Lifts Its Gory Head 151

The Diffident Earl of Mara   153

The Astounding Luck of Maeve Greatly   169

Lilylight of the Blasket Isles   181

The O'Rohan Blazonry   201

Aggie the Post   209

Kilfaddon's Reach and the Dark O'Foyles   219

The Twelve Dead Queens   231

Little Miss Costello's Shop   239

The Thicket of Gold   251

The Sorceress: Horror upon Horror Piled   259

Veiled Lady in the Shuttered House   265

LIST OF COLOR ILLUSTRATIONS

The Dandy Gambler and The Sporting Buck   *facing page*   1

Lira from the Sea   51

Potatoes and Babies   109

The Diffident Earl of Mara   153

Kilfaddon's Reach and the Dark O'Foyles   219

Foreword

IN the foreword of my former book *Ghosts in Irish Houses,* of which this one is a
younger brother bearing strong family resemblance, I said: "The stories I have
chosen present a panorama of the infinitely varied Irish scene." The present
collection is, I believe, equally representative of the intensely personal Irish ghost.
When I compile a book that deals with a controversial and, as in the case of supernatural manifestations, a suspect theme, I have ever in mind Cervantes' admirable summary of the reaction of the public in general to whatever book may be
presented for it to read and criticize. "He who publishes a book," said the creator
of Don Quixote, "runs a great hazard, since nothing can be more impossible than
to compose one that may secure the approbation of every reader." With this
quotation as my standard against attack, I offer my ghost stories equally as legends
of a given countryside and as chronicles of the frightening, dangerous, or humor-
ous wanderings of the unquiet dead.

If anyone asked me to say why ghosts in Ireland hold my interest more than
ghosts anywhere else, I would answer that they are more immediate and glowing
in intensity. When ferreting out details of supernatural occurrences in the remote
"back country" of Ireland—such inland counties as Roscommon, Monaghan and
Tipperary whose boundaries at no point touch the sea—I have invariably found
that the countrymen and the tinkers or "people of the roads" are the real gold
mines of information. That these gentry invent details and embroider preposter-
ously, only adds colour of passing richness to the tales they tell.

I have called my stories *More Ghosts in Irish Houses,* although some of the manifestations described take place out of doors. For instance, there are the fiery float-

ings in space of Glana O'Herlihy in "The Sorceress," which do not occur within any house. Nevertheless, Glana's horrendous Ratha Castle in County Tyrone—now a flame-riven hulk whose crag bastions, hewn from the living rock, are scarcely discernible—looms always as the lair from which the sorceress' ghost might still at any time pounce on an unwary traveler.

I was twelve years old when I encountered my first ghost—a tall, hollow-eyed, cadaverous creature in a tattered black military cloak who more closely resembled a huge bat than any man out of Gaelic history. He was of the class called "unknown" ghosts. That is to say, he has been seen by many persons, and always striding across a bridge over the River Nore in County Tipperary, yet there has never been any story to account for his wanderings.

Since I met my "unknown" ghost, I have seen more apparitions in various countries of the world than I have ever documented or even can count. There are those in this world who may dwell for years in notoriously haunted houses, where unquiet reigns to the degree that others flee the place, and yet never see nor hear any untoward happenings. Authorities on supernatural lore say that such people are of a nature entirely unresponsive to ghostly manifestations. My own nature is the direct antithesis. When accosted by ridiculers and unbelievers, I can only repeat Sir Arthur Conan Doyle's retort to Margot Asquith, Lady Oxford, when she baited him too acidly, before the rapt guests at an Asquith dinner party, about a certain ghost of whom he was telling. Sir Arthur looked Lady Oxford coldly in the eye and said, "If I feel a vibration and think strongly that I see an apparition, then I have definitely seen it." There was a pause as he held the lady's gaze. "You can say the same thing, Lady Oxford, for you are looking at one now." A few weeks later Sir Arthur died.

Besides writing about ghosts that I have seen myself, I have traced the stories of scores of others of whom I have only heard, in an attempt to learn in minute detail what motivated their desire, when in the state of what seems largely fictitious "peaceful death," to arise and wander the earth. The events which led up to these supernatural manifestations are in many cases dramatic human documents.

For stark example, there is in this book the tale "The Beautiful Mrs. Oranmore is Dead." What first attracted my attention to the story of Helena Oranmore, one of the greatest beauties of her time, was the change that took place in the life of this fashionable, witty and improbably beautiful woman at the very height of her celebrity. As a crested heron, effortlessly and carelessly soaring the empyrean, heedless of the falconer slipping the jesses from his gyrfalcon in the plains below, is suddenly taken unawares by the beak and talons of the lethal hawk, so was Helena Oranmore untimely pierced to the heart by Fate. From that day out, her spiritual journey down the pathless way to the shades of death is a tragic saga of the Edwardian period.

In direct contrast there is the heart-warming story of "Aggie the Post" who delivered mail to outlying farms and country houses in remote Connemara—not only letters, by a long shot, but even five Easter bonnets to five different women all on the same day. For as Aggie the Post said firmly, "I am a servant of the crown; I do as I'm bid."

A reviewer once said of me, "Reynolds is hugely addicted to pageantry." He could not have been righter. I myself could add that I am as hugely addicted to ghosts as well, and to the telling of their horrendous, dank, or shimmering stories.

JAMES REYNOLDS

The Endless Mountains Lodge
Bedford Springs, Pennsylvania
April 14, 1956

The Dandy Gambler
and The Sporting Buck

CARRIGHIVORE CASTLE, COUNTY KILKENNY, 1755

AT THE HOUR of high noon on a brilliantly sunny June day in the year
1755, a tall man walked restlessly up and down the quay at the fishing
port of Dundalk in the County of Louth. Lovely Louth, where the silvery-
green hills—or "miniature mountains" to the farmer tilling the springy turf fields
—undulant as ocean swell, thrust foothills into the Irish Sea, causing them to be
called in song and poetry the Sea-Nymph Mountains. The man was attired, from
crimson lacquer heel to crown of ribbon-tied powdered peruke, in a style of some
opulence. It would seem to the casual observer not acquainted with the reason
for this splendour that it was ostentation, if not downright faulty taste, for any
man of whatever rank to display such haberdashery at uncomfortably humid midday in a small fishing village.

But hold. What casual observer would chance to know this man's condition
in life, or his present agitation? He was the Right Honourable, the Marquess of
Mountgarrett, yclept the Sporting Buck, or, by his intimates, Johnny the Rake;
nonpareil of fashion, paragon in the stylish sports of the day, and one of the ten
members or "fingers" on the Devil's Two Hands, a small and fanatically exclusive
club of incorrigible offspring of aristocratic fathers. It was not remarkable that his
lordship should be seen in an obscure port, dressed to the teeth at hot high noon,
for he was an infatuated if visibly aging lover, awaiting, in heat that had nothing
to do with the thermometer, his adored mistress who was scheduled to arrive by

1

packet boat from Le Havre "any hour after sunrise" her letter from Paris had said.

If one knew the full facts, Lord Mountgarrett had been forced to leave his inamorata, the sultry and flagrantly tempestuous beauty Amberia Carloniani, in her native Venice—vastly against his own and Amberia's desires—and hasten home to his demesne of Carrighivore Castle to attend the obsequies of his mother. Now, three weeks after his departure at a moment's notice from Venice, "the red-gold Carloniani" of the long auburn tresses in the true Titian tradition, was joining him as the two had planned should he find it impossible to leave Ireland within the month and return to Venice. Wrapped in his thoughts, for the most part those picturing with a painter's as well as a lover's eye the ravishing curves and warm ivory flesh of Amberia, he heard a bell in the harbour master's tower above the quay ring out shrilly upon the quiet air of noon. Mountgarrett was instantly alert, peering through his quizzing glass towards the sea. Through the narrow entrance to the mole the trim black-and-white French packet "Étoile de Rouen" sailed slowly, stately as a swan, into harbour.

Eager as a youth for the sight of his first love (though if the truth were out he had long ago lost count of his amours), Mountgarrett was first up the gangway directly the navvies hoisted it aboard the packet. It was but a moment before the crimson-and-white furbeloved Venetian beauty, who had caused such open admiration among the passengers on board ship, was enfolded, a confusion of veils, necklaces, ribbons and ruffles, within the arms of her ardent Irish lover.

And so the idyl that had begun on a note of frantic ecstasy in Venice in Mountgarrett's fiftieth year, when his amatory prowess was, from overindulgence, slightly chancy as against the fresher viewpoint not only of Amberia's expectations but of what was decidedly her due in bed, was all set to flower—a second blooming at Kilbarry House, a small but charming residence in the simpler Palladian taste which had once been the dower house for the ladies Mountgarrett but lately had been maintained in almost cloistered calm as the abode of Johnny the Rake's mother.

It was this particular curlicue in Mountgarrett's elaborate design for living, of "seating" his Italian mistress *in flagrante* at Kilbarry, that had so outraged the members of his family when they gathered in the darkly curtained library of Carrighivore Castle to hear the reading of the monstrously involved will signed on her deathbed by that congenitally pious, extremely plain-faced woman Arantha,

Marchioness of Mountgarrett who, born Arantha Tredegar of Meryoneth, Wales, had "for her sins," she continuously whined, borne Johnny to blight her days.

The assembled Tredegars and the Clonallens, his father's family, had habitually squabbled violently whenever the two clans met. Now for the reading of the will there reigned for a brief space an ominous quiet. Barrister McGoffiny finished reading the long list of "I hereby bequeath." He wiped his lead-rimmed spectacles on an immense square of bright canary-yellow silk, which did double duty as a muffler and a sort of tent under which McGoffiny in his own house snored away his after-dinner nap, and left the library preparatory to returning forthwith to his chambers in Dublin to wrestle with the intricacies of Lady Mountgarrett's meandering and vague last testament. Johnny rose from his chair beside an open window giving on the paddock, to escort McGoffiny to the door and see him settled inside a four-horse coach which he had provided from the amply-furnished Carrighivore stables for the barrister's comfort during the tedious drive to Dublin.

Directly the two men had left the library, pandemonium burst the gates of sound. Everyone appeared to be talking at once, though it was the stentorian-voiced Welsh Gwenillian Tredegar who attained and held the floor against all bidders until she had had her say. Aunt Gwenillian rallied the members of her family to her cause.

"Look you—Johnny's past extravagancies have shocked us all. Two wives dead in their beds from grief and ill-usage by this libertine nephew of mine. My poor dear sister"—her eyes flew heavenward and the lady hastily traced the sign of the cross on her ample sable-velvet bosom, adding portentously, "God rest her tortured soul. Again look you, I hold that my sister Arantha's will has been tampered with. I would not trust either Johnny Mountgarrett or his henchman, that Dublin quill-finagler McGoffiny." But the remaining members of the assembled "bereaved" were not so sure that this wild statement was wise for the airing. Jason Clonallen, who had little to gain and nothing to lose, in any case, offered his opinion.

"No, Gwenillian, I think you leap too far and too fast. McGoffiny is all right —a good man—none better. Has handled our affairs for years. And Johnny don't care a tinker's curse what we do. He's always ridden his own course. Not our style maybe. The truth is Arantha would have left every farthing she possessed to the church if Johnny hadn't seen her drift and, in some manner we do not ken, forestalled her. So the small bequests you are all so agitated about will have to be endured. Johnny will do as he pleases for anything in skirts who catches his fancy.

I for one will sit on the fence and hugely enjoy myself watching the lot of you chew your bitter bile—and watching as well that ferocious Italian piece ride his lord-ship Mountgarrett down at a gap. I wonder who the fellow will be."

Channing Garroty, a purported "favourite" cousin of the deceased Lady Mountgarrett, a flinty-eyed waster who had, to his manifest chagrin, been fobbed off by "dear Arantha" with a few parcels of clothing and jewels of no particular worth, spoke up. "What fella will be *what,* Jason?"

Jason smiled wryly. "Some strapping bucko in the world of fashion, handling a full purse with loose strings, though damn me if I know who, will follow our rakish Johnny, perhaps sooner than he expects, in the exhausting bed-battle of the stormy Carloniani. I too knew Amberia, in Rome a year or so ago. She loves 'em lustily but not for long."

And so it turned out that the assorted Tredegars and Clonallens departed from Carrighivore loudly mouthing threats of vengeance for such shabby usage as all proclaimed had been dealt out to them "by the deviousness of his high-and-mightiness" Lord Mountgarrett. The only relative who remained on friendly terms with him was Cousin Jason, who hoped for a bid to stay at Kilbarry House. He regaled a group of cronies at the Kildare Street Club, when the roast had been done justice and port was going the round, with highly-spiced tales of the eccentricities of Amberia Carloniani. Rising from the table, he smiled ruefully at his friends. "I'm not the same bucko I was before I met Amberia, and I'm still a good few years younger than Johnny."

Kilbarry House, situated in the rolling meadow lands of Kilkenny, lay hidden from the view of passers-by on the frequented coach road from Dublin to Clonmel in Tipperary, by a high stone wall enclosing the modest reaches of the demesne. The beautifully spreading trees in the park were immemorial beeches, both the silver and russet variety, the yew walk was famous for density of foliage and was richly green as the deepest Han Dynasty Chinese jade. The house itself had been built of Connemara stone, bone-white in the sunlight but with the curious chameleon-like habit of assuming a dark amethyst-purple in the shadows. Of two minds the style of architecture as well, having the purity of proportion and line by which the Italian Renaissance master Andrea Palladio of Vicenza so influenced the architects of the civilized world, while the details, such as the delicately pil-lared entrance porch, the gracefully swagged pediment and Greek amphora-shaped urns which acted as finials on the enclosed balustrade at the roof line, showed definite Regency influence of the period when the classic motif was so successfully employed to lighten the noble dignity of baroque taste.

The interior of Kilbarry had been done up originally in light, luminous colours. A primrose-yellow brocade salon. The Verte Emeraude Chamber, as Johnny's French grandmother Franceville had called her intense malachite-green drawing room. But during the tenure of his mother, when Johnny seldom visited the dower house, all these delicious-coloured, elegant, airily-furnished rooms had been shut tightly because of the pious dowager marchioness' predilection for more sombre colours. Her bedchamber was hung with dreary moleskin-gray corded silk. The Crimson Salon, shadowed and ill-heated in winter, of a particularly darkling sepia tone, had been her retreat wherein she had received visitors. Here she dined by the light of one candle, for the lady's parsimony marched with her extreme piety.

For the advent of dashing Amberia Carloniani, who lived in a perpetual extravaganza of brilliant, even garish colours flicked over with gold and silver threads and galloons and hung with flashing jewels, the doors and windows of Kilbarry were thrown wide to the summer sunlight. An army of servants brought from Carrighivore yanked the old mildewed dust covers from the long-shrouded furniture and used them to cleanse the murky windowpanes.

Arriving, in a red-and-yellow lacquered coach drawn by four black Spanish barbs, at the stone plinths guarding the entrance to Kilbarry demesne, Amberia, a vision of coolness in white silk mull garlanded with red ripe cherries, her wide-brimmed chip hat fly-away with red and green taffeta loops, first noted that the plinths were topped by the lead image of chanticleer heralding the rising sun, the Norman device of the marquesses Mountgarrett, whose name out of Normandy had originally been Montois.

Unaccountably Amberia, whose laziness about taking any unnecessary step out of doors was proverbial, ordered the coachman to halt. A footman let down the coach step and the new chatelaine *pro tem* of Kilbarry House approached at leisurely pace the shallow flight of marble steps leading to the green lacquered front door. As it was swung wide and welcoming by Marko, the butler, the lady entered the flower-decked hall; her indigo-blue eyes, set in heavily-drawn lines of mascara, took one sweeping look about her and liked mightily what she saw.

Hard on the wheels of the coach which had borne Amberia from Mountgarrett House in Dublin, came the marquess himself. He had ridden his gray hunter at a perishing pace, considering the summer heat, and in no little rage because Amberia had left his town house alone half an hour earlier than the time he had set to accompany her in the coach to Kilbarry. So it turned out that his lordship was not in the best of moods when he flung himself off his gray and into the Primrose Chamber, where Amberia was taking a soothing cup of chocolate. But the sight of the scarlet-and-white deliciousness of the lady spurred his ardour to the point that the chocolate was never drunk, for Amberia was whirled upstairs into the White Rose bedchamber where at tall, wide windows the light filtered in through the leaves of a russet beech and the afternoon wore away to a cool starlit twilight in the dalliance expected of two lovers hot for each other and domiciled in the silences of a country retreat.

For a fortnight neither Amberia nor Mountgarrett left the demesne of Kilbarry. Surprisingly the heat held on, intermittently breeze-cooled, sometimes cloudy, but without rain for days. The drouth was ominous. The farmers crossed themselves and murmured when Johnny, out riding, met them, "Is it the world's end, sir, yer lordship?" Often he and Amberia retired to the White Rose Chamber after an early *souper froid* under the russet beech—a sort of symbolic tree by this time, for from under its shade the two could look upwards to the room where they "all the pleasures proved."

Then came the day of restlessness for Johnny. He decided suddenly early one morning to ride his gray, Conqueror William, over to Balronal Castle, seat of his crony Rathmarty near Clonmel, to look at a gamecock which had been advertised for sale in the monthly *Gentleman's Gazette*. It was often said of Mountgarrett, behind his back and to his face, that he "defined all the fashionable vices." He would laughingly retort to the direct accusation, "Too true, with reservations. One or two I skip as not my métier." Whereupon there would be great wonderment, even a bet, if the bettors could discover which *two* he eschewed. Among sports, it was the vice of gambling on the outcome of a cockfight that held most allure for the Sporting Buck. At Carrighivore, in a glade of ash and alder trees beside a sheet of ornamental water, he had built himself a small, perfectly appointed theatre to be used as a cocking main *al fresco*. Winter or summer, it mattered not, prodigious sums of money bet on the victory of "Old Rowley" of Gascoigne's or "Raker Red" exchanged hands over the curved backs of rococo cocking chairs. The rakes of Dublin participated, as well as more sedate country squires sitting astraddle their chairs around the main.

So Johnny went off to Balronal, leaving Amberia to her beauty sleep which he knew would consume the entire forenoon.

The red Chinese lacquer clock on the landing of the staircase had just chimed eleven when Amberia was awakened by the clatter of hoofs. A horse was being ridden at all-out speed up the driveway paved with crushed oyster shells. Not being aware that Mountgarrett had ridden away from home that morning, Amberia, still half asleep, surmised that the horseman, whoever he might be, had on some business come to see the master of Kilbarry. She was somewhat surprised when a few minutes later Kilty, her maid, scratched at the bedroom door. *"Avanti—or—er—come you in,"* she called out.

Kilty stood halfway in the open door. "Madam—it is his honour Mr. Denis Daly from Dublin below. He asked fer the master an' him out and away. So now he asks may he be after seein' herself. Take yer time, he says. There's no hurry on 'im, the morn."

Amberia sat up, her feet swung over the edge of the bed. She yawned widely. "Denis Daly—I have not met him. Who is he, Kilty?"

"Well, Madam,"—a shade nervously she creased the French rose rug with the toe of her buckled brogan—"they calls 'im in Dublin the Dandy Gambler. He's the great crony ave his lordship. The twa ave thim's a grand, great pair together." She hesitated; then, noticing the look of extreme interest in the eyes of the beautiful but slightly disheveled lady before her, took the plunge. "They—all an' either do be callin' thim the Flamin' Rakes in the way they do be burnin' the wits out ave all wimin. It's a caution, so it is, from a tweeny below stairs to a duchess in 'er coach—no woman's a virgin in 'er own mind after she's clapped eyes on either ave 'em."

Her lips drawn to a thin line of defiance, fearing the worst of tirades against her, Kilty awaited the blast. But Amberia lay back on the coverlet and roared with gales of laughter, great shouts of lusty merriment. Finally, her breath still choked with laughing, she leapt off the bed.

"Oh, Kilty—I have—as you say—convulse. I will see this Denis the Flame. I have a tenderness for his sort. And"—she wagged her finger at the now beaming Kilty —"I have not been a virgin in my own mind or anyone else's since I was rocked in a cradle. Go down now—I come in five minutes."

It was in fact a good half-hour before Amberia, resplendent for this early hour of day in lilac silk and rose-pink ribbons, came slowly down the stairs. Denis

Daly, tall, lean, his hair as red as the plume-like tail of Reynard of the hedgerows, came forward to greet her. His smile was wide and provocative, his eyes admiringly tender. In a flash Amberia of Venice, Italian Aphrodite and sundry other redundant appellations, in effect fell flat on her face in love.

In her complete capitulation to love, oblivious of the reservations and restrictions so galling to her lovers by which she had conducted her legion *affaires de coeur* previously, Amberia, her true Latin emotional intensity unveiled, would have found herself the central figure in sheer disaster if more cautious Denis Daly had not arranged their cloaked and masked rendezvous in Dublin. As a notable Lothario he had conducted scores of clandestine meetings with married ladies, or with those even more closely watched who were at the time "under the protection" of some fashionable Dublin rake or other. It was decided that an elderly woman cousin of his who conducted a dressmaking establishment in a spacious house fronting on Dame Street should be consulted in the interests of fashioning an autumn wardrobe for Amberia.

For a space of weeks good fortune favoured Amberia and Denis famously. The first raptures of having his inamorata all to himself night and day in the charming seclusion of Kilbarry had palled on Johnny Mountgarrett sooner than he would have thought possible on the hot day when he idled, restless as a fractious horse, on the quay at Dundalk awaiting Amberia's arrival from Paris. Now it was here for a dinner and cockfight or there for a boxing match featuring "Prodder" Queston, the British boxer under the patronage of Lord Randerly. Prodder's star seemed impossible to dislodge from its zenith. He was fighting all the crack Irish pugilists at semiprivate boxing matches held at country houses, according to the *Gentleman's Gazette* "the secluded seats of the mighty."

Amberia, soon after her tumultuous meeting with Denis Daly, had left Kilbarry House to take up residence at Mountgarrett House in Dublin. At first so enchanted by the sylvan beauties of the country demesne which had been fitted up for her exclusive use, she now vowed that country air with its gusty rainstorms and damp mists threatened her health. Johnny seemed not to notice the fact that he seldom encountered Amberia during the daytime in his town house. In the evenings he escorted her to routs and card parties held in the houses where ladies of suspect virtues were received. She was always a ravishing vision, even though her taste favoured the garish juxtaposition of bright colours and far too many jewels. It was a great cross to Amberia that she could not be presented to "the Viceregals" at the Dublin Castle balls. But even the unpredictable Johnny Mountgarrett, who flouted convention and social usage right and left if it so humoured him, dared not essay this sort of shindig. He still visited Amberia's bedchamber occasionally, but with less and less ardour, for he found her mind distant, her libido unresponsive to his advances, and her disposition full of crotchets the like of an Abbey Street strumpet wary of counterfeit coin.

The autumn racing season at Phoenix Park opened auspiciously. A new stewards' pavilion of whitewashed stone, its tin lambrequin awnings painted in red and white stripes, was christened by a big splurge of festivity. But again it was impossible for Johnny to introduce Amberia to the stiff-backed British vice-regal pair during the reception, or to procure for her an invitation to the ball to be held that night at Dublin Castle. Amberia flew into a towering rage. Her facile tongue spouted abuse and recriminations.

"I will not be so treated by these proud and so ugly Irish women. So old they are, too. Who are they, with their long noses red at the tip and their big square jaws, to say I am a whore? What woman isn't if she gets the chance? You are too blasé, and always away at the sports. Of you I am at an end. Of Ireland I am at an end long ago." Amberia swept into her bedchamber and slammed the door in Mountgarrett's face. From that night out she barred her door. In a few days Johnny took himself off to London and by so doing gave Amberia and Denis a free hand.

It was when he returned to Dublin just before the Christmas holidays that Johnny was informed of the liaison between his friend the Dandy Gambler and his mistress Amberia. Mountgarrett surprised his informant more than a little by stating, "Oh, I have known for some time past how the wind blew in the Italian quarter. I know Denis, too. He'll ditch her soon just as she ditched me. That's what I'm waiting for. I have a card of my own to play when the time comes." So saying, the Sporting Buck sat down at the card table to play at the new game of faro. Candles were changed three times that night in the red-brocade card room at McChancy's Gilt and Silver Club in Abbey Street. At sunrise, when the third set of bayleaf-scented "waxers" had guttered in the sconces, Johnny Mountgarrett rose from the table. All through the night he had been a consistent winner.

For breakfast he took a roast quail and a goblet of French brandy offered him by the club steward as "Smuggled, lovely as a quencher an' a reviver, yer lordship," and ordering his coach to be sent around to the club from the Mount-garrett stables, he posted straight out to Kilkenny and Carrighivore.

As for Amberia, her luck flew out of the window as the first rays of an October sun reached in at her lodgings in a tall old house in the Smock Alley Quarter and gilded her rather too full and rounded cheek. First she received the shocking news that Denis Daly, habitually smiling, silent, devious, a mystery man to Dubliners, had flown the coop. His debts, forever mounting to alarming proportions, had engulfed him. Cornered by Amberia, who created a scene of impressive force at Daly's lodgings, his valet "believed" his master had gone to Paris. No—he had left no address. The man coughed and ventured, "Nor did he pay me arrears, arragh. And they amountin' to half a year's wages. I'm left that destitute. Me lady ye'll understand."

But Amberia wasn't interested in advancing any moneys to a valet when her own future was in jeopardy. While in the heat of his passion, Mountgarrett had been generous with money and with presents of jewels. Denis had been the reverse. Two or three times when his gambler's luck had gone awry he had borrowed substantial sums of money "to go on with," he had said. Now he had gone on with a vengeance and with her money too. So—there was only one thing for Amberia to do. She must humble her pride and ask Mountgarrett to take her back. Perhaps, she reasoned, if he had lost all his original interest in her charms he would at the least provide her with passage back to Venice. After all, Amberia philosophized as she surveyed herself in a mirror of wavy glass hung in a dark corner of her dressing closet, her figure was perhaps too full for the taste among fastidious Irish bucks, but to the Italian male her abundant curves were the perfection of ripeness.

Carefully, from her still plenteous and fashionable wardrobe, Amberia dressed herself becomingly but not too richly, lest she seem in opulent circumstances and so queer her pitch, and set out in a hired chaise for Kilkenny. A day of rain in torrents, of driving mist, and a foreboding. In all ways it was a drear thing that she did at all, for the Old Woman of Gonn, handfast with Death himself, rode athwart her coach top, though little did she know it at the time.

When Amberia, drenched to the skin from the deluge that penetrated the leather cabriolet hood, reached Carrighivore late in the afternoon, Mountgarrett was in his book room arranging on shelves a set of books on the art of cockfighting compiled by Joshua Babcombe, an ardent English enthusiast who had traced every facet of the exhilarating sport since the days when the Roman Emperor Tiberius set Greek and Asian gamecocks to battle to the goriest death on the terrace of his Villa Tiberio on the Island of Capri. His interest probing deep in a book illustrated with aquarelle paintings, Mountgarrett wished no interruption from anyone. Certainly not from his castoff and, in his lexicon, perfidious Italian mistress, wet or dry.

Amberia made the dire mistake of outcry when he point-blank refused to receive her. However, considering the demented condition of the weather she had driven through, along tortuous quagmire roads, he ordered a footman to conduct the protesting lady to a bedroom where a fire of turf was already laid. Here she might rest and repair the damages to her appearance caused by buffeting gales of rain-sodden wind. He issued an order to Amberia that although he considered that he had nothing whatever to discuss with her, he would entertain her at a repast to be set in front of his book-room fire at precisely six o'clock. Amberia's temper had raged at the affront of his refusal to see her immediately on her arrival, and she made the disastrous error of demanding to speak with his lordship immediately she had arranged her gown and repainted her face. For half an hour the harassed footman was sent skeltering up and down stairs bearing vituperative demands to Mountgarrett, who sent back to the virago Amberia equally furious but adamant messages adhering to his purpose of receiving her at table at six o'clock and not a damned instant sooner.

The upshot was that Amberia sailed down the staircase, her panniered skirts belling out like the sails of a galleon dipping to battle attack in a choppy sea, and beat with both her clenched fists upon the Barbados-mahogany panels of the book-room door. This fishwife attack on his privacy by unwanted Amberia, Johnny Mountgarrett viewed as more than too much. Now Johnny was a man of congenitally high temper, swift to mount to fantastical heights, though commonly kept strongly in check lest he do the object of his wrath an injury. His wrath burst the bounds of reason when Amberia proceeded to grasp one of a pair of rare and favourite Chinese porcelain vases, amethystine silver, illusive in hue, lovely to Johnny as the first luminous prelude to summer dawn. Shrieking as if demented, Amberia crashed the vase to smithereens against the door. A kind of red rocket seemed to explode in Johnny's brain. Seizing a riding crop that lay across a table by the fireplace, he ran to the door and flung it open. Amberia, leaning against the newel-post, was using her lawn fichu to staunch the blood that flowed from a deep cut on her upper arm where a ricocheting shard of porcelain from the broken vase had struck her.

Instantly reading the look of hatred in Mountgarrett's eyes as he advanced towards her, his riding crop raised as if to strike, she turned to run up the stairs. In her haste to reach her chamber and bar the door against a chastisement, she failed to realize that the folds of her long skirt had become tangled in one of the paste buckles on her shagreen slipper. Amberia stumbled, clutching at her skirt. She had nearly reached the top of the long steep flight of stairs when her ankle turned, causing so sharp a pain that she lost her balance and plunged backwards down the stairs. Her head struck the carved oak newel-post with such force that when Mountgarrett stooped to lift her up, it lolled crazily on her broken neck.

No one—guest in the house or servant—had seen the mortal outcome of the battle of words between Mountgarrett and Amberia. But there had been plenty of keyhole listeners, guest or servant no matter, who had heard with varying degrees of misgiving—as one listener reported later on to the lord lieutenant of the county—"a pure charade of venom. The verbal battle of the century. Dash it all, I feared it would end in murder all round."

Mountgarrett caused the broken body of Amberia Carloniani to be encased in a lead coffin, and he personally conducted her remains to Venice. There, reposing in a catafalque of carved ebony partially concealed under a sable-velvet pall, she was borne in a gondola by torchlight to the cypress-shaded Isola Morta, lying lonely and serene in the shallow tides of the Adriatic called Lacuna Grande.

And then Donna Fortuna, a shade more antic than usual, practiced a bit of finagling. She arranged that Johnny Mountgarrett should meet Denis Daly in Verona, where he had repaired to a small villa which he had taken a year ago wherein to enjoy the first transports of passion with Amberia. Denis, ever wary to skirt a mile at any signs of inconvenience to the even tenure of his days, was for giving Johnny a wide berth, even to getting away out of that and not stand on the order of his going. But a curious change had taken place in Mountgarrett's feelings since Amberia's death. He dwelt his days fully convinced in his own mind, though nearly exonerated by his cronies and the Irish at large, that he had been the cause of the tragedy. "That I, the avid worshiper at the shrine of feminine beauty I sought out, should have been the cause that such beauty is no more! It is a thought, and a state, scarcely to be supported." In his secret heart Johnny knew as much as need be that it had been the strong Latin passions glazed over with a patina of her stupendous beauty that had so enthralled the weak-spirited Denis. Johnny reasoned that many a man with far more character than his friend Denis Daly had capitulated hands down to Amberia when she opened her predatory assaults. He sought out Denis to rekindle their friendship, but was horrified to find that here was no more gaiety, no broad winning smile of youthful freshness. Denis was a skeleton of a man, his cheeks flushed, his body aged before his time by the ravages of lung fever. He was nearly penniless. Mountgarrett took Denis into his villa. Each afternoon the two friends played cards—mild games for small stakes, but enough. Scarcely a fortnight had passed when the Dandy Gambler died one evening in the garden of Villa Amberia Cypressa, of excessive heat and choking dust raised by a brewing storm.

Lord Mountgarrett saw an omen in the deaths, first of his once-idolized mistress, then, so soon afterwards and in Italy too, of the essentially Irish friend of his rakish days in the fashionable world of Dublin. He was afraid that himself would be the third to die. Three times, on successive nights, he had dreamed he was lying dead, floating in an inky sea under a raging storm, but above the intermittent howl of tempest blasts he heard voices shouting in Italian.

So—Mountgarrett set out to range the world. He raced his horses in France and Hungary. He dallied over the game of love in Spain. He shot stag and wild boar in Austria. Over deeply-rutted forest paths, only by courtesy called highways, he drove, harnessed to a light shooting-trap, a spike team, two horses abreast and one leader in front, into the fastnesses of the ancient Kingdom of Bohemia. While stopping at a reputedly vampire-haunted castle set high on a crag in a darkling wood, Johnny Mountgarrett was introduced to the rugged sport of hunting bears with knives. It appeared that Count Trokala, lord of hundreds of thousands of heavily-forested acres, despised the use of firearms or even crossbow and arrows for killing these animals. He convinced his intrepid Irish sportsman guest that there was far greater thrill in attacking the great hulking black, sepia-brown and rusty orange-red Carpathian bruins at close quarters than in shooting them with a rifle at the distance of a hundred yards. Johnny listened to his host eagerly. The method, he learned, was to attack the bear, armed with a cudgel in his left hand and holding in his right a long slender sharp-pointed hunting knife "such as are used for all purposes of existence by Romanian gypsies," the count had added. A great bowl of steaming arrack punch was brought to table at this point in the conversation. The count proceeded to demonstrate to his guests how the hunter must face up to the bear, beat him off with the cudgel and wait his opportunity to drive his knife into the beast's chest. "This is the ancient way," Count Trokala said, wiping from his improbably luxuriant blue-black beard the foam of beaten egg-white stirred in to "froth" the punch. "A survival of ways to cope with wild animals in the days before firearms had come to be. Tomorrow we go into the Gava Valley on my domain. The bears are plentiful there."

It was just at twilight the following day when Johnny, still deep in the forest and separated from the main hunting party, heard the growling of a bear somewhere off in the underbrush. Turning quickly, taking a stance of defense, he grasped for the cudgel slung by a leather thong to his belt, and held at the ready angle his hunting knife. Then it was that two startling things happened simultaneously.

Directly in front of him an immense, towering black bear seemed veritably to hurl his bulk out of the larch thicket at Johnny, while at his right there appeared the quietly-smiling apparition of Denis Daly, his face white with the livid pallor of death, his clothing in tatters as if from grave decay. Johnny was so startled by this incredible appearance of Denis Daly's ghost that he split his mind in twain at the wrong moment. A sharp pain in his arm just above the hand that gripped the cudgel recalled him to the sense that, ghost or not, this was the moment to defend his life. Focusing his aim, he plunged the knife into the exposed chest of the bear, which at this point, a smirk of utter surprise on its face, its huge, crooked, fur-matted arms outstretched, was about to crush out Johnny's breath of life. Johnny, with his mauled arm bleeding profusely, made his way towards the sound of a hunting horn being furiously blown off to his right. The apparition of Denis Daly at this time and place had unnerved the hunter of bears far more than the sudden onslaught by a black furred giant of the forest.

It came to pass that each night for a week Johnny was awakened from deep sleep by a touch of icy fingers on his shoulder. Standing beside his bed was the ghost of Denis Daly, the pale skeletal figure in tattered remnants of grave-clothes emitting a faint odour of mouldy earth. Then, oddly enough, the apparition would motion towards a small painting by Guardi, propped up against a bedside candlestick, depicting the Grand Canal in Venice at sunset —a picture greatly favourite of Mountgarrett, so much so that he habitually carried it in his luggage when traveling. Always the ghost would point towards the painting, then point into the darkness in the direction of Venice.

But it was to Ireland that Mountgarrett next traveled. He shut himself up in his castle. Save for a bit of rough shooting in the wide reaches of his demesne and occasionally an early morning ride through the groves of monumental beeches whose silvery bark gleamed magically in the "grace of the morning" mist, the marquess seldom left the quiet of his book room. And then the midnight visits of Denis Daly commenced again. Identical with the visitations that had occurred at Castle Trokala. Always Denis would point at the picture of Venice now hanging on the wall at the foot of Johnny's bed and then point off and away in the direction of the Italian city on the winding lagoons.

One night when Johnny was taking lonely coffee before his book-room fire, he was amazed to see the figure of a woman wrapped from head to foot in a cloak of brilliant king's-blue silk walk hurriedly past the open door and disappear from his sight in the direction of the hall staircase. Johnny rose from his chair and started to walk down the short corridor to the circular hall from which rose the sweep of delicately balustraded stairs. He came through the arched door just in time to hear a horrendous shriek comparable to that last cry of Amberia's that had so often rung agonizingly in the cells of his memory. But there was a curious difference in the backwards fall of the woman who seemed to have just gained the top of the stairs. With a cry of surprise and fear, she raised her arms above her head and seemed to float, not hurtle this time, backwards down the stairs. Slowly —slowly, as Johnny intently watched, the blue-cloaked figure drifted upwards until she reached the glass dome set as a skylight at the apex of the stairwell. And then it was that, as Johnny watched, the apparition dissolved into thin air, and he heard the softly-cadenced voice of Amberia murmur, "Venezia—Venezia—Venezia returno." The words seemed to reverberate across the high stone groinings of the arched roof, to die away in murmurous memory of sound.

A few weeks after this occurrence Lord Mountgarrett, haunted by the whispered words "Return to Venice," shut behind him the front doors of his ancestral castle of Carrighivore. He caused the high iron grille gates to his demesne to be closed and chained shut until such time as he would again return from traveling and take up residence. But the gates remained chained shut for thirty years. Mountgarrett never returned to Ireland again. Or not in life.

Having a deep foreboding that Venice meant him ill, he eschewed its pleasures. For a time he resided in his villa near Verona. But the ghosts both of Denis Daly and of Amberia were so insistent during their nocturnal appearances that he decided suddenly to close his Villa Amberia Cypressa. On short let he took an apartment in the Palazzo Aldobrandini on the Grand Canal in Venice. Shut away as a recluse, in a sort of immolation, Lord Mountgarrett whiled away his time at cards, playing a solitary game that he invented himself. He called it

"Triangle" for the pattern in which he laid out his cards. He sometimes engaged musicians to entertain him. And then he had his ghostly visitors. Both Denis and Amberia were constant in their attentions. Though Denis seemed to become more odorous of cerements as time passed—or perhaps, Johnny thought, the smell might be augmented by the miasma of Venice in summer—Amberia forebore her backwards pitch down a staircase. But she was still attired in a blue cloak, slinky-appearing as if but lately drenched by the torrential rain of the Irish bogs.

But Johnny paid little attention to his ghostly companions now. He had obeyed their wishes. He had returned to Venice. He was aging rapidly; the once notoriously virile Marquess of Mountgarrett, the Sporting Buck of the Dublin round, was a tired, mightily disillusioned old man.

One evening, as twilight was deepening, he set out in his gondola for a glide through some of his favourite *canale piccoli,* the enchanting flower-hung side canals of Venice. When his gondola glided away from the water entrance of the palazzo he waved a languid, lace-cuffed hand to old Mia Marietta who looked after him so carefully and with such wit to match his most bitter observations of life as it went on around him. The gondolier poled his long, slender black craft for perhaps half an hour. When the prow again touched the seaweed-rimed stone steps of the water gate at Palazzo Aldobrandini, where Tongatta the waterman and Mia Marietta were waiting to lend a hand to his lordship in alighting from the gondola, Lord Mountgarrett was dead.

Later, John Barry, a barrister out from Dublin to bring the body of the Marquess of Mountgarrett back to Carrighivore Castle, found, while examining some of Johnny's personal papers, a letter pinned to his will. It was written in violet ink on a blush-pink vellum paper—a hasty scrawl, undated. Barry raised his eyebrows, wondering as he read:

"Yes, *Giovanni mio,* you will die in Venice. I foretell it.

Amberia."

Jocko the Monk
Dances Finnegan's Jig

THE OLDEST DANCE in Ireland is said to be Finnegan's Jig. All along the West Coast from County Cork to Sligo, this tribal dance from out the mists of remote antiquity has been tripped as a means to express the emotions of celebrants at a christening, a wedding or a wake, or just from sheer exuberance of spirit. Down the centuries there have been many claimants to the title "fastest jigger in Holy Ireland," but as far as I can find out the palm was always awarded to Lowney Bastable, the Playboy from Aran, a champion "from infancy to the grave."

The story I am about to relate I heard entire from a retired sea captain. Captain Kinkaid had once run a small coastal steamer from Clew Bay to Bantry, across to the Blaskets and the Aran Islands, a triangular route.

One day in the year 1910 the captain noticed that when he put into Kilronan on Aran there was a young man dancing a jig, a veritable whirlwind of intricate steps, accompanying himself meanwhile on a fiddle. A large crowd had gathered on the quay, a farewell party of well-wishers, for today Lowney Bastable was leaving his birthplace to fare forth into the wide world. As Lowney knew nothing in life except to dance, he had, in effect, traded an inarticulate tongue for a pair of fantastically articulate feet. His tongue since babyhood had been "tied be a halt on it," as his grandmother, with whom Lowney had lived his entire life, often said of his shyness. "But the ladeen's feet can talk faster than a starling twitters." So— when Grandma Bastable died she left a gray woolen stocking aclink with ten golden sovereigns, the savings of a long hard-working life, to her "dancin' playboy, may God keep a weather eye on 'im," and a last breath of whispered advice, "Go from here out, Lowney, childeen. Aran's a bleak, tortuous acre. 'Tis the mainland fer ye—go away out of Aran." And died on the words.

From the moment Lowney set foot on the quay at Mallarany he started to jig, and from all I have been able to learn of his will-o'-the-wisp life, a happy one by all accounts, he never stopped jigging long enough to get a night's-length sleep. What with a profligate generosity to assorted handsome strumpets, those bold-eyed streelers that traipse the Atlantic Parade at this humming port, and for his own adornment buying bright odds and ends such as cravats rivaling a Connemara sunset, rakish hats, and a pair of varnished leather shoes ("from the Rue de la Paix in Paris," whispered a foxy-faced shyster who accosted Lowney with all sorts of wares and shady propositions of how to "triple his wealth"), it was not long before the simple dancing boy from the Aran looked at the palm of his hand where reposed the last one of his ten sovereigns.

At evening, when everyone in Mallarany who could walk habitually took advantage of the fine sunsets to stroll along the Parade, Lowney fell in love. Quick as a flash of lightning can sear the heart of an oak. It was love at first sight when a little Sumatran monkey, hardly bigger than a rangy alley cat, caught hold of Lowney's sleeve as he was passing the pitch of an organ-grinder who, having lost interest in his occupation and tethered his monkey to a cleat let into the sea wall, had sloped off to quench his thirst in a nearby pub. Lowney sat down on the sea wall and took the affectionate little monkey on his knee. The little fellow wore a blue jacket frogged in cheap yellow cords and a pair of red Zouave trousers hid his spindly legs. But the most engaging item was a red-and-yellow cap with a shiny black-leather visor that had *Jocko* embroidered across the front of the cap. While Lowney was occupied in getting acquainted with Jocko, the monkey's owner, a dark-visaged Lascar sailor from some ship in harbour, returned to collect his monkey and his hand-organ. It was an odd thing entirely— many of the lazily sauntering passers-by noticed it particularly—that when the Lascar sought to lift Jocko to his shoulder, the little monkey cringed away as frightened and tearful as a baby. Then and there Lowney placed his bid. Would the man sell him his monkey? Well—perhaps—. He would gladly sell him organ and monkey—bad cess to them both. He was for taking ship away to foreign ports again. What would he pay? Gold. The Lascar's eyes widened. So for the price of one golden sovereign the bargain was struck and Lowney Bastable found that he was now set up in business as an organ-grinder, complete with a monkey in a Zouave uniform holding aloft a battered old tin cup.

From this time out the legend grew. Few persons in this world, whatever their station, become a legend while yet alive. But all Ireland and beyond came to hear of Lowney the Organ and his monkey Jocko. For however adept, swift, and vital was Lowney at dancing Finnegan's Jig, Jocko was better. Lowney taught him all the steps himself knew, but clever little Jocko invented a number of startling new ones on his own. For example, there was a dance in which Lowney incorporated a series of somersaults for them both as a grand finale. Three somersaults was a unique touch, which invariably added many coins to the shiny new tin cup which Jocko passed around after each performance. But this was all too tame for Jocko. After Lowney would finish his somersaults, puffing and gasping for breath, fighting dizziness more than a little as the years progressed, Jocko would leap into the scene and perform a circle of breath-taking backflips with such rapidity that this small object of flying colour brought thunders of applause and a harvest of assorted coins from a never-failing audience. Up at dawn every morning, Lowney and Jocko often traipsed the frequented roads or lonely cross-country lanes and bogs to perform in the open on fair days, on wet ones, in pubs and bar-parlours. Sometimes they were even invited into the better-class hotels. Everywhere the two danced their success was uproarious.

A London music-hall manager traveling in Galway offered a bid for Lowney to come to London to jig "on the 'alls." "No"—Lowney shook his head and smiled shyly, a small boy's smile for all his forty years. "I do'na think Jocko 'ud like it. I'm hearing tell there's danger in the streets of London." What Lowney did not tell the man from London was the fact that he was worried, more miserably worried than he would admit even to himself. Jocko was sick. Yes, his treasured little Jocko the Acrobat, who was his "heart's heart" as well as the best jigger in the land, was miserably sick.

But if Lowney thought there was danger lurking in the streets of London, he failed to realize that danger lurks wherever man treads. Danger is Destiny and Destiny danger. One day when it had rained for over a week the coast was sodden. The fields, the alley cobbles, the great flat stones of Eyre Square in Galway Old City, where Lowney and Jocko were dancing at a street carnival under canvas, were treacherous with the slime left by incessant rain. Lowney and Jocko, who grew more and more listless at his tricks these days, were just finishing a fast jig.

The straggling crowd of watchers shouted approval; a few flung coppers clinked as metal struck the stones. Someone shouted, "Bucko, give us Finnegan's Jig—er are ye too old to tread ut? The monk's a bit mealy-lookin' too. But here—." The man tossed a few coins into the ring that was faintly chalked on the wet stones. It was a rolled coin zigzagging across the pavement that was Lowney's undoing. Just as he grasped his fiddle and called out "Up Jocko boy, tighten yer chin-strap," he slipped on the coin, slid across the pavement and straight under the wheels of a brewery dray. The heavy ironbound wheels passed over his body at the armpits. When the broken body of Lowney Bastable was picked up by the drayman and his helpers, he was dead.

It is told to this day in Galway that never was so pitiable a sight as the distracted little Jocko. That he kept clasping his arms around the neck of his friend Lowney, crying like a small child bereft of its mother. No one knew quite what to do with Jocko. But he solved that problem for himself. Sometime near dawn after the tragedy the monkey slipped out of a window of the pub, where he had been taken by a kindly proprietor who sat up for hours feeding hot broth to the shivering animal and who sought his own bed only when he thought Jocko asleep and well bedded down for the night. When all was silent in the dark pub, Jocko disappeared off the face of the earth—or so it seemed.

A few weeks after Lowney Bastable had been buried in Old Spanish Town Cemetery, a man chanced to be passing by, taking a short cut to his home near the Gypsy Claddagh, a clutch of houses outside the old walls of Galway. There, on a small wooden cross marking Lowney's grave, sat a monkey. The man was a newcomer to Galway, and knew nothing of the circumstances of accident, death and disappearance. As he stopped to ponder at this oddity, wondering what he should do, he distinctly heard the sound of music—a ballad of the jouncy sort played by itinerant organ-grinders up and down the byways of the world. As the man, more puzzled than ever, watched, the monkey jumped to the ground and started to dance a jig. Then he bowed, touched the visor of his cap, held out one skeletal little hand as if holding a cup and, as smoke melts into the air, faded from mortal sight.

And so the stories grew. Men and women told of seeing a little monkey dressed in a red-and-blue suit, a small cap cocked over one eye, jigging for dear life, sometimes atop a wall on a garden terrace, or perhaps agilely balanced on the ridgepole of a roof. This apparition, it was reported, would appear suddenly in most unlikely places all the way from Clew Bay to Kinvara or Doogle's Head, a watering place where Lowney had spent many summers entertaining trippers in a carnival show. One time it was reported by a dancing clown at Tramore in Waterford that during the course of his turn he looked down beside him to see what was causing the audience to stare in silent amazement. There the clown saw a little monkey, curiously pale in colour, a kind of figment of mist, dancing a wild class of jig beside him. As suddenly as the apparition had come, it cut a nimble lepp and then no monkey was there.

I am partial to the story of an American lady who was out walking in Old Spanish Town, Galway, one evening during the long summer twilight that illumines Irish summer skies. Coming out from under the arcade she happened to glance upward and beheld on the slate roof of a cottage what at first she thought was a small child in a blue coat, who had somehow got stranded atop the roof. She called out, "Oh—child, child, *do* be careful! I'll get someone to help you down." Then what she had supposed was a child began to jig madly, jigging all over the steep-pitched roof. The woman was conscious of roars of laughter from behind her. She turned to look. Two young girls in shawls were laughing and pointing to the jigging monkey on the roof.

One girl called out: "That ain't no childeen, lady—that ain't even a monk. That's Jocko, a *ghost* of a monk."

The Beautiful Mrs. Oranmore is Dead

TEMPLEARVOE, COUNTY MAYO, 1910

HOW OFTEN it has been said "Beauty lives." However the world and its ways may change down the centuries, the *beautiful,* as applied to nature, to an expression of art, or to a human being, forever retains its magic. It is a word illusive of definition, yet potent to revive one's memories of beauty once seen or beauty to be sought.

When starting out to tell this story of Helena Oranmore, I define a woman who walked in such beauty of person that in her time and in her world it was said of her "Helena is the veritable definition of Beauty." I remember one day in England when a friend, Mrs. Morton, was showing me the rare and lovely roses for which her garden in Kent is renowned among rose fanciers. I was struck by a particularly beautiful ivory-white rose faintly tinged with violet-pink, called Madame de Huissard de Hauteville. I cupped the slender opening rosebud between my fingers and studied carefully the unfurl of delicately veined petals. I detected an odour, not strong but compelling, more of mignonette, of the shadowed fern brake in some forest, I thought, than of rose. I flicked a questioning glance at Mrs. Morton and saw that her eyes were watching me.

"You have a tale to tell me?" I asked. "There is something about this most beautiful rose in your garden that is not right, something that eludes me. It seems curious that I suspect a taint in such evident perfection."

Mary Morton nodded her head and smiled wryly. "Yes," she said, "there is a

25

story. A mystery to horticulture. A rose too heady from its own beauty and that on reaching perfection destroys itself. Anne-Marie de Huissard, Comtesse de Hauteville, was called by the Duke of Wellington, when he danced with her at Her Grace of Richmond's ball on the eve of Waterloo, the most beautiful woman in Belgium. It appears that Madame de Hauteville always wore a corsage of these roses that were later named for her."

Mrs. Morton paused and started to pull the petals of the rose back upon the calix to disclose brown spots of mould spreading around the heart of the rose.

"Tell me more of Madame de Hauteville," I said. "This, I am persuaded, is only the prelude to an entrancing story."

"It is soon told," she answered, "as the life of this rose is soon over. Far sooner"—she waved her hand across the expanse of variegated roses—"than that of any other rose in my garden." Crumbling the petals in her hand she thrust them into a pocket of the basket she carried on her arm. "I cannot even keep the petals for a potpourri." We moved along the allée bordered by standard rose bushes. She continued her narrative. "The taint in the rose is the same as that which consumed the life of Anne-Marie de Hauteville. After Waterloo she married an Irishman, Captain Michael Daveny, who had been one of the few survivors of Wellington's ill-starred Garde d'Honneur. Countess Daveny, as she styled herself in Ireland, had made a cult of her own beauty. After the death of her husband in a dueling accident, and the subsequent ruin of her beauty by a protracted illness, she took her life by poison."

Mrs. Morton was silent for a moment, her brows drawn together in thought. I did not interrupt her, but waited eagerly for what else she would reveal. Finally she spoke. "But the countess left a son famed for his good looks and little else, I believe, who married a Veronica Trail, an heiress from Belfast. An amazon of no particular looks, who devoted her life to breeding and showing horses." Here Mary Morton turned to me. "Now comes the part of my story which should greatly interest you. It was Veronica's daughter Helena, granddaughter of Anne-Marie de Hauteville, who for her marvelous beauty became the toast of Europe in the great Edwardian days."

As Mrs. Morton had talked on, "threadin' the needles to stitch the story together," as the Connaught man has it, I had been wondering why this saga of beauty triumphant and beauty destroyed had touched a familiar chord in my mind. I stopped in my tracks and put my hand on Mary Morton's arm. "You mean the woman that bore a kind of title, the Beautiful Mrs. Oranmore?"

"Yes I do," she said. "The woman of whom Edward VII said, 'There has never been so glorious a beauty in the world as Helena Oranmore.'"

And we walked on silent, amidst the scent of roses.

A cold, darkly rainy month of November was drawing to a close of sound and fury in the year 1892. The elements seemed bent upon a last heroic fling, massing demented wind, torrential rain and a dense pall of fog into a last assault to harass to the breaking point the mariners sailing the two seas that bound Ireland. For the landsman who must till his small holdings for survival, crops were ruined by the overflow of bog water to the case that all work upon the land idled to stoppage. So that when morning of November twenty-fifth dawned bleakly over the water-wastes of County Mayo there was little of cheer in a high-ceiled bedchamber of plain-faced, huge, dun-gray Templearvoe House, commanding the reaches of Lough Mask. But the woman lying wakeful within the rose-red dusk of her canopied and damask-curtained bed, warm and protected from the chilly air of the chamber and in reasonably good health, was unaware of the ferocity of elements without, save that the wind from off the lough seemed to blast the corner of the house where her bedroom lay, with greater fury than she could remember. But Helena Oranmore had other things to think about than the habitually chancy, too often, as now, demented Irish elements. This was the day that she must arise and face the stares of friends and strangers alike in Dublin. Her appearance at a reception for the Polish ambassador and his lady, at Dublin Castle, would be her first since her widowhood.

For eight months Mrs. Oranmore had remained in complete seclusion at Templearvoe, not once appearing in society since her husband Eric Oranmore had been drowned while sailing his yacht in a regatta off Achill Island. Today's weather reminded her of the terrible days of waiting after the sudden storm when three small sailing yachts had been swamped, or battered to bits on the jagged lethal teeth of Cathedral Rocks, when of all the victims Eric's was the last body to be found. Then the identifying of a corpse so cruelly mutilated by rock-gashes and the gnawing of marine life that it had sickened her nearly to death for days, so that she had been unable to attend her husband's funeral. His high-stomached family had taken her absence as purely blasphemous. She knew full well, from scraps of gossip that had filtered in to her mourning seclusion, what the Oranmore tribe thought of her. Envy and jealousy among the female members rampant and unjust. Various members had inferred that no woman, no matter if she was touted as the greatest beauty of her day, should be so weak in the knees that she could not stand the sight of death, however distressing, and bear up to pay her last tribute to her husband. No, they snorted, Helena was coddling herself as usual. Mrs. Oranmore smiled wanly as she recalled a remark tossed her way by a gossip. "Probably Helena feels mourning black is unbecoming to her *beauty*," had commented acidulous Miss Margaretta Oranmore, Eric's spinster sister, whose life, with which her irreverent brother had taunted her, was given wholly to "wasting your money on charity to a lot of wastrels and wiping your eyes and nose at funerals, wearing weeds to outdrear the widow." Helena remembered that Miss Margaretta had emphatically outweeded anyone she had ever seen when the red-eyed lady had come into the library after the funeral at Toormakeady Church, to relive to the last tear the obsequies of her brother and to eat her weight of the funeral baked meats.

But whatever these harpies had thought of her condition, Helena had really been off her feed for weeks. And the unsettled condition of her health had for the first time in her life caused her cream-and-roses complexion to turn a bilious, livid greenish white. This condition was, of course, not to be displayed in public. So for the first weeks Helena had closeted herself in her boudoir overlooking reed-fringed Lough Mask, with its invigorating panorama of the "haunted" Partry Mountains lying mystery-wrapped in amaranthine silence off to the west, and had just vegetated until her beauty in full flower should return to its temple. To be sure, beauty was not laggard to the extent of delaying for eight months. But Father Finnerty from Toormakeady, her friend and confessor, a priest of stern rectitude though mildly infatuated by Helena's beauty, had told her sternly that one year entire was the proper length of time for a widow to live remote from the world, but that for good behaviour he would deduct, as it were, a month or two from her "sentence for vanity," as she privately called it.

In the midst of Helena's reflections on her past life and the days of the present to be faced, there came a knock, a discreet rat-a-tat-tat at the door.

"Yes, Frollie," she called out, "I am awake. Bring me my tea." Helena exhaled a prolonged sigh and sat up in bed to receive her morning tray of tea and buttered rusks.

At ten o'clock in the forenoon Mrs. Oranmore, out of mourning for the first time in nearly a year, descended the long winding staircase at Templearvoe, attired in a traveling suit of palest violet broadcloth created by the French house of Redfern. The jacket was cut snugly to her tall, lithe, exquisitely-curved figure, with a wide peplum flaring out from her waist in the manner of the "baccarat coat" once so admired by the French gallants at the Court of Versailles. Helena Oranmore surveyed herself in a long mirror hung at the foot of the stairs; where the flawlessness of her complexion was concerned there was no more severe critic alive than herself. While Frollie Burrage, acting in the exciting capacity of lady's maid to this marvelous lady, and her Dublin bound, busied herself excitedly stowing luggage into the boot of the traveling barouche waiting out of the storm under the porte-cochere, Mrs. Oranmore checked off for perfection every inch of her reflection in the mirror, from slim alligator-hide slippers to a toque of black velvet set fashionably aslant over the eyes, which in colour took on deeper depths of allure from the pinion feathers of two deep Parma-violet wings of some bird known only to the milliner's art, which were poised at either side of the crown as if for imminent flight. What the lady saw was a face delicately oval in contour. Although her skin was constantly referred to as "of marble whiteness," she knew that it was not coldly so, for her blood pulsed healthily close to the surface to add a warm tinge of the Andalusian south, a treasured heritage from her Spanish maternal great-grandmother from whom it was certain, too, that she had inherited her luxuriant raven-black hair.

Some women, the ones Helena always referred to as "irritants," said that the curve of her lips was more than a little voluptuous, as if, one female critic had vouchsafed, dear Helena either used too much rouge on her lips or some woman from the sensuous Levantine had contributed to the bloodline of the fair Oranmore. Helena, who in her young days was always a good sport when the envy-tinctured barbs of social intercourse pricked the armour of her beauty, had parried, "Well, wherever I got my looks, or how, doesn't signify—to me at any rate. Here it is. So I make the best use of it I may."

As always when gazing at her image in a mirror, Helena was enjoying herself unmindful of the passing of time. It was Frollie who, prefacing with a discreet cough, brought her mind back as from a far place. "Madam—Johnny Carty is ready now that the wind's died down an' the rain over." Helena answered, "Yes, Frollie. Bring me that black velvet cloak from the closet under the stairs. I will need it in the carriage. And you, too, be sure and bundle up warmly. This will be a long, hideously uncomfortable drive."

She extracted a rabbit's foot from her handbag and dusted a film of rose-ivory powder across the classic regularity of her features, which brightened so winningly when she smiled. "We're off," she called, and so they were on the long drive to Dublin.

It was late that night when Helena Oranmore made her enterance alone up the Grand Staircase of Dublin Castle to pay her devoirs to the Lord Lieutenant and his Lady standing on the top landing to receive guests. She had had an exhausting day journeying from Templearvoe, her coachman Carty having insisted on driving at full-out gallop most of the way, necessitating three changes of horses at posting taverns en route. They had made it in time, but only just. She had arrived at her sister-in-law Mrs. Trescott's house in Rutland Square with only time for a hot bath and immediate change into *grande tenue*. Now, in great looks and apparently as fresh in health and spirits as she had ever been, Helena walked serenely up the stairs, a vision to fill all eyes beholding, gowned in a robe of champagne-coloured satin cut splendidly *en train*, its illusive pale golden colour gleaming as a perfect foil to her parure of sapphires and diamonds.

The return of Helena Oranmore to society spiked the already brilliant Dublin winter season to a feverish rivalry in entertaining. In the last decade of the nineteenth century society in Dublin was most assuredly spelled with a capital S. The splendidly spacious and richly appointed town houses of the Irish peerage and "nabobs," though not quite so affluent as during the "grand, wide, lovely and prosperous opening years of the century," as the witty chronicler and social arbiter Mrs. Mary Granville Delany described the peculiarly Irish Dublin scene, still shone brightly. At night long lines of carriages drew up to and away from the doors of houses from whose windows shone the glow of scented wax tapers. Balls and "twilight receptions" were the order of the day, to follow water picnics, to which the Irish of any condition of life have always been addicted, racing and country pursuits. So, during a stay of two months at Amelia Trescott's house, Helena enjoyed exceedingly her return to life and gaiety.

I need not mention that her suitors were legion. They spared her neither night nor day. Yet she flirted them to her in raptures or fended them off in pique, as easily as she breathed. At a soirée one evening a callow young man had the temerity to ask Helena her age. This was after she had told him to run along, that in making such protestations of undying love for her he, a mere stripling, was away out of his depth.

Flicked on the raw, the youth retorted, "Well—as to that. Just how old are *you?*"

Helena lifted her chin and quickly unfurled her black lace fan beneath it. For a moment her famous violet-blue eyes flashed fury. Then, ever of tranquil disposition, Helena cooled. She laughed engagingly and said, "Flannery, my boy, I am twenty-eight years old. And there's not a man or woman in this room that will dispute it." Noticing the widening look of abashment in Peter Flannery's eyes, she continued, "For you see in Dublin anyone who is even remotely in the public eye is known to a T, as to age, disposition and financial circumstances. Now— come stand up with me. I'm sure you waltz—er—energetically."

It was April and the London Season was approaching. Helena was in great looks and her health their counterpart. She went over to London for, as she told Amelia Trescott, "no possible reason else than to enjoy myself and see how the English beaux stand up to the Dublin ones, of whose rather ferocious attentions I am just a shade wearied."

Nothing could have been more felicitous than the timing of Helena's arrival in London. A wedding between the richest and of course, according to the British press, laudatory wherever the aristocratic or the titled families were concerned, the *handsomest* young duke in the land and the passing lovely daughter of an earl, was to take place at one o'clock at St. Margaret's Church. Helena did not attend the wedding itself, but she was asked to the reception at the Park Lane house of the bride's parents the moment that lady was informed that "the beautiful Mrs. Oranmore" had arrived in London for the Spring Season.

During the morning, Helena had received at her hotel a note from Laura Wrenton, an acquaintance whom she had met in Dublin while Eric was alive. Characteristically gushing, Laura wrote that she had only just heard of Helena's advent in London, that she must see her immediately, adding a heavily under-scored postscript "There is *so much* to tell. L." Helena had found the "dashing" Mrs. Wrenton, who notoriously had "slipped the bridle" of two marriages in rather suspect circumstances and was now on the loose, but who was nevertheless received everywhere in society, extremely tiring in the long run; her flippant, empty conversation was a constant repetition of court calendar gossip and was more than sufficiently catty. However, it was decided that they should lunch at the Cavendish and go on later to the Sellbridge-Barminster reception.

During lunch Laura said, "Well, Helena—I must say you appear more ravishing than ever. I do not know how you do it." She gazed with what Helena thought tired, dissipated eyes. Laura saw a flawless complexion, delicately modeled features alluringly shaded by the brim of an immense burnt-straw "Devonshire" hat massed with black-and-white aigrettes. She said in her petulantly shrill voice, "I expect now that you are free you will marry a duke—or a marquess or an earl at the very least. I've often wondered why you never married a title long since. God knows you had plenty of chances in your *younger* days. Or *are* you free? I'm pretty sure those ardent Irishmen have chased you immoderately."

Helena laughed. Taking a dark-red damask rose from a vase on the table, she pinned it under the black velvet ribbon that formed a girdle to her white mull and Limerick lace frock.

"Indeed I am free, Laura. And hope to remain so, at least for a good long time. Yes—the Irish male flaunted his manhood to exhaustion, both theirs and mine. But I am free as a Galway Bay breeze." She toyed with a dish of Cornwall strawberries a waiter had just set in front of her. "As to why I never married one of the titles offered me in, as you say, such profusion, I fell extravagantly in love with Eric Oranmore early on in my career. I was actually eighteen when I spent a summer in Connemara. He first asked me to sail with him in his 'pinnace,' as he called it, around Slyne Head. I nearly died of shyness and the suddenness of love assailing me all at once. So—I married him. I had eight years of a wondrous happiness with Eric." Helena paused for a moment, reflecting, then added, "In spite of his stiffish family, every member of which he was so refreshingly unlike."

But Laura was waiting openmouthed to be off again on her favourite theme. "I know—I know, Helena, everyone said you and Eric were deliriously happy; but you would have so graced a title. You really should consider it now. Seriously."

Helena rose from her chair and started to draw on her long bisque kid gloves. "But Laura, all my married life I *have had* a title. Conferred on me, it would appear, by the world at large. One that has pleased me no end." She watched a frown of perplexity crease the heavily-powdered brow of Laura Wrenton. "Yes," she said in her most caressing voice: "The *Beautiful* Mrs. Oranmore."

At Sellbridge House there was a large throng of guests, attracted to be out and about as much by the perfect weather, with air still and agreeably warm, as by the desire to wish the bride and groom Godspeed on their wedding journey to Italy. A marquee for dancing had been erected in the walled garden. Helena had been wandering among the guests for perhaps twenty minutes, greeting friends she had not seen since she and Eric had visited London three years before. Suddenly her attention was attracted by the figure of a tall, fair man wearing a dark suit, who was at the moment in the act of handing an ice to a lady sitting half-concealed by a potted syringa bush placed to mark the entrance to the marquee.

Helena caught her breath sharply. For an instant a pain of longing clutched at her heart, the stranger so reminded her of Eric. As she stood still watching him he turned his head and looked straight into her eyes. A provocative, confidently male look of admiration. Helena quickly caught hold of herself, turned and moved across the terrace to speak to Lady Lomond, newly arrived in London from Scotland.

Only a few minutes passed before things began to happen with a suddenness and swiftness to make even a women as poised as Helena Oranmore gasp for breath. Later in the night watches of the years that found her wandering over the face of Europe seeking from some man, if not love as she had known it twice in her life, at least sympathetic companionship, Helena accused the Fates for her dilemma. They had not played fair. She had been woefully unprepared for this onslaught. The expert and sophisticated methods of David Brinsley to gain his own ends where a woman was concerned were far too whirlwind for her to withstand.

Until Lady Lomond introduced Brinsley to her, Helena had not realized how greatly during the long months spent solitary at Templearvoe she wanted just this kind of admiration from just this worldly kind of man. One word from David and her defenses were down, nor did she lift a finger to raise them. She had raised defenses only against a lot of Dublin "flirters." Let them lie; she had no want of defenses now. Once again Helena was in love, as headlong and gloriously in love as ever she had been with Eric Oranmore. And with a man of whom she knew absolutely nothing. Knew only that he came from Wales, was asked everywhere, and that he was vastly popular with men and women alike.

For a few weeks her life seemed to whirl. It was dining in the smartest restaurant one night, and then, as contrast, seeking out David's favourites—"a little place—wonderful food and romantic atmosphere," he would say—in Soho or the purlieus of Covent Garden Market. By day there was Ranelagh and Phyllis Court for the polo. Racing at Ascot and Sandown. She was never tired at night, so she accepted invitations to a plethora of balls and musical parties all during the London Season. Sometimes Helena would take a long breath and wonder just where David Brinsley, at all times her leisurely cavalier, obtained the money to treat her to such gaiety, to send such magnificent baskets of hothouse fruits and flowers. She was increasingly glad that Eric had provided her with a sufficiently stable income, derived from his large land holdings in Belfast, to enable her to dress the part of the great beauty of her time.

Certainly no period in English history so complimented a woman of fashion who possessed the tremendous beauty of Helena Oranmore as the late Victorian shading into the Edwardian. True, the aging Queen Victoria, nearly recluse at Windsor or behind the fawn-gray walls of Buckingham Palace, kept no brilliant court; but her son the Prince of Wales, a great lover of life, indefatigable in all its pleasures proved, held a brilliant, sophisticated court of his own, more away from London than in it, progressing from one sumptuous country house to another and followed by a retinue of pleasure-loving friends. Yes—Helena loved this era extravagantly. Its luxurious living spiked her imagination. She would often sigh, lying encircled in David's arms, murmuring, her lips lightly pressed upon his mouth, "This is the time of all centuries in which I would have *chosen* to live."

But even in her moments of ecstasy Helena was often brought suddenly aware that this idyllic state of things could not last. There must come a time of pause for breath. A time to spread the pattern of their lives before them both and map out a course to follow at less hectic speed.

It was David who, during lunch on the river terrace at Roehampton one day in July, introduced into their heedless relationship the thin end of the wedge. He asked in his casual way, "Helena darling, shall you be returning to Ireland soon?"

As between them there had until this minute never been the slightest hint of even temporary separation, Helena looked at him sharply, a sudden fear causing her to remain silent for a space of minutes.

"No, David," she said presently, trying to keep her voice at an even, conversational tone. "I had not given it the slightest thought. Why do you ask?"

Although David, with his urban, nonchalant charm, was in private the most ardent lover any woman could wish, he never made the slightest demonstration of affection in public. He now reached across the table, and taking her hands in his caressed them tenderly.

"Perhaps I was too abrupt, my darling—you know my failing of speaking my thoughts too hastily. But I really must leave you for a time. I simply must go down to Wales." He wove and unwove his long fingers, drawing his eyebrows into straight lines of perplexity. "It is difficult, Helena, to explain—and no end embarrassing. But my funds are running low. I have business interests in shipping, in Cardiff." He lifted one of her hands, turned it palm upwards and kissed it impulsively. "Do you for a moment think I *want* to leave the loveliest woman in the world?"

And for a time that was all that Helena knew of David's life in Wales. A few days after this conversation he departed for Cardiff.

On the same day Helena went down into Devonshire to spend a weekend at Colborne Hall with the Daintrys. During the following week, a shadow of foreboding clouding her mind, she crossed the Irish sea and went back to her own demesne of Templearvoe. But although David wrote to her every few days saying that he throve in his native Welsh air, adding humorously that he was beyond belief busy rehabilitating his fallen fortunes, these were short notes rather than the affectionate letters that she so longed for.

Summer passed—a round of days during which Helena listlessly accepted invitations to various parties. She even roused herself a few times from this lethargy of the spirit and entertained at Templearvoe a few guests for racing fixtures in Galway or the local horse shows.

It was at breakfast one morning in late September when the postbag was delivered to Helena that, glancing through a packet of letters, she saw a long, apparently legal envelope. It bore a London postmark. Idly, hardly wondering at all what this letter might contain, she slit the flap of the envelope. It took her only a moment to read that she was named corespondent in a divorce case instituted by Barbara Waybright Brinsley, wife of David Owen Brinsley, Esquire, of Cynthanen House, Caernarvon, Wales.

The divorce proceeding brought by Barbara Brinsley against her husband, naming the beautiful Mrs. Oranmore as corespondent for having alienated her husband's affections while he had been staying in London the preceding spring, and demanding heavy damages, was, as such marital delinquencies go, a *cause célèbre*. While David Brinsley was no celebrity, Mrs. Eric Oranmore—"The Irish Venus" as one paper heralded her entrance into court—was famous enough throughout the British Isles and the continent of Europe to fill with the rank and fashion of London the courtroom where the case was being tried. Some persons even journeyed up from remote shires to be present at what one gossip writer called "the Oranmore levee."

In the ordinary way Helena seldom wore black; she had always felt that it did not become her. "My hair gives the needed touch of black to a toilette—

and I like colour," she would often say. But in her appearances in court she dressed entirely in black, a wide-brimmed hat of black velvet casting shadow to the tip of her shoulders. Her white face, on which she used no touch of rouge, identifying only her full lips with colour, was veiled in black mesh which she raised only when giving testimony, so that eager spectators were more than a little disappointed not to have full-time enjoyment of the face of the reigning beauty. Enterprising photographers took snapshots of Mrs. Oranmore on her entrance into court, enlarged the shots and hawked them in the street, calling out, "Here ye are. The Veiled Irish Beauty, saxpense. Quick, they'll soon be gone." And they were indeed in popular demand as souvenirs. Even in Dublin some of these pictures appeared, to the fury of the Irish supporters of Mrs. Oranmore. One Irishman became inflamed to the extent that he delivered a harangue in O'Connell Street, arguing "The lovely Oranmore did no wrong. Er—if she did 'twas her right, with the grandeur ave her beauty on 'er an' men what they are."

Divorce was awarded to Mrs. Brinsley, as well as damages to the amount of one-half of her demand. Helena returned to Ireland to consult Senator Mc-Neely, her counselor and godfather, for she must plan her future expenditures, perhaps must even sell Templearvoe now that the case had gone against her. As she sat in her stateroom on the small steamer plying between Holyhead and Kingston, she thought, as she had done so many times during the blasting publicity of the divorce proceedings, that one thing was true as the heart of Mary Mother. She had *never* known, never even suspected, that David was married. If anyone in London had known it—and some witnesses protested they did not, while others nonchalantly answered that of course they did, and so must Mrs. Oranmore have done—no inkling of it had ever reached her ears. In court she had disclaimed all knowledge of his married state and David had upheld her in that deposition. She remembered with bitterness what a friend had told her, that Laura Wrenton had said airily, "But *of course* Helena knew David was married. Tied, even in absentia, to a church mouse buried away in the dreariness of Wales, to be sure. But there she *is*. David was not going to queer his pitch, when the pitch was the ravishing Helena, by admitting to having a wife." Then Laura had tossed her head, and the venomous tongue of an aging, rather plain woman had forked and spit upon the air: "Something like this was in the cards. Helena has always been too damned beautiful and too damned sure of it."

As it turned out, due to careful survey and manipulation of her finances by Senator McNeely, Helena did not have to sell Templearvoe. But she must retrench considerably. Her income would, for a period of years, be reduced by nearly half. So it was decided that she should put her house up for let, at least for five years. She was now eager to leave Ireland for a time. In her own mind she wanted it to be a long time. The Tribe Oranmore had behaved with excessive bitterness all during "Helena's shocking behaviour," as Miss Margaretta had voiced her spite. Immediately Helena had arrived back in Ireland, all the Oranmores bared their fangs and let loose with criticism and advice on how a woman so disgraced before the world should behave in future to save *their* good name from further objectionable publicity.

So, in her thirty-first year, her looks no whit impaired by the intense emotional ordeal which she had for many months been through, the beautiful Mrs. Oranmore packed her loveliest gowns, her great picture hats, her jewels and her furs, and went to Paris. From here she would plan just what to do with her life.

The morning after her arrival she sat, in the softly-gilding Paris sunshine, on a balcony of her hotel overlooking the Seine. It was spring again, and Helena had heard no word of David Brinsley save a chance remark from a man she had met in Dublin, that David had "gone out to South Africa—somewhere —prospecting," for what he did not know. *Café-au-lait* was brought to Helena while she lazed on the balcony. And so on this lovely morning she began her temperamental journey through half the capitals of Europe and many of its less agreeable towns and villages. It was to be a journey lasting for years. Lonely at times, lonely to heartbreak, and Helena always remembering and treasuring her memories of life with David, never giving up hope that her superb beauty might yet gain her another chance at love.

For a few years the beauty of Helena Oranmore held true to people's extravagant descriptions of it. Pictures showing her superbly gowned, being entertained by the vicomte D or marquise Z in a box at Longchamps or a loge at the polo match at Deauville, frequently appeared in the illustrated weeklies of London and Paris. Ever mindful that she must watch her finances as well as preserve her tall undulant figure, Helena stayed at small hotels or *pensions,* of good address and repute if perhaps not the first rank of smartness. She ate sparingly whether dining on her own or by invitation. She had always made friends easily and effortlessly. And kept them within her circle. Her beauty gained immeasurably, or so everyone said, by her urbanity, her friendliness and her un-temperamental disposition.

This constant moving from one city and fashionable watering place or mountain resort to another, more often than not as the guest of agreeable persons only too pleased to have her, was for a while delightful to Mrs. Oranmore. But with the years it began to pall; its allure grew stale. Her associations with the men of leisure that she met seemed never to reach the stage of a serious attachment. Almost without exception the men desired the one thing Helena was not interested in, nor prepared to give them.

One day at the last minute she decided to join an English friend journeying to Dresden for the Christmas holidays. This decision proved to be a happy one, for, staying in that lovely rococo city, attending the opera and the superbly produced performances at the Dresden Theatre, she was introduced to Baron Karl von Kesserwald, who became so infatuated with her beauty that he placed at her disposal his *schloss* in the Bavarian Alps.

After the New Year Helena accepted the baron's invitation. As she told her friend Lettice Westernly, "I feel a great *tendresse* for Karl. He reminds me of Eric in many ways. But then"—her eyes misted over with the poignancy of remembering—"so it was with David when I first saw him. Still—I have a feeling that months of rest in the quiet of the mountains with Karl and his sister, after all this racketing about, will convince me that I love him enough to marry him."

Helena was standing in the salon of their suite in Koenigs Hotel, looking out of the window across the Koenigsplatz. She did not see Mrs. Westernly shake her head nor hear her murmur, "I wonder—I—wonder."

The visit to Schloss Hochwald was restful, the mountain air invigorating, her hosts indulgent. But there it ended. Baron Karl spent days away from the castle on interminable shoots. In the summer he absented himself in Vienna and in the autumn he sent for his sister to join him there, but did not mention wishing to see Helena again. She journeyed alone to Buda-Pest, a city she had had a fancy to visit ever since, as a young girl, she had read a torrid romance about a beautiful Irish horsewoman who had made a conquest as fiery and as colour-starred as the barbaric, partly Turkish city of Buda-Pest itself lying athwart the lazily flowing Danube. It was during her train journey that Helena opened her mind to herself. She took a long-overdue inventory of her resources, physical, financial and in a sense spiritual, although she had never been a devout woman. Why was it she tired of the companionship of the men who desired her so ardently? In the past ten years she had had a score of proposals of marriage from suitors of nearly as many nationalities. Men of great charm and even greater position in the world. But Helena was quite honest with herself. It was still the image and memory of Eric that held the secret recesses of her heart, and, blurred a bit now by long absence, his silence and his trickery, David, Eric's successor because, she admitted, he had been so like Eric in looks and effortless charm.

The night Helena arrived in Buda-Pest was a dark and cloudy one. The wind blew across the Danube, cresting the ruffled waves with white caps of foam. For a while Helena sat in an open window of her hotel on the Corso facing Pest, a heavy velvet cloak thrown across her shoulders, watching the lights prick out in villas among the heavily-foliaged trees surrounding the base of the rock from which rose the gleaming white baroque mass of the Imperial Palace. Finally the wind was too strong for comfort; Helena rose and went into her room. She sat down at her dressing table and lighted two paraffin lamps flanking the mirror. Suddenly, by a trick of the pointed flames, she saw her face reflected in the dark depths of the glass, a careworn mask of loneliness and spent vitality that caused her to utter a sharp cry of pain. She realized for the first time that her beauty was fading. She faced that shattering moment that comes to every woman who has lived by and for the legend of her loveliness, when she knows that from now on every moment of her life must be a battle to preserve the *illusion* of beauty as long as her breath may endure.

After this unhappy night a curious change came over Helena. She sought solitude in the oddest ways. She purchased endless varieties of cosmetics. She would spend hours upon end at her dressing table, then, apparently satisfied with the result of what she saw in the mirror, would don her loveliest gown and go out alone to dine in some restaurant frequented by the rank and fashion of whatever city. When, as so frequently happened, some man, seeing this extraordinarily beautiful woman, turned out in the height of fashion, dining alone, sent her his card by a waiter, she would smile and return the card with the message that she was unwell and wished to be alone, or that she was waiting for a friend—the friend who never arrived. Little by little, but with characteristic, even alarming thoroughness, Helena withdrew into her secret self. Her only companion became her image in the mirror. Her beauty became a fetish. She must at all costs preserve it, for she had convinced herself that it was the greatest treasure in the world.

It was in Venice that Helena caused perhaps the greatest stir in all her wanderings. It was on a summer evening when the kind of sunset so exquisitely painted by Turner lay saffron and orange and pomegranate-red upon the façades of the old palaces and turned the still lagoons to molten gold. That day Helena had received word that her house in Ireland had been sold for a good price. For this stroke of fortune arriving at a crucial moment when her finances were frighteningly low, she might treat herself, she thought, to a little fête. With utmost care she massaged, creamed, painted and powdered her face. She piled her hair high upon her head *á la grecque,* dispensing for this gala occasion with her usual severe style of parting it in the middle and dressing it in waves over her ears. She placed a diamond sea shell, couching in its flutes a pigeon-blood ruby, in the front of her hair, as she had seen a jewel worn by a beautiful and dashing Roman marchesa. Then she called a maid to hook her into a svelte gown of sea-green satin. This done, she surveyed the result in a long cheval glass and found it perfection. She bade the maid summon a gondola. "A private one tonight, Angela," she said. "With two gondoliers. Be quick about it—I want to drift in the full glow of the sunset."

And that is how Venetians first saw Helena Oranmore, as the golden evening died into green and silver twilight. A woman of ravishing beauty clothed, like Venice herself, in the illusive green of shimmering sea water, lying back against the crimson cushions of a black and gilt-touched gondola, drifting through the canals that spread like a filigree of silver lace through their divine city. But the romantic Venetians looked askance at this. For one reason—the lady was alone. Such beauty *alone?* Certainly this woman, this night, this Venice—such a thing should not be.

What, I wonder, would these Venetians have thought if they had known that the beautiful Mrs. Oranmore on her lone was not poled about the canals until nearly midnight, her startling loveliness a magnet for all eyes, from the lack of an escort if she had wanted one. Solely because she wanted no one man or woman to accompany her, lest their presence detract from the vision of herself. For by this time Helena Oranmore had become completely obsessed by her own beauty, wooing it, caressing it, adorning it for display. As for herself, she was jealous of sharing with anyone alive.

Of course it was inevitable that over the years various traveling Irish compatriots and even English and French friends of earlier days should catch a glimpse of Helena at some Continental spa or, encountering her, always alone, wandering listlessly in some park in Rome or Florence, speak a few words with her, offer an invitation perhaps to dine or attend a theatre. On such occasions she would brighten for a moment, exchange a bit of news of the day or a fragment of social gossip, make her excuses, invariably decline whatever entertainment was offered, and go leisurely on her way. Persons puzzled by her diffidence would recount these meetings in various words but all in the same vein. There was usually the question, "How did Helena look?" To be answered that she was simply but fashionably turned out for whatever season, that her figure was elegantly slender as ever but, alas and alas again, the incomparable beauty of her face was sadly fading. Her cheeks under heavy maquillage were lined and sunken. In her famous hyacinth-blue eyes lurked an undeniable expression of loneliness, of a mind forever haunted by poignant memories of the past and despair of what the future might hold.

During the years of the First World War Helena was in Italy. She had become acquainted with a Tuscan family named Roccobene who lived in an old manor house surrounded by vineyards, near Florence. The family consisted of two spinster sisters, Signorinas Elda and Maria, and their invalid elder brother Cavaliere Apronto. While the family was locally reported to be immensely rich from the cultivation of extensive vineyards, the Roccobenes lived frugally in almost total seclusion. However, Helena roused from complete solitude, for during the war she nursed the wounded who had returned from the front for convalescence in the hospitals of Lucca. Details of this period of her life are largely obscured. The only information is that "Signora Oranmore" was an indefatigable worker. To patients under her care "the Irish lady" was an angel in beauty and of a tenderness beyond compare.

In the year 1924, in the village of Chiavari, Liguria, not far from Rapallo, there lived in nearly complete seclusion a woman of mystery—or so she was spoken of by the servant, a countrywoman called Rosanna Lepi, who was the only person La Signora apparently ever talked to at any length. Rosanna did all the marketing, she kept in spotless order the tiny *villino*, so small that there were only two rooms on the ground floor and one large bedroom above. Always Rosanna kept the big terra cotta jars filled with flowers, for La Signora, as Mrs. Oranmore was known in the locality, expressly insisted that the rooms of Villino Sylvana should be always adorned and the larder well stocked with food against the sudden arrival of a long-expected guest. While Rosanna would in all ways comply with La Signora's requests, she shook her head in wonderment nevertheless. For three years now she had prepared daily for this "guest" who never came.

Every day La Signora rose at midday and appeared in the patio or the salon dressed in lovely trailing gowns; but even Rosanna, who never went further afield than Rapallo or Santa Margherita, knew that these dresses were not in the present style and that they were much mended, the elbows of long gauzy sleeves darned in exquisite stitches worthy of the nuns at Santa Eufimia's, who actually did the repairing of La Signora's wardrobe. The convent, one of the few places where La Signora ever called, was the first gate down the lane towards Chiavari. Then, while Rosanna busied herself about the house or worked in her vegetable garden—for she liked her vegetables to be pulled fresh to her cooking pot—La Signora would read from books and magazines with many pictures, which were sent out to her from a country she called England. As evening approached, she would walk up and down, up and down, the paths of the long, narrow flower garden. What was most difficult for emotional and adoring Rosanna to bear was that when the twilight hours came and she would go down the cypress allée to fetch La Signora to dinner, she would often—too often as time passed—find her mistress sunk down upon a bench, weeping uncontrollably.

One hot day in August, the kind of day that comes to the Liguria when from morning to night the cicadas take over the show, shattering the quiet of a shady garden with their nerve-racking rasp of whirring, Helena Oranmore ordered a carriage summoned from Chiavari. She said she wished to go into Rapallo directly after early lunch. The habitually voluble Rosanna was so startled by this unaccountable demand that she was for the moment speechless.

Then she gasped and said, "Signora, you do not go alone? I will accompany you?"

Helena shook her head. "No, Rosanna—I will go alone. It is no journey." Rosanna started to protest. "Do not be foolish. I—" Helena raised her chin defiantly, "—I am not *that* old that I cannot go about where I wish by myself."

The long drive to Rapallo had been hot and dusty. Why had she come, Helena wondered? Why leave the coolth of her cypress-dark garden on this blisterer of all days? And, she mused, all because of these dreams she had been having. Well, she would have an ice at Giova's—one of those delicious apricot ices—

would rest awhile under the awning and then return home by starlight. She pulled a pale rose-coloured chiffon veil over her wide-brimmed black straw hat and adjusted a bow of the same rose-coloured satin on her breast. Ranolfo, the boy who drove her carriage on her increasingly infrequent drives about the countryside, assisted her to alight at Ristorante Giova in the Piazza Mare.

The heat of the afternoon had tempted a larger than ordinary crowd to take an ice or cooling drink at popular Giova's. Helena raised her veil on the back of her hand so that she might drop it on the instant in case anyone stared at her. She walked to a secluded table at the back of the terrace and ordered her ice. Using a lorgnon, for her eyesight was not what it once was, she surveyed the scene before her. Her eyes swept the crowd. No—no one here that she knew even by sight. A waiter had just placed an apricot frappé before her when she froze to immobility. Her fingers stiffened so that a spoon poised over her ice dropped onto the marble table top with a metallic clang. Two gentlemen and a lady had just alighted from a carriage in front of the terrace and stood looking about for an empty table. Helena quickly dropped her veil over her face. She had paled to stark whiteness under her heavy dusting of rose-ivory powder. So—her dream had come true. She had dreamed that once again in her life she would come face to face with David Brinsley. For there was no shadow of a doubt that the tall, remarkably straight man in the fawn linen suit, a carnation in his buttonhole, carrying a malacca stick and a Panama hat in his hand, was David. Her first thought was instant flight. Her second was "How well he carries his years." She did a bit of mental totaling. "David must be sixty years old now," she mused. "He is two years younger than I."

It was while driving back from Rapallo in the last blasting heat from the rays of a setting sun that Helena made her plan. For years, long before the recurring dream, she had been sure that somehow, somewhere, she would run into David again. She had in her mind rehearsed legion ways of procedure come the day. That she would dominate the scene, carry her colours high, flaunt her beauty in her betrayer's face, win him back to her, she fully believed. For a woman of her glorious beauty and spirit any other course was unthinkable. And now she shuddered in shamed pride. Her dream had come true. That she would meet David in a restaurant, and in Italy, as she had believed it would occur from the misty remembered pictures of her dream. And she had cravenly veiled her face against recognition, and distractedly sought escape from Giova's by a rear exit from the terrace. She could not face David, fearful to the point of horror of what he would see and think of her, and he remembering. The mask of withering age which, con-nive as she might with massage, maquillage and interminable periods of complete rest, she could not claw from her face, as in frenzy at her reflection she had often wished to do, appalled her. This mask of age. No, this was the end. She realized she could never face David again.

Arriving at the villino, Helena refused Rosanna's ministrations—"Signora, a change of dress—food—a little wine." She went directly up to her room. All night she tossed upon a restless bed. By the first sun-rays of another hot, airless morning Helena had planned to the last detail what she must do.

When Rosanna brought her *café con latte* at nine o'clock Helena said to her, "Rosanna, I want you to go into Rapallo on the tram. I will give you a note with a name written upon it. Go to each of the large hotels along the Passeo di Mare. Show this note to the clerk or the desk porter—you will find someone to ask at the desk in the entrance hall. I wish to know at which hotel an old friend from London whom —" She paused, conscious of Rosanna's black eyes regarding her speculatively, to find precisely the right word—"whom I once knew, is stopping."

Rosanna brought pen and paper and put a writing pad across her mistress' knees. As Helena wrote out a short noncommittal note she suddenly realized that this idea was a shot in the dark if there ever was one. David may have been just passing through Rapallo. He might be visiting friends in any one of the scores of villas strung out along the shores of this lovely stretch of Tigullian Gulf. But she must not leave anything to chance. She folded the note and handed it to Rosanna. "When you find out—and do not give up easily if the porter says Mr. Brinsley is not registered—then return here as soon as you can."

After Rosanna had left, Helena rose, put on a sheer chiffon and lace negligee and went down to pace the cool paths of the cypress garden during the long wait until her messenger returned.

In the vitiating heat of mid-afternoon Rosanna, perspiring from every pore, came out into the garden where Helena was resting though wide awake, her usual siesta having eluded her. But her first glimpse of Rosanna's smiling face and bab-bling "Si—signora—it is good—yes—yes—good," instantly assured Helena that her errand had been successful. Rosanna handed her a now damp and crumpled note. Written in a strange hand in English were the words: "Sig. Brinsley of Cape Town S.A. is registered at Excelsior Hotel." The note was signed "J. Carrio."

Helena let the piece of mauve paper flutter into her lap. In a voice that seemed to Rosanna to come as from a far place, her mistress said, "Rosanna, go up to the convent. Ask Sister Maddelena to come and dine with me tonight. Then go on to Father Anselmo's cottage. Ask him to come here at nine o'clock. It is urgent that I see them—both of them—tonight. Ask Sister Maddelena as well to send Filippo to me. I shall have a letter for him to deliver to the Excelsior Hotel the first thing in the morning."

As Rosanna hurried off, Helena closed her eyes and her head sank into the upraised palms of her hands. "Oh God," she whispered, "grant me that he will not have left Rapallo."

After dinner, Helena handed a sealed envelope to Sister Maddelena with instructions to open it on Orta Sunday, only a week hence. "I am leaving the village for a long visit," she said. "This is something I want the Saintly Mother in Christ, Sister Dominica, to have."

Then, seated alone in the garden with Father Anselmo, Helena confessed herself of many things that she had done in her life. The moon hung in the sky directly over the chair where she was sitting. When she had finished talking she noticed that Father Anselmo was looking at her fixedly, that in the depths of his widened eyes a look of horror dwelt, his lips were parted, and as if the gesture were prompted by his subconscious, he traced with trembling fingers the pattern of the cross upon his breast.

Before Helena had received Father Anselmo in the moonlit garden she had repaired to her bedroom and removed every trace of the rouge and powder make-up which she had applied more heavily, more sharply defined, with the years. Then she had laved her face with cold water and gone down to face her confessor virtually unmasked, certainly in a state in which no man or woman born had ever seen Helena Oranmore since she had discarded schoolgirl sashes. As the full rays of the moon had streamed down upon the face of the lady sitting with clasped hands before him, a trick of light had suddenly revealed to Father Anselmo a gaunt, bone-white face in which were dark, purple-black pools of shadow. There was no glint of life in the sockets of the eyes. Here, he thought, was set upon the living, breathing body of a woman a death's-head skull.

After Helena had dispatched Filippo to Rapallo with a short note to David Brinsley, bidding him come to see her at five o'clock that evening, she set about arranging the stage. First she summoned Rosanna and bade her cut sheaves of yellow lilies and scented stock and roses from the walled garden and to arrange them in vases in her bedroom. This must appear as the "bower of Venus" that

David had always called any room she occupied. Instead of eating lunch she went up to her room, flicked a flower or two into place for symmetry of arrangement, and called to Rosanna.

"You called me, signora?" A big woman, Rosanna always arrived breathless from haste.

"Yes, Rosanna—I want you to take some lingerie to that woman in Chiavari who launders delicate laces so beautifully. Take your time about it. I suggest you visit your sister while in town. Take her some fruit, even stay with her for supper. I have a great deal of writing to do. I think this will be enough." She pressed a packet of lira notes into Rosanna's hand.

"Now—go on and have yourself a little fiesta. Do not hurry back, I shall be quite all right." —and to Rosanna's surprise the signora put her hands on her maid's shoulders and kissed her affectionately on the cheek.

From the window on the terrace Helena watched Rosanna walk with her oddly waddling gate down the cypress path, cross over the little humped bridge, and go out through the tall iron gates onto the dusty road leading to Chiavari.

"Good Rosanna—good creature," she said watching the departing figure. "How devoted you have been to me." She turned from the window and went up-stairs to her bedroom. Between the windows stood a painted Venetian *cassone*. Lifting the lid she took out a robe of crinkled white silk, patterned with lightly-traced golden vines. An artist named Fortuny had designed it. She had bought it years ago in Venice—in the days when Mario Torrigiani had been in love with her. He had called her Hebe, Aphrodite, Artemis, all fused into one. She laid this dress carefully on the bed, watching the sunlight filtering in through the jalousies shimmer across the long folds of thin silk. She opened wide the door at the head of the stairs—wide so that anyone ascending the stair would get a full view of the room on entering. Then she did a curious thing. She pushed her light rococo dressing table into the middle of the room, so that from the door-way the mirror obscured the sight of anyone who might be lying upon the bed.

Helena brushed away a film of dampness from her forehead. Sudden faint-ness nearly overcame her. Her head swam. *"Dio*—this heat," she murmured, thinking that this was no time to be moving even spindly rococo furniture about the room. She paused for a moment, steadying herself against the table. Then she drew the dressing-table stool over in front of the mirror and sat down.

For a few moments she sat stiffly upright, staring straight ahead into the shadow-ringed eyes that stared back at her from the mirror. Calmly, as if preparing her face for a gala, Helena spent a good hour applying to her features the most elaborate maquillage that ever she had done. Satisfied with her appearance, she went leisurely about arranging the cool folds of the silk Fortuny gown, loosely tying the golden cords about her waist. She went to the window looking over the garden and away to the mountains, and flung the jalousies wide, standing for a moment bathed in the radiance of the sinking sun. Then she turned and walked over to the dressing table. She took up a pot of lip rouge. Dipping her finger into the rouge pot she wrote, in large, boldly-limned script a sentence, diagonally across the surface of the mirror. She leaned back on the stool and surveyed what she had written. Then she leaned forward and kissed the lips of the face reflected in the glass between the lines of rouge.

Helena paused a moment—listening. She had heard the sound of carriage wheels. But whoever it was driving abroad in this heat passed by her gates. Time was running out. She must not be laggard. Not looking down, still regarding her reflection in the mirror, Helena opened a drawer in the table. Her fingers groped for a small silver filigree vial. She had bought this once in Paris in a mood of despondency. A fortuneteller to whom she had been recommended sold her for a staggering price a poison that was, so the seeress had said, painless and immediate and left no distortion of the features. Helena rose slowly from in front of the mirror. She walked over towards the bed. Sitting on the edge of the mattress she unbound her hair, still raven-black with only a faint tinge of silvery white showing at the roots. She pulled out the blue glass stopper of the vial. Placing the opened bottle to her lips she tilted her head back and let the soothingly sweet liquid slide down her throat.

When an envelope containing a note written in deep violet ink in a somehow familiar handwriting was delivered to David Brinsley at his room in the Hotel Excelsior, as he was just finishing dressing for lunch, to be taken at Blue Grotto in the company of his friends the Latterbys, his highly-developed curiosity was aroused. As he slit the flap with a fingernail, a thought crossed his mind that he used to buy bottles of purple ink for Helena, long—so long ago. And then, straightening out the single sheet of mauve stationery, he saw the signature—the one word "Helena." For a moment he felt weakened by a rush of memories; his eyes seemed to cloud over. Then steadying himself he read:

"David—*amore*—

"Yesterday I chanced to see you at Giova's. You were with strangers to me.

So I did not speak to you. I want so much that you come to see me. Come to-day at five o'clock. Ask any concierge in Rapallo to direct you to Villino Sylvana, Strada Leo, Chiavari. I shall be alone. *Amore mio.* Come. Helena."

When David Brinsley alighted from a wheezing taxicab at the gates of Villino Sylvana, he paid the man off, not having the faintest idea what all this would lead to, or how long he would stay with Helena.

He walked up the winding terra cotta path to the front door which he noticed was wide open. He pulled a wire bell cord and waited. He heard a jangle somewhere within the hinder parts of the house. Then silence, a long silence, that seemed somehow oppressive—not even an evening songbird trilled among the ilex trees. He pulled the bell again. Still silence. Then he entered the oval hallway and called. "Helena—oh, *Helena*—it's David." Still this ominous quiet.

He never knew what, exactly, prompted his next move. Perhaps it was a waft of heavy perfume, a scent tinged with the sensuous eastern odor of amber that drifted down on the stifling air from the landing above. David put his foot on the first stair. He called once more loudly, *"Helena—where are you?"* No answer. Rapidly he mounted the stairs to the open door at the top. The impact upon his senses of what he saw as he looked into the sunlit room drained every ounce of strength from David's body. With both hands he grasped the door-jambs so that he would not fall. Windows flung wide, jalousies raised, the room seemed to blaze with red-gold glare of the last rays of the setting sun. He knew that on the bed lay the body of Helena, for he could see the waves of black hair streaming across the pillow and one white hand clutching a tress of hair. But the face was hidden from him. What unnerved David most was the dreadful finality sealed by the words written in crimson across the mirror:
"THE BEAUTIFUL MRS. ORANMORE IS DEAD."

As Helena was a beautiful, lone, wandering woman in life, just so she continued in death. And just as she was obsessed by the ruin of her fabulous beauty, the heartache and futility of her life, when she wrote her epitaph in rouge across her dressing-table mirror in a remote Ligurian villa, so is she still obsessed with the thought. Her ghost will not let the living forget her. Nor that she bore all her life long, as a noblewoman would a heraldic title, her own personal device, a verbal obeisance to her classic beauty, THE BEAUTIFUL MRS. ORANMORE.

I have often stayed in Chiavari, where, in fact, I designed a villa for my friends the Daniel Lavezzos. One day I heard some women talking at the table next to where I was lunching at a restaurant near the sea.

"Oh, yes, it's true." The woman spoke in a strident voice. "These English people that let the Villino Sylvana for three months in the summer moved out within a fortnight. It seems that nearly every night there was heard hysterical sobbing at the end of that long cypress walk. And a woman in white with a veil over her face was seen walking to and fro. Ghastly it was, I hear."

Another time Signor Veducci, a friend in Rapallo, told me that a gardener employed at the villino used to find small bits of ribbon, or a torn piece of pale violet stationery lying on the garden path, or perhaps, on a windy day, blowing about the garden. Written across the paper in some oily red substance like crayon were the words "The Beautiful Mrs. Oranmore is dead."

The ghost of Helena Oranmore comes back to Ireland, too. Indeed she is a famous ghost, for here she goes about the rooms of Templearvoe and walks the paths beside the Lough Mask in full beauty as she was in the days when she and her husband Eric lived there. But apparently wherever Helena goes she cannot refrain from leaving her epitaph about for someone to see, to remember her beauty and her lonely, frantic death.

She died of the stain at the heart of the rose—that stain which began in her heart when Helena fell in love with David Brinsley and was unjustly accused of adultery.

A Mrs. Roebeck, who lives on the adjoining demesne to Templearvoe, told me the most fascinating of all the stories I have heard about Helena's ghost. It appears that a few years after Helena killed herself in so dramatic a fashion in Italy, a friend of Mrs. Roebeck's came to Sheevana House in the quiet reaches of County Mayo, to recover from an unhappy love affair. It was a case of a young man jilting, for a flighty young French actress, a woman of great beauty but a goodish few years older than himself. I will call this lady Mrs. V.

One night, she told Mrs. Roebeck a strange, rather wonderful ghost story. She said that when she was crossing the English Channel she was disturbed while resting in her stateroom by the feeling that someone else was there besides herself. She switched on a light. Sitting bolt upright on a jump-seat in a corner of the cabin was a woman dressed in deep mourning. The wide brim of her hat was covered by a thick black chiffon veil so that Mrs. V. could not see her face. At almost that same moment of discovery, three short, sharp blasts of the ship's whistle were heard—the announcement of arrival. The woman rose slowly. She turned and faced Mrs. V. and lifted her veil, disclosing a face pale as death, but of such regal beauty as Mrs. V. had never seen in her life. An instant afterwards the figure in black was gone. Then it was that, as Mrs. V. was gathering her bags to leave ship, she discovered a small twist of paper. It bore the sentence in red lipstick "The Beautiful Mrs. Oranmore is dead."

But that was only the beginning. Mrs. V. saw the ghost of Helena Oranmore frequently during her stay at Sheevana House. And here it was, in her native Ireland, that the apparition went unveiled. As Mrs. V. put it, "She was a raving, tearing beauty."

The last time that Helena's ghost appeared to Mrs. V. was possibly the most dramatic of all. It seems that the young Frenchman had not been too happy in his affair with the fickle actress. He found out where Mrs. V. was staying in Ireland and wrote an impassioned letter to her, declaring his undying love, abasing himself, declaring what a fool he had been, and so on. Would she be the angel he had always thought her and let him come to her again? Mrs. V. sat down at a desk in the library of Sheevana House one evening to answer the young man's protestations sternly. She intended to say to him in no uncertain terms that she wished never to see him nor to hear from him again.

Just as she poised her pen to write the first words of her letter, she felt a cold wave of air envelop her and the pen was incontinently knocked from her hand onto the floor. Understandably startled, she looked up to see the figure of the same woman she had seen so many times before. Now she was not beautiful, but haggard and hollow-eyed. The eyes of the ghostly creature blazed as if with terrible anger. A white skeletal hand dashed the note paper onto the floor to follow the pen. Then with a sharp cry, as of mingled pain and anger, the figure vanished into thin air.

When Mrs. V. leaned down to retrieve pen and paper, she read a boldly-underscored sentence scrawled in red across the top of the hitherto blank sheet: "The Beautiful Mrs. Oranmore is dead."

Lira from the Sea

BALLYMORONY, COUNTY SLIGO

"One foot on sea, one foot on land,
To one thing constant never."

T HE LONG, low, whitewashed stone house, called Ballymorony, with its three levels, one of which is an arched causeway extending for two hundred yards out over the rocky lough that winds in from the Atlantic, has great character. Architecturally, it is unique. It is often called by travelers the Irish Chenonceaux. One long wing, which is built over the arcaded retaining wall, is, in construction, very like the beautiful François I chateau built over the River Loire.

After that, the resemblance ends. Chenonceaux flaunts the very peak of French Renaissance; Ballymorony owns to three periods: the Irish feudal castle style; a wing of rose-red brick added in 1660, more or less the period of Charles II in feeling; and a Palladian portico built in 1738 by the Honourable Desmond Drax Cellbridge Morony, who also had an arched driveway entrance cut into a courtyard to make the causeway wing a separate house adjoining the main building. After his unconventional second marriage, Desmond Morony caused to be carved over the entrance arch, at his wife's express wish, some historians relate, the motto "One foot on sea, one foot on land, to one thing constant never." On this cryptic admission of a sea-born free spirit, the Morony family base their claim that the world-known legend of the Lady from the Sea is theirs originally, theirs and no one else's. The fact that there are, among disparately situated families, thirty-four versions of the mermaid-transiently-turned-mortal theme, in no way swerves the Sligo Moronys from their belief.

Gabriele D'Annunzio wrote of this woman in *Donna delle Mare*. Ibsen immortalized her in *The Lady from the Sea*. Greek legend gives us *Undine*. And many families as widely scattered as Stavanger, Norway, Tennant's Harbour, Maine, and Santa Punta, Portugal, claim this legendary mermaid as an ancestor. All this diversity of claimants notwithstanding, I give you the story as I heard it in regard to the Moronys of Ballymorony, County Sligo.

The Honorable Desmond Drax Cellbridge Morony was the second son of Lord Beltanna. The title had been bestowed on Desmond's grandfather by James II of England for supplying money and armed men for the Battle of the Boyne. Desmond's father accepted the title for a time; then, having had a row with the Earl of Westmoreland during the time when the Earl was angling for the Lord Lieutenancy of Ireland, Lord Beltanna renounced his title as being British-bestowed and so unworthy of an Irish patriot. He refused to let his son claim it. After Lord Beltanna died, the title was voided. However, we find Desmond Drax prefixing "The Honourable" to his name.

When he was eighteen, Desmond had married the daughter of a neighbouring landowner. She bore him two children. While Honoria Talby, the mother, never enters this story, the children themselves do. They are the survivors. Desmond's second wife, known as the Lady Lira from the Sea, had little interest in either of the boys.

On a bright morning in May, 1739, one year after his wife Honoria's death, Desmond Morony went out in his fishing curragh as he had done countless times before. Having been born and reared at Ballymorony, Desmond spent half of his life either sailing on the sea or swimming in it. Schools of porpoises make a playground of the mouth of the lough that forms an inlet from the sea, disporting themselves the like of playing a game, weaving in and out of the arches of the causeway. There is a frieze of carved marble, in the dining room of Ballymorony, which depicts sea-nymphs riding porpoises. The porpoise is taken as the personal device of the Morony family.

After Desmond had fished for a while, he felt that the sun was too hot for comfort, so he headed for a cool cave he knew of a mile or so away, where he ate the lunch which his old nurse Kathoe Conheedy had put up for him.

Old Kathoe was a woman from Ballinasloe near Athlone. She was of the "fey" White-hooded Women of Ballinasloe, who wove and wore the circular white homespun shawls from which they of Ballinasloe took their name. A withdrawn, antique creature was Kathoe. She spoke only Gaelic, and her love for her nursling Desmond Morony amounted to idolatry. Desmond thought at times the care which Kathoe showered upon him was a bit too thick. But since she had nursed him as a baby, he kept her on at Ballymorony as a pensioner, although she was far too old and crippled to work.

Once he felt the coolness of the cave, lassitude overcame Desmond and he soon fell asleep. What time it was when he suddenly awakened he did not know. He was so violently propelled from sleep into full wakefulness that when he got up from the rocky floor of the cave, where he had been lying on a length of sail-cloth, his foot caught on some slimy seaweed and he pitched forward, striking his head on a jagged rock in the pool a few feet below where he had been lying.

Slowly, so slowly Desmond hardly knew whether he was awake or still dreaming, he came back to consciousness as from a far place. His head pained him. But a strangely cool hand seemed to be rubbing back and forth across his aching forehead. Desmond put his own hand up to see who this was that had come, unknown to him, while he slept. Grasping the hand, he looked up into the most fascinating face he had ever beheld. A young woman, a girl she seemed to be, was bending over him. Her eyes seemed slightly aslant in her face. She had an ivory pallor that seemed to have a hint of green in it, but that was probably the play of light and shade from the water in the pool. Her hair, he noticed, was of an odd colour, an iridescence. It was at once black, bronze, golden, flecked with silvery lights. A drowsiness was spreading over Desmond's mind again. As he felt himself sinking into oblivion, he put his hand behind him where the girl's thigh pillowed his head. The last thing he remembered was the curve of the girl's body—covered by cool, wet scales.

Early the next morning, Desmond appeared at Ballymorony. When he had felt strong enough to rise from his seaweed bed, his head throbbing like a continuously-beaten drum, he had searched for his curragh, but the tide had come in during the night and carried the little boat out to sea. He had walked the six miles along the coast in the misty dawn. Kathoe was, as usual, waiting for him. Once she saw the big cut on his forehead, she hustled him up to his bedroom and tended him as she would have done the little boy in her charge so many years ago. He never told anyone where he had been, never explained to anyone, even to old Kathoe, how he came by the cut on his head.

After a few days Desmond, who had, ever since his return from the sea cave, become ominously quiet, started to take long walks at night. He would leave the house soon after dinner, which he barely touched, and not return until dawn rolled in from out the east. Always these days he was silent. He saw little of his two motherless children who, although they had a younger woman for nurse, spent most of their time with Kathoe.

One of Kathoe's tricks was to hang signs upon the doors of dining room, drawing room, bedroom, wherever she chose to admonish the occupant. Knowing only the Gaelic herself, and not being able to write at all, she had had Desmond print a few caustic Gaelic phrases on pasteboards. This had happened years ago, when he was a growing boy. He had forgotten all about these credos. When he returned one morning, tired and disheartened, he found one of the admonitions hanging on his bedroom door: *Bionn daoine c'eille na gcodiadh sa mheadhonidhche* (People of sense are asleep at midnight).

Unable to forget the hauntingly beautiful face which for one moment he had seen bending over him, Desmond had taken to prowling the beach at night. For hours on end, up and down, up and down. Ballymorony to Kinvara to Liscannor, and miles beyond. Every night he sat for a while at the mouth of the cave where he had first seen the lovely girl with the slant eyes, the pallor—and, as he must admit, the scaly hips. But she did not appear again.

Then, one night of soft air and shatteringly brilliant moonlight, Desmond found the girl he had watched for. Stilly, she came to him. Out of the sea she came. She carried a wet, shimmering, scaly bundle under her arm. To Desmond Morony this girl said, "I, too, have not been able to forget. So now I come to you. I am not mortal. My father is Lir the Sea God. But I love no man but you. I have slipped my skin, that binds me to the sea. Take it and hide it where I can never find it. If I ever do so, an old longing for my home in the depths of Ocean will overpower me. Hide the skin well."

Ten days later, Desmond Morony brought back to his house a bride. He answered few questions. His bride answered none. Desmond said, simply, that he had met his wife in Galway Old City. She was of Spanish descent. She had not the Gaelic and knew little English. That was all.

From the first, old Kathoe took a violent dislike to the new Mrs. Morony. It was more than dislike. It was bitter hate, and fearsome distrust. Kathoe, one of the "fey" Ballinasloe people, knew dread. She knew what she knew in the dark of night. This marriage boded ill for the House of Morony.

Outwardly all was serene. Mrs. Desmond Morony was quiet. She smiled, a slow, rather teasing smile, at everyone. Very little speech passed her lips, and then in stilted language. She was imperious, in a softly mannered way. Old Kathoe told Mrs. Carheely, the cook at Ballymorony, "It's grand and wide she's after bein' in her ways, at all. Sure ye'd think she's after bein' a queen or other." Then, gazing with filmed old eyes into the distances of the sea, Kathoe continued, "She may well be a queen—she came from a far place. She holds himself in thrall. Och and ochone, there's a dark end in it fer him an' his."

It was soon evident the new mistress of Ballymorony had spiked the curiosity of all the neighbouring populace. The farmers and fishermen made one excuse or another to talk to her. The gentry called on her. She was shyly gracious, but somehow they always felt uneasy in her presence, as if they had been subtly snubbed. Few visitors came to Ballymorony after the first flush of local interest had worn thin. Life moved quietly at the big white house built out over the sea.

Desmond, so much in love with his strangely alluring wife that he never left her side, seldom went out into the world of men. He gave up all his old pursuits, such as hunting or racing his horses at Galway meetings, seldom even caring to fish the richly rewarding waters at his very door.

A portrait, purporting to have been painted by Sir Joshua Reynolds but unsigned and perhaps done by a clever pupil, now hangs in the drawing room of Ballymorony. It is a three-quarter-length picture of Mrs. Desmond Morony. She sits in a contemplative mood. One long, pale hand supports her right elbow, the right hand cups her narrow chin. It is said to have been painted after she had been married eight years and had borne Desmond five children. It is a bewildering face. The girl might easily be in her early teens. Yet there is an old-soul look in her slanting green eyes. Perhaps the painter deliberately forced the hint of green in the pigmentation of her fair skin. What arrests the eye when looking at the painting, and haunts the mind afterwards, is the illusion that one is viewing the figure through water.

One notices that Mrs. Morony's dress is oddly out of period. In the eighteenth century, for gala dress all sorts of ornaments, such as tinsel ribbon, roses and flowery garlands, ostrich feathers and jeweled pins, were worn in the hair. In her portrait Mrs. Morony has none of these accessories. Her hair is plainly worn, parted down the center and drawn back into a small knot in the nape of her neck. The hair is, strangely, of no particular colour. It shimmers in metallic bronze, black shadows, and dull gold. Her dress of satin is in feeling more a Greek robe than anything else. It is blue, green, rusty-black, all these colours, yet none of them entirely. It might be a picture to evoke the luminous illusiveness of Undine.

In 1742 Desmond's elder brother, Michael Morony, came to visit at Bally-morony. He promptly fell madly in love with his sister-in-law. He handled the tense situation well, it seems, as did Lira Morony. Apparently there were no re-grets, nor bitterness, and Michael soon went on his way. Lira was the name which the nameless "lady from the sea" had conferred upon herself when she learned from Desmond that mortals must bear names by which to call them. Lir was one sobriquet for the Gaelic god of the sea, so she, his daughter, would be Lira. It caused little comment. Mrs. Morony was odd on any count, everyone thought. She was a foreigner as well. No one questioned her name.

From the first days of her marriage, Lira Morony had loved to sail, or just drift on the lough in a barge that Desmond had had made for her in Galway. It was a longboat, fairly wide amidships and painted green and silver. It was called after her children. At first the boat was named Lira; then, as each child was born, its name was added to the prow in this manner: Lira-Grania-Desmond-Maeve-Donard-Duirmuid, and then the baby's, Brigid.

When Brigid was still a babe in arms, Mrs. Morony said one day to Desmond, "While you are away on estate business in Limerick I shall have a water picnic. The weather has settled in for early summer warmth. The twilights are long and bright. All the children clamour to go out on the wide stretch of lough where it bends in at Oranmore. The blue herons and the wild swans from Coole nest there. I promised them swans' feathers to make a snow-white crown for Maeve. She's their chosen Queen of Beauty for the carnival." Desmond thought this a grand idea. He kissed her cool lips and went off to Limerick.

That night, after all the house was quiet, Mrs. Morony went up-attic to find some fancy-coloured carnival dresses for her little girls to wear at the water picnic on the morrow. After selecting from a big chest the costumes she wanted, she started to go down the winding stairs.

This attic was in the oldest part of Ballymorony, the feudal castle that had been built in 1390. The stone groining arched over the stairhead. Lira noticed that one of the large stones had worked loose. It looked so insecure it might prove very dangerous. She put down her bright dresses and reached up to re-move the stone. Tomorrow she would have one of the servants replace it with mortar. As the stone came away from its place in the arch, a loosely-tied bundle dropped out. The binding cord broke—a dry, gray-green garment lay at her feet. Mrs. Morony's heart strangled in her throat as she saw what this garment was. Her hidden scaly skin. So that was where Desmond had put it! As she had bade him, he had never told her. Now, with recent winds tearing at the roofs, the stone had worked loose. As if compelled by some force she was at a loss to define, she picked up the curiously flexible bundle, and going slowly down to her bedroom, she closed and bolted the door.

All night Lira Morony paced the floor. Great waves of longing swept over her. In her ears she heard the wind in the sea caves, many fathoms below the surface of the ocean. Before her eyes she saw the waving fronds of vivid sea flowers undulate across the ocean floor. The feel of the pliant scales in her hand, just a hint of cool depths of ocean, decided her.

Next morning dawned so golden-bright it was hard to look directly at the sparkling water. The picnic party set out. Two strong fisherboys stood in the stern and sculled the barge. The course was set for the wide lagoon at Rathheel Point. All day the children, Lira's five and the two half brothers, swam beside the slowly moving barge. Even baby Brigid was dandled in the water. Lunch was eaten drifting in the lagoon. Widely scattered swan feathers were gathered by the children and were fashioned into a magnificent crown for Maeve. As twilight was setting in, the barge hove in sight of Ballymorony, set so commandingly on its arcaded rock. Mrs. Morony, who had been preoccupied all day, motioned to the oarsmen to stop.

She rose to her feet and, taking little Brigid from her nurse's arms, she set the baby on her shoulder. The children, who were sitting in the stern of the barge and spinning tops, all turned to look, hoping that their mother would sing for them one of the strange and haunting songs about the ocean maidens. But she was gazing in a fascinated manner at the still water of the lough. Not a ripple stirred the water as far as one could see. The air was so clear and quiet that they could hear the splashing of the rock bass and see iridescent fountains of diamonds as porpoises dived under the arches of the causeway. Then, as the children watched, Mrs. Morony did a frightening thing. She unfurled the bundle which had been held in her hand all day. It enfolded her like a live thing. It gleamed silvery gold in the rays of the setting sun. Still holding the baby Brigid on her shoulder, Mrs. Morony gave a great cry of longing and leapt from the prow of the barge into the dark emerald waters of the lough.

Desmond Morony was inconsolable. He blamed himself, for as soon as he saw the stone removed from the attic groining, he knew the whole tragic story. Word was given out that Mrs. Desmond Morony had met with a fatal accident while out on the lough, close to where it runs in from the sea. She and her youngest child had been drowned. But the two young boatmen knew another version of the story. They told it as they had seen it with their own eyes.

During the next year the Morony children skittered about the open waters of the lough as they had always done. Sad as the drowning of their mother was, it was no reason for them to shun the sea, surely. One afternoon Maeve and her twin brother Donard, aged twelve, were out in a fishing curragh. They were after sea mullet, a delicious fish that Mrs. Carheely would dust with barley meal and ground herbs, and grill over the peat fire. A little way off the Kilcolgan Reef they felt a strange tugging at the prow of the curragh. A pale green-white hand shot out of the water, there was a shout and a scream, a plunge and a dive. Ripples. More, widening ripples. Silence.

Later that evening, a boy walking along Kilcolgan Strand reported to a nearly demented Desmond Morony that he had heard a sharp cry and seen the curragh sucked down into the sea. "Quick as that." The boy snapped his fingers. "There was no storm at all. The day was as clear as a virgin's eye, yer honour."

And so it went. Each year Mrs. Morony, or Lira the sea god's daughter, whichever you wish to call her, came back and took one more of her children. No matter whether they were forbidden to set foot in a curragh or barge, somehow they managed to get out on the lough or the sea.

When Duirmuid, aged sixteen, was fishing from a breakwater at Shinagheela Castle while on a school holiday, he leaned too far over the low parapet and fell into the sea below. A boy who was with him said that just as Duirmuid leaned over, a long-fingered white hand with a curious slimy green pallor reached out of the water and grasped Duirmuid by the arm. Splendid swimmer though the victim was, he never rose to the surface once he had fallen in.

Finally Desmond had left to him only the two boys by his first wife, Sean and Kevin. Taking these two with him, he went to live in a villa at Tivoli, in the hills above Rome.

Before Desmond rented his house and left Ireland to live in Italy, two things happened that are interesting to note. In a bedroom in the wing of Ballymorony which hangs over the causeway, Desmond found these words scratched on a pane of glass in a window looking out to sea: "The Queen of Wonder, and the most feckless of women, dwells in this house." It was in this bedroom that Desmond's infatuated brother, Michael Morony, had slept during his short, unhappy visit to this house.

The other incident happened the night before Desmond was to leave Ballymorony with his two sons. He went early to bed. According to his diary or memoirs, which, through the years, he meticulously kept, he finished writing, then dropped off to sleep immediately. During the night the image of his drowned wife Lira floated through his dreams. Once he roused, just as he heard the staircase clock strike twelve. He thought, in his half-awakened state, that it was raining in at the open window, or that the mist was heavy and driving in from the sea. Well, no matter. As he was sinking again into sleep, it was as if a pair of icy-cold lips bore lightly down on his own. Instantly he sat up in bed and put his hand to his mouth. His lips were cold and wet.

When he came down to breakfast next morning, old Kathoe waited for him in the morning room. She was so very old now that she had nearly shuffled her coil, but her eyes were remarkably keen. After his morning salutation, "God go with you this day," the old woman bade him come with her. "Go on out of this," he told her, but old Kathoe held her ground and would not brook dismissal. He followed her at last to the entrance door. There was a trail of slime and seaweed on the black-and-white marble floor, and stains of greenish water marks, as if someone had trailed wet fingers along the white walls of the hall.

Wherever possible I have made a close study of the various ramifications of this legend of the lady from the sea. In 1934 I stayed in the Von Lindtner house, which is situated on a wild stretch of coast a few miles from Stavanger, Norway. One night I was awakened from sleep by a curious sound that at first I took to be someone sluicing down the corridor outside my bedroom with buckets of water. But as I turned on the light beside my bed and glanced at a small traveling clock, I saw that it was only half-past-two; I felt that even the most conscientious servants would hardly be up and about their cleaning duties at this hour. I rose from bed to investigate. Opening the door, I saw that in patches the uncarpeted floor-boards gleamed slimily, and my eyes were drawn instantly towards a double window opening onto a balcony at the end of the corridor. Passing as lightly as a wraith of sea mist seeps through the cracks of loosely-joined window frames, I distinctly saw what appeared to be a huge fish with the head and torso of a mortal woman.

In the morning I was assured by members of the family that this occurrence took place so often that they themselves usually slept through the visitation undisturbed. My hostess remarked a shade wryly, "It's just part of our family history. An adventurous ancestor somewhere in the seventeenth century went swimming in Skagerrack once too often." Unconcernedly slitting the envelopes of her morning post, she added, "A messy ghost, I assure you. Slime and draggles of seaweed on the floors do not endear her to my servants when they clean up after her visits. And always she keeps to the upstairs rooms of the house. That is why most of the rooms remain uncarpeted."

Again, when I stayed at Ballymorony, which was frequently in the autumn for fishing and rough shooting, I encountered the ghost of Lira of the Sea dozens of times. One hot noon I saw her lying prone, as if exhausted, on a rock under the shadow of one of the three arches that support the Charles II wing of the house, the wing flung out across the inlet from the sea. Pale greenish-gray was the scaly skin, and that pallid "human" skin of her upper body was faintly luminous. At first the woman I took to be no other than Lira seemed panting for breath. Then, as her half-closed eyes spied me watching her intently from the rowboat in the middle of the stream, she seemed suddenly alert and, with the undulation of a porpoise, slipped into the shadowy depths beneath the arcade just as any startled aquatic creature would do.

Fisherwomen at Killyhanna Strand, and they scraping fish on the quayside, tell tales of Lira which always seem to be a variation on the main theme. A particular friend of mine, heroic-bosomed, massive-thighed Rossie O'Gullan, expatiated on the qualities of motherhood attributed to Lira by the women who had seen her ghost. "She's handy wid her childer at all, the crathure," she said. "She'd no call t'leave 'er dark depths at all in the first place, save"—Rossie accented her words with a great slash of her *spada*, or scaling knife, viciously disemboweling a fine specimen of sea bass—"save love taken. A strong temptation all we women have—arragh." She suddenly straightened her muscular back and gazed out and away across the sands. "I do be seein' that Mrs. Morony sittin' on a rock feedin' the little babo she hurled into the sea along wid herself. Quiet-like she is, payin' mind to none nor either. The babo sucks away just like me own childer, but"—Rossie bent over the scaling trestles and resumed her work with the same ferocity of movement as before—"I often wonder, does the babo suck mother's milk er salt sea wather?"

BLUE FLAME

Sulphur Burns
a Blue Flame

A CROSS the humped shoulders of Slievnamon (in the Gaelic tongue the word is fulsome, meaning Mountain of the Beautiful Woman), the moonlight lay silver and serene. A late walker on the road to Letterfrack felt a great peace athwart him. A grand night it was entirely, still and soft the evening air. He chuckled to himself. "It's a free heart I have, no less." He tamped a gobeen of black Sailor's Plum tobacco into the bowl of his pipe, lit up, and, elated with pure contentment, strode on his way. He passed a farmer standing at a stile. "God's grace to ye, man alive," the traveler called out in good nature. "All the world's well." To which salutation he was answered, "And all in it."

A mile or more along the road the man came abreast of a spinny of alder trees, when, on the instant, all the demons of hell seemed suddenly to ride the air. It started with a thunder of galloping hoofs as a horse approached along the flinty road. The traveler leapt onto the grassy border, transfixed by fright, teetering on the edge as the horse came on headlong at furious pace. But the man had not leapt in time, for, as he fought to retain his balance, there was a crushing impact, a shriek of terror rent from the walker of the roads as he plunged into a rock-strewn ditch forming a culvert at one side of the road. The maddened horse bearing a blood-streaming rider on his back exuded a strong smell of sulphur mingled with the sickening odour of fresh, hot blood. On, on the horse plunged, to be enveloped by shadows of the night.

63

Next morning a dairyman early on his rounds spied the form of a man heavily bearded, clothed in dingy homespuns, sprawled on the stones of the culvert. As he bent over the body he noticed that the red-rimmed eyes staring skyward were dilated with fear, as if the man had seen the devil himself and his heart had stopped at the sight. There was another curious thing the dairyman observed. One side of the ragged wool coat was singed; the rusty black surface gave off the acrid odour of sulphur.

Many persons, whether they liked the two brothers Lawlor or not, often remarked that it was a catastrophe that two boys should have to grow to manhood under the brutality of a father the like of that beast Trooper Lawlor. A cruel and devious father was Trooper, so called because of early days spent in the Inniskillen Dragoons. His record of inhuman conduct towards his fellow men, stranger or family alike, no matter, dated from his return home from fighting with Wellington at Waterloo, when, he boasted the length of his life, "I carved the Frenchies into rashers ave bacon, a saber in each hand, an' frizzled the rashers black wid me flamin' tongue." Yes, all agreed, a bully and a braggart was Trooper.

Soon after Terrence, the younger of the boys, was born, Trooper's unhappy wife had turned her face to the wall one night and died in the weariness of an old grief. Save for a sketchy kind of care from a passel of raffish women dubiously referred to as "housekeepers," the Lawlor boys grew up on the biggest farm in the valley, alone, undisciplined, wild as coneys in a burrow, completely illiterate, their behaviour vicious towards one another. Pado, the eldest son, was five years older than Terry. He was a tall, strong, coarsely handsome brute of a boy who crowed it over the weaker, more spindling youngster.

"Terry, me whey-faced rabbit, come to heel instanter," he would call out, or "Bring me a bucket ave oats fer me lovely little mare Valley Lass, and don't be after dyin' on yer feet doin' it, er I'll scald ye to redden ye up." All day long and half the night Terry Lawlor ran hither and yon, harassed out of his weak mind by his father and Pado.

But, dire as this life was, he could have put a better face on it if only he had been allowed to feed, to exercise, or to ride in from the hill pasture the most wonderful horse, to his mind, ever foaled on Irish turf. This was Blue Flame, sired by his father's great gray stallion Sulphur. It was Sulphur that his father had ridden at the famous charge of the Irish Dragoons at Waterloo, a horse of diabolical temper and a devious viciousness akin to the Lawlor tradition for male brutishness.

When Terry was about sixteen he was assailed with a congestion of the lungs. Always of frail build, his constant coughing wore the boy down until he looked, as Pado yelled at him one morning, and himself off to the exercise ring behind the stables, "Be the livin' Holy, ye're a crowdy mess ave skin an' bones. Ye put me in mind ave a featherless bird fallen from its nest. I hate the sight ave ye, ochone. Now be after lettin' that barred gate swing wide to let this son ave Sulphur through. He's already apin' his da be breathin' out brimstone on the air."

Meekly as always in the face of his savage brother's tirades, Terry pretended not to hear; outwardly at least, he paid Pado no mind. But a watcher, and he wary, might have detected a glint of loathing in the boy's eyes as he followed Pado, astride Blue Flame, up the hill to the grassy plateau where were set up the schooling jumps. A class of ring usually referred to as "the devil's loop" had been laid out where Trooper Lawlor had schooled his steeplechaser for lepp, speed and pace. Most of his neighbours grumbled that he set his jumps too high, his ditches too wide, that he not only wore out his young horses too soon, but ruined their tempers forcing them to jump too great hazards for their age. Terry watched his brother ride in his arrogant thruster fashion around the course. Blue Flame had once been gentle in the extreme, a horse of beautiful manners. But constant forcing him to take gut-tearing obstacles soon brought this chancy temper to the boil.

Terry straddled a high boulder on the stone wall—his usual seat—to watch, ready to replace a branch of brush or a stone loosened from a jump. Terry never knew whether it was by accident or by design that, settling back to lepp a big brush jump, Pado wheeled Blue Flame just as the horse was close to where he was perched, riding so close to the wall that Terry was knocked backward onto some loose rocks. For a moment he lay stunned. And then his dormant temper rose like a rocket. Memory drenched his thoughts. All the dreary years of his growing-up, during which he had been scorched by the cruel tongue and often beaten by the crueler fists of Pado, whirled through the hurt boy's brain. He slowly lifted himself from the ground. Pado had dismounted and, while laughing in great shouts at Terry's discomfiture, he leaned down to adjust a twisted stirrup.

Swift as a swallow dips in flight, Terry stooped and picked up a jagged piece of rock. Shrieking hysterically at the top of his voice he beat Pado across the shoulders, the back of his head and, maddened by the sight of spurting blood, somehow exalted by mastery at last, Terry beat his brother's face into a jelly of bloody flesh. During this fearful attack Pado had held onto the reins of Blue Flame; he even still clutched the reins as he plumped to the ground dead. The horse snorted wildly, his frantic neighing high-pitched as the scream of a woman in mortal agony, as a horse will do at the sight of blood.

The clamour on the hill had attracted the attention of some harvesters working in a field on the next farm. The men threw down their scythes and binding-cords and started at the double for the spot where they saw the plunging stallion. But they paused at the wall to better take in an astonishing sight. Blue Flame, with flaying hoofs, was trying to savage the boy Terry, who in turn was attempting to mount the maddened animal, to ride him for once in his life as he had always wanted to do. Given some unbelieved strength in his extremity, the boy succeeded in swinging into the saddle.

Farmer Tim Shanley called out, "Be God's pity, Terry boy, get down out o' that, ye'll be murdered sure. Ye can't manage that beast. Ye'll—" But he was shouting at the wind. Grasping the bridle reins low down, as many's the time he had seen jockeys do, Terry lay low in the saddle, his quaking knees grasping Blue Flame's barrel for dear life. After the first wild plunge the horse caught the bit in his teeth, held it there and settled down for, as the harvesters referred to it afterwards, "the runaway ave the century."

Out across the schooling field, down the hill, a maddened lepp across a reedy brook that in the ordinary way even Blue Flame would never have attempted no matter how spurred to do so, he flew as on wings. Terry had closed his eyes, clutched the reins tightly and let the horse streak. Told over and over again down the years by the dazed watchers on the hill, the story of this ride gains momentum as did runaway Blue Flame. Onlookers say the horse, bearing his rider half-dead from whipping by low branches, ran for nine miles cross-country. Until, plastered with foam from a slack tongue, sweat streaming into his eyes, the horse was blinded. At a crossroads he misjudged his course and barged head on into an ancient Celtic stone cross rising like a fortress keep at the junction of the roads. Farmers returning from Linarra Market found the broken bodies of Blue Flame and Terrence Lawlor. It was assumed the boy had hit his head on a low bough somewhere along the maddened ride, for his skull was bashed in, the features of his face unrecognizable.

So—the years passed. Old hellion Trooper Lawlor died, but not a quiet death. He had been haunted and distracted for years by the re-enactment of the tragedy that had happened on the hill pasture. Sometimes it would take place in broad daylight and arouse the countryside, for Blue Flame was no respecter of persons nor property rights, but on his fatal run had bolted regardless across castle demesne and cottage garden or farmyard. But more often, just as Trooper had drunk himself into a daze and stretched out on his disheveled bed, the sound of hoofbeats would be heard, a maddened horse approaching the house, and to the befuddled father of the dead Pado and Terry it would seem that his bloodied sons were hurled right across the foot of his bed.

It is a curious fact that the manner in which this manifestation takes place varies in form. Sometimes it will be noted that Blue Flame bears upon his back the battered and bleeding form of hysterical Terry. At other times it will seem to be Pado reeling in the saddle, blood gushing from his crumpled skull.

A farmer once told me that he was tossing hay in his rick one noonday. All was quiet afield—he said "what we Irish farmers in the south counties call 'bee-buzzing quiet.'" Suddenly pandemonium broke loose as a blood-spattered roan horse came galloping across the field, steaming with sulphur fumes. As if tied onto his back by invisible cords were the battered bodies of two red-haired young men. As swiftly as this apparition had materialized it passed into the shadows of a grove of trees and the air was again hot and bee-buzzing quiet.

The manner of my seeing the ghost of Blue Flame and, I shall always believe, the ghost of Pado Lawlor swaying in the saddle, was as spine-chilling as any manifestation of the supernatural I can remember. Certainly it was no spindly Terry but a brawny corpse, huge-thighed and broad-shouldered. I had been hunting with the Tipperary Hounds. The day had been a perisher for squalls of cold wind more than a little laced with sleet. I was hacking slowly along a byroad, a short cut to the house where I was spending a few days with friends.

Of a sudden my usually quiet mount Battledore shied violently, nearly pitching me over his head. I had just settled again warily in the saddle when the animal, his pricked ears jerking nervously, made a second determined lunge for the side of the road. Quivering in every muscle he sidled, tossing his head in alarm. It was then that I heard far off in the mist the sound of hoofbeats thundering towards me. I immediately thought of a runaway horse perhaps having shipped his rider returning home, or perhaps a farm horse broken out of some farmer's field. So I tried to quiet Battledore. I pulled over as close as possible to the stone wall which bordered the narrow bohireen. But by that time my horse was dancing in circles, evincing every sign of maddened fear and an inclination to run away himself on the instant. Suddenly—out of the mist—loomed a blood-streaked blue roan horse, its huge eyes bulging like balls of red fire. The precipitate ghost of Blue Flame, snorting like a Kerry bull, roared past me. Engaged as I was in keeping my horse on his feet and my seat on his back, I yet managed to get a good view of the rider. A man with a terribly battered head.

In the flick of an eyelash the ghostly manifestation was over. It took me a few moments to quiet Battledore. As we set out to continue our journey home I became aware that the horse had joined me in sniffing the odour of brimstone so noticeable on the damp November air.

God Forbid I Bear a Pooka

MALLARANY STRAND, COUNTY MAYO, 1890

FOR THOSE who do not know all the curiosities in Gaelic lore, let it be known that a pooka is a creature, relatively speaking, cousin-once-removed to a leprechaun. The old bards sang that a pooka was a water sprite, liable one moment to appear as a water thistle or primrose by the river brink, then suddenly to transform itself and appear to mortals as a mannikin, in size usually an infinitesimal object easily accommodated in the palm of one's hand, or perhaps knee-high, but never higher than that, or so it is told by persons who brag that they consort with pookas. A kind of arrogant boast proclaiming them immune to some disaster which, superstition insists, follows intimacy, however casual, with a pooka.

Shakespeare immortalized a pooka as Puck in *A Midsummer Night's Dream*. A pooka is the literal incarnation of mischief. The antics of the Italian Harlequin, the German Til Eulenspiegel, and even, in a sense, the American Tom Sawyer all bear pooka traits.

To illustrate in brief the way we Irish regard a pooka and a pooka's contempt for the ways of man, I present the following incident as a preface to my story itself. In the County of Wicklow is situate Pollaphuuca Waterfall. An ancient, arched stone bridge spans this mighty splash of gorge-hurled water. It is told that once upon a time, close to midnight of stygian darkness, a wayfarer far gone in drink taken—"because ave harassment be conviviality," he would probably have excused himself—wandered far off his homeward way. He barked his shin cruelly on a stone abutment, crying out loudly, "Be the holy God, where am I lost to?"

Out of the mist spewed up by the waterfall below, a small, shrill voice answered, "Ye gaum, it is the Bridge ave Pollaphuuca yer tryin' to kick into the gorge."

Then, revealed in an aura, an odd class of phosphorescent glow, the man beheld a tiny pooka dressed all in the green of water rushes, a bright red peaked cap set awry on his bald head. "Arragh, I'm murdered be the great stones crushin' me leg," the man moaned. "I've only the breath left in me to git to me coteen before I clutch the cross in death. Will ye set me on the road to Enniskerry, me fine little man?"

"I'm not a fine little man, I'm a pooka and well ye know it," the pooka retorted. "I give nothin' away. Fer a silver coin, knowin' ye'd not be carryin' *gold* on yer sodden carcass, I'll set ye right. I'll even give ye this"—the pooka held aloft a spear of water fern which glowed like a giant firefly in the night—"to light yer path."

The man fumbled in his pockets. He found a coin, fingered it carefully, smiled covertly to himself. "A silver ducat fer yer good nature," he said, and handed it towards the pooka.

The creature accepted the coin and was about to place the fern taper in the man's outstretched hand. But in dealing with chancy strangers a pooka is always cautious. Placing the silver coin between tiny pointed teeth, he bit the ducat. A look of rage spread redly over his face. "Ye blackguard ave the world," he screamed, "t'is counterfeit!" On invisible wings the pooka leapt into the air. He grasped the man by an ear-lobe, tweaking it sharply. With a wide grin he said, "You may Pollaphuuca but you can't fool a pooka." Still grasping the ear he hoisted the astonished mortal high in the air and dropped him over the parapet of the bridge into the torrent below.

Along about the year 1890 a streeler or wharfside prostitute named Kitty McClosky lay dying in a hot, dingy room under the eaves of a lodginghouse facing Sailor's Furlong, a narrow walk above the ship-caulkers' yards in Waterford Harbour Town. Beside Kitty on the narrow bed lay a baby girl born only two days before. A woman of middle age busied herself about a cupboard, preparing a draught to induce sleep. The doctor who had attended the birthing of Kitty's baby had said that morning to Mary Ranley, "It will quieten the woman McClosky, put her into the sleep she'll likely die under and a good thing, too. She's no blood in her veins and no strength in her heart. This childbearing so late in life and in her condition of health called the tune." So Mary Ranley, the owner of the house, was, in effect, performing the last rites.

As a dark, chill twilight deepened, Kitty McClosky died. Wrapping in a blanket the nameless scrap of humanity that tossed fretfully beside the corpse, Mary silenced the child's whimpering. "Like a kitten mewin' ye are" she said. She closed the door and went down the narrow attic stairs to send her son Timmy out in the town to find a pair of "shrouders," the bleak furtive-eyed women found in every Irish town who wash and shroud the charity dead.

For all that it was a bright Sunday in late May and the young boys and girls of Waterford Harbour Town trooping past Mary Ranley's house were dressed lightly for a day on the water and carried picnic baskets heavily laden with meat patties, cheese rolls, cakes, fruit and Stone ginger beer, she had not been able to persuade her foster daughter Reenie McClosky to join her neighbours for the sailing party out to Fethard Point. Mary often thought about the strangeness of it all at a time like this when Reenie would sit like a wooden image on the top step of the house, watching but apparently never giving a thought to joining in any of the games or outings so much enjoyed by boys and girls of her own age. It was then that Mary's mind would range back over the fifteen years since the dismal evening when she had lifted a nameless baby from beside its dead mother and had taken the child to bring up as if it were her own. Mary had named the baby Rianna, because she was forever laughing. And in the old tales that Mary's grandmother had told her, long days back on the farm in Tullaroan, Queen Rianna was the Gaelic goddess of all the pleasures, with the gift of laughter as her boon to young girls. But as the years passed, Rianna became a lovely name that somehow was never used. The child's playmates bestowed on her the nickname Reenie. She grew in years and prettiness. She seemed to care less and less for her foster mother, Mary Ranley, and the simple but pleasant enough home of which she had been made a part. No, Mary mused, Reenie, now sixteen years old, was all for cutting her skirts off nearly to her knees, tying big bows of red, blue or green ribbon in her naturally golden fair hair, and prancing out at all hours of the day and night to walk the quays with girls of the ilk of Bridie Callahan and Kesty Lanner. And so brooding Mary would sigh and busy herself with wetting down the tea leaves in the big brown earthen pot. Perhaps if she could catch a glimpse of Reenie sitting in her favourite vantage point on the top step in front of the street doorway she would call out,

"Reenie allanah, come now, join me in a bowl ave tea, I've things to tell ye. Sure these days fer the once ye come into the house ye go out twinty times." But like as not Reenie, even if she was atop the front steps surveying the Sailor's Furlong, would only nod and smile, "No, thank ye kindly. I'm waitin' fer Bridie."

To which Mary would murmur bitterly to herself, "Waitin' to scan some low-caste waterfronter more the like."

And no one could blame the waterfronter, "low-caste" as Mary put it, or not, if he made the most of the come-hither glances of a girl as pretty as Rianna McClosky was at sixteen years. When she favoured a long look in the mirror, which amounted to whenever she could find one, Reenie saw a girl of medium height with a figure that was the definition of "a manifestation of nature." Wherever there was a curve of breast, thigh, buttock or shoulder, Nature with perverse prodigality doubled the usual portion. The face of Reenie was perhaps not outright beautiful in the classic sense, but as one of her admirers had said on the night of her last birthday party in Bridie's lodgings, "Hell and tornado, but you're a *distraction* being so damned pretty. Come on along of me." In two words he had hit the nail squarely on the head: Reenie was "distractingly pretty." During the all too short night when Reenie had lain naked beside the big young sailor from off the Belfast packet boat, she had listened entranced to a long "line" of endearments with which he punctuated his ardours. As she kissed him farewell in the morning, then and there Reenie made up her mind. "This is the life for me," an inner voice cajoled.

A few weeks after her sixteenth birthday, Reenie came into the house on Sailor's Furlong at the hour of evening tea. Mary Ranley sat with her husband and a brother and sister at the tea table, eating prawns and battercakes. "Come along, Reenie," called out Marty Ranley. "Sure it's the grand sight fer me eyes ye are. Sure I niver see ye at all any more. Here"—he held out a plate of fried prawns—"have one ave these beauties done to a turn. They're Mary's specialty, ye know."

Reenie turned with her foot on the first step of the stairs. "I can't stop now, Marty. Thank ye all the same. I'm packin' a few clothes. I'm goin' on a little trip with Bridie."

For a few minutes there was silence in the room. All at table were wondering, thinking the same thoughts. Then it was Mary who reached for the big earthen teapot. She poured strong red tea to the brim of each empty cup. Then she spoke. "So it's come at the last. As I knew it would. I know the ways ave thim streelers ave the quays. Kitty McClosky's daughter. Once we bid Reenie good-by tonight we'll none ave us see her again. Never no more."

For a while Bridie Callahan and Reenie "toured" the seaports. Howth outside Dublin knew them briefly for a pair of skittish flirts who were avid for money to the point that a young garda officer complained, after testing the charms of both,

"Terrible quick with the down an' up and a hand outstretched fer the reckonin'."

Seaside resort Rosslare Strand was sampled for a couple of months in the summer. But it soon appeared these downy birds were outclassed by smarter members of their Dublin sisterhood. After a few verbal bouts with forked tongues employing invective of rare colour, and a few brush-ups featuring incarnadined fingernails to raking effect, Reenie and Bridie, like the proverbial Arabs, upped their tent poles and in the night watches silently stole away.

They chose Bantry, that delectable seaport on Bantry Bay. Here was, in effect, although she probably did not suspect so at the time, Reenie's spiritual home. The population was prevailingly male, rogue male, various and transient. Strong young mariners off ships sailing the seven seas formed a kind of ring of fire around Reenie. Her pompadour, a veritable nimbus of pale-gold hair, and her predilection for sheer blouses artfully trimmed with what at the time was known as peekaboo insertion, caught the eye of every randy male on the Parade. It was during her blissful sojourn in an "elegant second-floor front" at Mrs. Alto Cassidy's Select Resort that Reenie spent a great part of the days and nights on her back. At this period a paraphrase on Mary Ranley's remark that "for the once ye come in ye go out twinty times" might run that for the once she was up she was down twenty times.

After a few hectic weeks in Bantry, Reenie and Bridie parted company in none too warm accord. Bridie accused Reenie of "cadging" her prospects when the two were on the night prowl or drinking in the waterfront pubs. The truth was that Bridie, ten years older than Reenie, was losing her looks; her face was sallow and blotched from careless living and bad liver. And when in drink taken she shrieked like a harp over money for services rendered. Reenie on the other hand bloomed like a Killarney rose. Her laughter was delightful under all conditions and her high spirits and good nature for a "come on, me strong girlo, let's have it again" were infectious and a prime contender in the popularity stakes. And

Reenie's popularity with men was uncontested. If ever Aphrodite fostered the fortunes of one of her chosen handmaidens on earth, it was Reenie McClosky.

Just for a holiday, a change of scene, Reenie decided to spend a week at Mallarany in the County of Mayo. Now Mallarany is celebrated far and wide among mariners and streelers for its waterfront dives and pubs. Sailors, from bronze-skinned, withered-visaged Lascars off rusty tankers, treacherous of habits as an adder, to tall, fresh-faced fishermen from Achill Island and the Stags of Broadhaven where women are scarce and the nights long and cold, roam the Strand waterfront nightly.

And so Reenie arrived at Mallarany Strand in great looks and definitely at the top of her sexual form, which was impressive at any time, lugging a yellow-leather portmanteau with seams bursting from hasty overpacking. By this time Reenie had collected a staggering array of her veritable trademark, filmy chiffon and lace blouses uniquely fashioned to reveal even to the most casual eye the pectoral magnificence of the one and only McClosky.

The first week of Reenie's holiday was, in her lexicon, "sheer heaven," for she entertained scores of stalwart clients equal to her own dexterity of performance on the mattress. And then—an odd thing happened, a sort of catastrophe for one dedicated to the aloneness of women pursuing the oldest profession. Reenie fell headlong and unaccountably in love. As she was falling Reenie remembered a voice of caution, at first sharply, then increasingly dimly, the echo of the wise admonition of Bridie Callahan, her mentor in the game of love for sale. Often Bridie had said of some particularly attractive fellow for whom young Reenie had conceived a "crush,"

"Niver fall down deep in love wid *one* man, girlo. Love 'em all a little and leave 'em lay."

To her few streeler acquaintances in Mallarany the cream of the jest was the fact that Rony Legheena, the object of Reenie's affections, was as odd an article of manhood as one would see even among the "freakies" at Kilorglin Puck Fair. He was grotesquely undersized, wizened of visage, more than enough long in the tooth, and so bowlegged that Lacy Muldona of the foghorn voice, the accepted pub queen of Mallarany, remarked in Reenie's hearing, "Arragh, ye could drive a jauntin' car between the legs ave that bhoyo Legheena an' never touch a shinbone on either side."

But Reenie was trapped by her own ardour. To the exclusion of every other male she hung onto her lover in a kind of bemused desperation night and day.

That lazy, inarticulate half-gypsy Rony was taking her for a good thing, pleasuring himself on her lovely body while dipping his hand into her none too full pocketbook for his keep and "little luxuries"—a fact which seemed for this time of continual ecstasies not to penetrate the whirligig of gray matter that answered for the brain of Reenie McClosky.

Then one day while out walking the Strand with her raffish lover, Reenie met a girl named Curry whom she had known at Bantry Bay. A dark, flashing, sloe-eyed creature, the classic Dark Rosaleen of Ireland. The girl went by the name Rosaleen as well, and was notorious for her sharp speech and congenitally bitter tongue. Rosaleen Curry took one look at Reenie's escort and let out a harpy screech.

"Holy Saint Anna—fer God, Reenie, where did ye pick up the likes ave him? He looks like a pooka."

That tore it, for Rony at least. He had for the past few days been undecided about staying on with Reenie. More than once he had said to himself that she was too damned demanding, he'd not the strength to run the course. So, sometime during the night watches he decamped from Reenie's bed, for parts unknown to her forever after. As is habitual with drifters, he traveled light, his gear consisting of the shoddy suit and heavy drover's boots he stood up in, and Reenie's pocketbook containing the last penny she had to her name.

And so ended the brief idyl when, for the first time, selfless love had touched wayward Reenie. For a few days she moped despondently alone. But her spirits were too mercurial, her appetite for the exercise of her libido too strong for fasting of long duration. In a fortnight's time Reenie rouged her pale cheeks and donned her black-satin skirt cut tight to the hips and froufrou at the hem, topped by her most seductive blouse of white Irish crochet lavishly sprinkled with scarlet and purple sequins. Standing before her mirror she fluffed out her golden pompadour to improbable proportions designed to catch the light of hanging lamps, and her visiting in the waterfront pubs. She sallied forth with the light of conquest in her eye.

For the length of two months or more, Reenie basked as never before in the indulgent smile of her patron goddess Aphrodite. She reaped a harvest of coin of the realm. And yet for all her somewhat excessive gaiety in the pubs, and her amatory prowess, which was effortless and consequently never forced, there was noticeable a curious awareness about Reenie these days. Little by little, as the weeks passed she withdrew from the society of the few acquaintances that made up her narrow world of intimates. Reenie took to walking solitary, wrapped in a dark shawl, unrecognizable to passers-by from any of the other "shawlies," wives of fishermen and port labourers who lived in the shale-roofed coteens strung out along the waterfront fringes of the port. The truth was—and a hard truth it was for Reenie to face—she was going to bear a child. Just why Reenie accredited its conception to undemonstrative, even feeble Rony Legheena, when she had lain with scores of other notably virile men since his abrupt departure, even Reenie herself could not answer. Somehow she was persuaded in her own mind this child was Rony's.

Pagan daughter of joy though she was, devoid of any religious beliefs, at heart Reenie was fanatically superstitious. Twenty times a day she recalled the evening when she and Rony had met Rosaleen Curry. She remembered Rosaleen's startled jet-black eyes, cold as a snake's, and her sudden laugh of derision. "Holy Saint Anna! He looks like a pooka." Well Reenie knew the tales abroad the land. Anyone who touched a pooka, let alone lay under his caresses nights upon end, was marked for a bad destiny. Reenie moaned to herself the ancient "Oh whirra-whirra" keening. The Old Woman of Gonn, the most dread of all the harpies from the noisome caves honeycombing the Cliffs of Moher, had cast her shadow athwart Reenie's shoulders. She knew beyond doubt that that was the way of it. During the night that followed this morbid reasoning Reenie lay alone in her bed. She felt extreme discomfort—a kicking sensation in her belly and a terrible unease, a sickness at morning that to indecently healthy Reenie meant death, no less, and the sooner the better, she thought in this stress.

Reenie was in her seventh month when one evening just at sunset she had a chance encounter with Rosaleen Curry, dressed to the nines in black-and-crimson finery, standing unaccountably at the end of the Long Wharf, a quiet breakwater where Reenie often came to sit.

"Hello, pooka girlo," sang out the raucous Rosaleen. "Be the holy, ye look a sight fer bein' draggled and worn thin. I niver see ye about the Strand any more. Where do ye keep yerself? In that old rookery where ye were livin' on yer last farthin' the only time I heard of ye at all?"

Reenie smoothed her hair, which she wore parted in the middle nowadays, and combed close to her head, the length of it wound into a psyche-knot low on the nape of her neck. This style she found the best way of dressing her abundant hair to wear under the shawl she had lately taken to wrapping about herself at all times, not entirely to hide the ruin of her once so admired figure but also that with its head folds she might hide her face against recognition. Reenie narrowed her eyes to slits as she gazed at Rosaleen, who looked as bright as a Malay Straits parrot that sailors off some India tramper often presented to a publican in exchange for a few drinks and a night's lodging.

"I live where I like, ye gypsy sluteen." Reenie advanced menacingly upon the leering streeler and with the flat of her hand swiftly delivered a stinging slap to her plump cheek. "It was yourself that spoiled it all fer me. That night ye called me Rony a pooka. Ye've a dirty mouth on ye. Full ave toads an' vipers, yer insides er a moil, ye tawdry bitch, an' yer a spoil-all to boot." Turning on her heel Reenie walked up the causeway—too swiftly, for at the top she nearly fell on her face in a vertigo from hurrying the climb in her heavy state. It was that night, when the pains in her belly were excruciating, that Reenie made up her mind to take what she had decided was the only way out of her predicament.

"God forbid I bear a pooka," she had said laughingly to her landlady, old Mrs. Creedy, early on when she had confided to the bawdy, good-natured old soul that she was carrying a child.

Maggie Creedy, a streeler of the first rank herself "a million years ago," she had confided to Reenie, had been shocked at such facetiousness. "Childeen, fer the love ave God don't be after jestin' about a thing the like ave that. Pookas is pookas, an' to touch 'em is as good as murder an' crucifixion. If yer disorganized in yer belly it's jist a baby like any other. Soon out ave ye, and yerself up an' at it again."

"Well," thought Reenie, murmuring to herself as she went down the stairs from her lodgings, out the door and away along the inland road towards the silences of Lough Feeagh, "that was all a long time ago. That was another Reenie entirely. I'll not bear a baby ave any kind, pooka or not."

By the time she reached the reedy shore of Lough Feeagh, false dawn had painted a swath of primrose light in the eastern sky. A light breeze out early to herald the coming dawn riffled the waves of Reenie's radiant hair. A long way back, her heavy brown homespun shawl had slipped from her shoulders and unheeded fallen to the ground. By now, her mind in a kind of trance, she was walking as swiftly as she could manage. So firm was her purpose that when she reached the shore of the lough and the shallow waters lapping the meadow grass, Reenie, her eyes closed as if in sleep, walked without hesitation into the sedges.

On she walked, her head thrown back, the dawn wind cooling her feverish cheeks until the water like strong hands grasped at her knees, her thighs, a cold pain shot through her belly, then enclosed her breasts and stifled the sobs in her throat.

Soon the first light of true dawn spread over the land and over the waters of Lough Feeagh, which concealed in sun-latticed depths the weed-entangled body of Reenie McClosky.

It is told in the pubs of Mallarany and Bantry that the ghost of Reenie Mc-Closky is of the category "anniversary ghost," which means that she appears for a brief span of days in early September, approximately the time when she drowned herself in Lough Feeagh. She is seen as a young woman wrapped in a dark wool shawl, the head folds fallen back to reveal a pale face crowned with masses of golden hair gleaming with an unearthly light, who moves swiftly along the Strand at the twilight hour of day. She seems always to be headed for a jetty called Long Wharf. Arrived at the end of the jetty, the apparition raises her hand and makes the motion of delivering a blow. Usually the slap is directed at thin air. But there have been other manifestations. Two or three women have related how they encountered this wraith-like woman and received for no reason a painful slap on the cheek.

Sean
Son of Ossary.

Connaught

The Ossary Legend

THE CASTLE OF UPPER OSSARY, COUNTY KILKENNY, 1100

THIS IS a sombre tale stemming from most ancient Ireland in the time of the baronies. Years before the Battle of Clontarf there dwelt on neighbouring demesnes two brothers, chieftains of Upper and Lower Ossary. Hate, fed by a lusting for power that one might dominate the other, and its handman, treachery, consumed the twisted minds of Liam and Conn Ossary so that the days of each man were dark and blighted as if a flock of evil, odorous rooks winged ever across their vision, blotting out the sun of reason. Yet there is a thread of poetry, poignant, ill-starred to be sure, that for a space somewhat lightens the broodiness of this saga. And because the Irish cradle their legends, this one has been kept forever green in the hearts of poets and they who have the gift of song, in the way of Tristan and Isolde's love death.

Duirmuid, son of Ossary "The Upper," woke on a cool May morn before the sun had fully lifted above the eastern rim of the world a face shining from its daily bath in sea water. He vigorously rubbed sleep from his eyes and for a few moments gazed about the long, narrow room just under the barbican battlements of the castle where he slept with his two older brothers, Sean the Hotheaded and Corun the Bull-necked. He noticed that both brothers slept noisily as was ever their way. Duirmuid did not tarry lazily in bed this morn as he sometimes did, craving to lie awhile thinking of all the things he might do with the long day stretching before him, his to enjoy. This day, he remembered, promised to be a momentous one, perhaps the day that would mark, for all men to witness, his growing-up, his elevation to the status of a young warrior, a status that to his adventurous mind had been far too long delayed. Today his father Liam, Lord of Upper Ossary, was setting out for Waterford accompanied by more than two hundred gallowglasses, or "spears on foot" as they were called hereabouts, augmented by half again as many horse. With this complement of armed men and with the prowess of his own sword arm and those of his two brawny sons Liam was prepared to ride out with all speed to assist the Mac of Clonnard in a foray against the Danes of Waterford.

As Duirmuid dressed, carefully winding the cross-garterings of deerhide thongs over the soft leather hose he wore when attired for a long ride across country, he thought of all the roaring and blasphemy he had heard in the last few weeks when his father and sundry neighbouring chieftains foregathered in the Warriors' Hall of the castle. They had discussed plans for what promised to be a full fearsome clash of sound and fury, a battle to the death and no quarter, as the barons cast for a final victory over the Danish usurpers; for without a complete routing of the enemy, his father had shouted, the Gael could not long survive. Bannor Roe McIllagha had even topped his father's bull voice by thundering above the din, "Gone are the days when we launch forth out of the glens to madden the Danish outposts the like of a swarm of gadflies worrying a herd of Kerry cattle. We leave a few Danes and our own dead and that is the sum of it. We gain no profit to our rightful account."

For many weeks there had been preparations going ahead at the castle. The courtyard and the barracks for men-at-arms had resounded to the clanging of hammers wielded mightily by armourers and smiths fashioning armour plate for man and horse. Duirmuid's gentle mother, the Lady Ailagh of Upper Ossary, had vowed that for the comfort of planning household tasks undisturbed or the quiet of an hour's length she would as lief reside in the maw of a great forge.

Duirmuid knew, by the sound of men gathering and donning battle gear in the courtyard below, that the notes of the starting trumpet were not far off. He pulled his laggard brothers into cursing wakefulness, then bounded down the narrow twisting staircase to be first at the morning "bending the knee to grace" without which, administered by herself, the Lady Ailagh would not allow forward advance even of a decisive war.

Watching from an alcove, Duirmuid saw his father, fully armed, a blue heron's feather cresting his close-fitting helm, kneeling at the back of the chapel.

Directly the Lady of Upper Ossary had finished her devotions she took up from the altar a small crucifix fashioned of arbutus wood and, slipping her arm through that of her husband, went out from the shadowed chapel into the arched portal and so came to close embrace of farewell in the brilliant morning sunlight of the courtyard. The Lady Ailagh hung the arbutus-wood crucifix about the neck of her lord by a chain of linked bronze rings. "God keep you for me, my heart," she said.

Duirmuid waited, his eyes riveted upon his father's face, for the word of summoning, for notice that he would be allowed to join the company of horse and foot from Upper Ossary. Out of the corner of his eye he spied his own horse Wind Hawk champing at his bit, forever restless to be off. Duirmuid saw a hempen saddlebag of gear, but none of his, strapped behind the high backrest of the saddle. As he watched, hoping for word to mount, it was Sean to whom his father motioned impatiently. "Up Sean, mount Wind Hawk," he called. It was then that Duirmuid knew that once again he was to be regarded as too young to follow into battle the blue-heron banner of his house. In the eyes of his father, and, even more galling to the boy, those of his arrogant brothers, he was still a child to be left home with the women of the household, the old ones and the rabble of children fathered indiscriminately by the lusty gallowglasses.

Just as his father raised both hand and voice to signal "Away—fly the blue herons and God's blessing attend all here," he motioned to Duirmuid to come closer to his stirrup iron. "I leave you, my third son, in charge of your mother and of your House. Watch well over all." Then he raised his hand to the keep tower in the gesture of a chieftain taking leave for a time of his fortress place. With this farewell Liam, Lord of Upper Ossary, took leave of his family and castle.

In the dread days that followed, when Liam of Ossary returned to his stricken house, he blamed himself for the terrible pride that had prompted him to strip the guardhouse of its usual complement of men so that he could make a great showing of might among his neighbour barons. On his knees, keening for his dead, Liam moaned that no man in all the world—ochone—had ever paid so sorely for the sin of pride.

Directly his father had ridden out of the gateway onto the road that would lead through his demesne to Carrick-on-Suir, where the barons were to meet, Duirmuid rushed, three steps at a time, up the same narrow stairs he had hurtled down only an hour before, and he in such high spirits of expectancy then. He gained the topmost battlement of the Heron Tower in time to see his father riding beside Padraig, the proud bearer of the blue-heron banner.

It always brought a clutch of emotion, a surge of boyish pride, to the throat of Duirmuid, son of Ossary, to see this symbol of his heritage stream upon the wind. Today the brilliant sun picked out the myriad blue and violet tones of the banner. His mother and her ladies had dyed the silk threads to the exact colours of a marsh heron's plumage; then, using actual feathers as a pattern, they had embroidered a heron in full flight upon a field of saffron-yellow linen.

Soon the company of armoured men breasted a hill and without pause took the down grade. The blue heron in flight against its own yellow sky disappeared from Duirmuid's sight. For a while he ranged back and forth along the battlements. He knew by heart all the crannies of this great keep tower, knew just where each cresset for holding a pitch-pine torch could be stuck in time of night battle or siege. Then he tired of this pastime of pretend, having done it so often before. Just as he started to go down from the battlement his eye was arrested by what at first he thought was a lone horseman watching the castle, half-concealed behind a savanna of alder trees on the brow of a hill on the western boundary of the Ossary demesne. But on looking more closely Duirmuid decided he had been misled, for he saw no watcher and no movement.

For the rest of the day Duirmuid wandered aimlessly through the rooms of the castle—rooms empty of life and quiet now that his father and brothers and all but a score of men-at-arms had gone over the hill, under the blue-heron banner, leaving behind them a great litter of broken straps, rusted stirrup irons and bits of oily sacking, stained red as with blood by the rust that had been wiped from every piece of armour, no matter how old or apparently useless. Liam of Ossary had found himself hard put to outfit all his gallowglasses in protecting plate.

All day Duirmuid wandered, the picture of restlessness. At the kennels he found brief amusement in a litter of staghound puppies only two days old—tawny, bumbling objects, frantically seeking their mother's teats, all head, it seemed, with eyes still gummed tight-shut. He was ill at ease, his skin prickly with sweat, for an unaccustomed heat had risen from the water meadows.

"This is an unhealthy thing. There is no wind stirring," his mother said to Duirmuid, and he meeting her walking on the Great Hall terrace, crooning to the baby Grain, his tiny sister who was still too small to walk. "No wind," his mother repeated, "to blow away the stench of rotted weeds in the bogs—an unhealthy thing entirely. I have a drear foreboding." Her face white, as if with a sudden unease, she went back into the house and up to her bower in the west battlements. Mounting the stairs, to herself she murmured, "Fey as I am, all and always, some ill threatens the House of Upper Ossary."

After a bowl of millet porridge taken standing in the buttery, Duirmuid lay down upon his bed at sundown and was soon asleep. Once during the night he was awakened by the excited barking of hounds in the kennels. The sounds died down to growls and whimperings, then silence. Again, only half awake, he thought he heard the sound of distant hoofbeats.

The morning dawned overcast but ominously hot and airless. Duirmuid was up and about early. He dressed in the coolest garment he could find, a kind of jerkin, such as his brothers wore under armour, cut from coarse, loosely-woven linen. He took his hunting bow and arrows of yew wood, cunningly fashioned for toughness and resiliency by old Barrow the Sword, the castle armourer, so called both for his craft and for the sharpness of his tongue if bothered by questioners while at his anvil. Passing his mother's room, Duirmuid softly lifted the heavy iron latch, pushed the door open a few inches, entered the chamber and peered into the shadowy alcove where stood the huge bed, curtained in green embroidered linen showing a flight of blue herons winging above the cunningly-stitched treetops of a forest of evergreen. Duirmuid bent over his mother and saw that she breathed gently in refreshing sleep, the baby Grain lying cradled in the crook of her arm.

Softly as a dragonfly lights upon a reed lily, Duirmuid kissed his mother and baby sister and went away out of the room, out of the Great Hall door, across the drawbridge and, by tracing the curves of a goat track across the marshes, found his secret and private cave—an old gray-wolf's den, no longer frequented, where he had often come to gather bracken and make himself a huntsman's "moonlight bed." He would lie with his head facing the mouth of the cave, his body half in and half out, and watch the moon rise over the bog. When it was at the full, its strong rays turned the bog mists to drifting scarves of silver. Although Duirmuid often made up songs in the manner of the itinerant bards and "magical men" who sometimes visited the castle, he scarcely sensed that there was more than a little of the poet in his nature.

After the long walk across the bog, up hill, down valley, and up hill again, the heat tempted Duirmuid to lie down to rest on his freshly-gathered bracken bed. Relaxation coaxed deep sleep. The brazen sun, a hot orange-gold disk in the bone-white sky, had climbed to the zenith and descended halfway towards the west when Duirmuid rose from his ferns, gathered his bow and quiver of arrows, and prepared to seek quarry. Red deer he hoped to start, or if no luck in this at least the agile flop-eared coney. It was while he stood irresolute, pondering whether to seek red deer across the valley or the coney-burrows under the bracken on the slopes upon which he stood, that a swift terror seized him. A stab of pain as if a hand clutched his heart and crushed it between strong fingers. Far off he heard faintly the sound of shouting. Duirmuid cupped his hands behind his ears in the gesture of a warrior endeavouring to place the field of a battle not far off but hidden from view. The clamour seemed to come from the direction of the castle, more than half a mile away behind an oak-crowned knoll across the river meadows.

Duirmuid felt as if his legs were the weight of stone. So intent was he, so stricken with fear, that he began to cough chokingly from holding his breath. When he regained his wind the latent strength of a young runner returned to his long, stripling legs. Like a stag Duirmuid bounded forward and raced, with a speed he had never in his life attained before, down the hill towards the castle.

Darting from the shadows of a spinny of alder trees that fringed a last rise before which lay a long stretch of sphagnum moss ending abruptly before the outer bailey wall of the guardhouse, Duirmuid saw a column of oily black smoke rising from the roof of the home place, "the tower of spinning, the bower of chatter," as his father called it. Here his mother and her ladies were wont to gather daily. Here, too, sat the "gossips" or women of the roads, female equivalent of the bards, who traipsed the roads and found food, shelter, and an eager audience of women at the lonely castles of the barons. Duirmuid saw to his wonder that the drawbridge was down. Just as he leapt the ditch that surrounded the earthworks set around the bailey, he heard the sharp clang of horses' hoofs on the courtyard pavement. Then he saw an armed horseman pass swiftly out under the bailey arch and across the wooden planking of the bridge, a smoking torch of resinous pine still clutched in his hand. Then it was that Duirmuid knew in his heart that the greatest dread of all dreads in the world had this day visited his father's house. The grass-green cloak of the horseman, belling out behind him by the speed of his flight as his horse took the bog road to the west, and the blazoning of a red wolf with rising sun blasphemously poised like a saint's halo behind the beast's head, proclaimed the lone figure to be a henchman of Bloody Blake of Menlo.

It was late in the night when Duirmuid completed his wanderings through the castle. His mind was fogged by now. The sights of death most horrible that he had seen—men, women and children put to the sword, run through by the pike—had veiled the boy's eyes in a mist of red, a mingling of the red smouldering of hate and of utter despair. His mind was in such turmoil that he could not think clearly. A slave to exhaustion, he felt his eyelids heavy with sleep. The terrible weight of grief beyond all conceiving pounded on his brain like a hammer. He had found his mother lying dead at the door to the solar, her head all but severed from her body, her outstretched hands clutching the baby Grain, through whose skull had been thrust a pike, the haft dark, stained and sticky with blood, still standing straight in the air as if, Duirmuid thought, the spearhead had been driven into the planking to mark the boundary for distance in a game of spear-darting. From the cellars to a cubby on the battlements where a man-at-arms on watch would take shelter from a storm, he had not found a solitary soul alive. It was only when he stumbled out across the drawbridge and bent down to look into the dead faces of the guards his father had left to man the castle, that he found one man alive—alive, but only just. As he bent over the sword-gashed face of Barto, an old gallowglass, gigantic in stature, who had taught all the sons of Ossary the use of the longbow and the spear, the man opened his eyes and recognized Duirmuid. In a voice blurred by a gush of blood from the wounds in his hacked throat, Barto managed to speak the few words:

"Go to your father—the Blakes watched 'im leave—this day they came in greater strength—than we." Barto coughed the rack of approaching death. Duirmuid eased the iron gorget from the old man's throat.

"Yes—yes, Barto. Which Blake was it? The Old Wolf of Menlo or his son Gavin—which one was it?"

Barto's head sank lower on Duirmuid's knee. "It was the twa ave thim. Big in their savagery. The Wolf of Menlo struck me down—it was Gavin who sworded yer mother."

And so, rising like a veil of mist, a miasma, from the massacre of an innocent household, came the Ossary legend. The way of it is this. From the time old Barto rasped out his last breath in the arms of Duirmuid until a pale moon rode high behind ragged clouds as if loath to look upon such a scene of rape and treacherous slaying, Duirmuid sat inert, stupefied, beside the mutilated body of his mother. Sometime in the night he had lifted her and borne her to the great canopied bed where he had last seen her alive at early morning. And as he sat beside her stillness, his mind went away out of him.

It was years, many and long, before a bard living lone and barren as a hermit, in a cave far up the rhododendron-clad shoulders of the Muckish Mountains in Donegal, took one day too much heat from the sun and was struck down with an ague, only to waken and find his mind restored so that once again he was his own man. Only then did he know himself to be Duirmuid, son of Ossary, and with the clarity of mountain spring water dripping along a birch twig, all his thoughts shaped themselves into a circle of terrible remembrance. It was then that Duirmuid laid his plan for revenge upon his mother's slayer, Gavin Blake of Menlo.

Duirmuid no longer walked the earth silent, alone, seldom accosted by his fellow men, who took him for an "awayer," a nameless somnambulist. So penetrating were his thoughts that he spent long periods of time lying on his bed of bracken—its rustling fronds gathered fresh each morning—laid among the mightily tangled roots of an ancient oak near the shore of the Lough of Allen. In remembrance he explored every cranny of his life from youngest boyhood until the hour when he had heard the sound of shouting coming from the direction of Castle Ossary and had run his headlong race towards home and its hideous carnage. He remembered clearly that there had long been black blood between his father and Brian Blake, the Old Wolf of Menlo, hated and feared for his savage treachery by all men save those in his pay. Often Duirmuid had heard his brothers beg their father to give them men and horses so that they might ride out against The Blake and his bestial crooked-backed son Gavin, the "Wolf's Fangs" to all men of the roads who, if young Blake chanced to ride past them and cast his shadow athwart their path, crossed themselves and called on God to deliver them from "the shadow of the cursed Blakes."

So—this had been the Wolf of Menlo's revenge on his enemy Liam of Upper Ossary. Always at this point in his remembering Duirmuid would fall into wondering how long he had been a hermit in the mountains and the bogs, for the ague in his bones spoke of advanced years. Where was his father, where and how fared his brothers? But as he sat under the gnarled branches of the oak, watching the sun sink behind the low blue and purple Hills of Garvy, watching the flight of herons, azure-and-gray feathered symbol of the House of Ossary, he knew that watching for the chance to meet Gavin Blake in some lonely place must be the thought uppermost in his mind. But Gavin, if alive at all, would be an old man now, and to enter the bleak Castle of Menlo was at best a chancy hope.

One day Duirmuid met a traveler on the road near Kylemore in the Barony of Mayo. Together, as a sign of friendship, they shared a hand-loaf of oaten bread and some dried fish and wayside berries, tasted cold spring water, and then sat down beside the lough to talk. It was during this hour that Duirmuid, and he covertly listening, careful not to betray his identity by look or word, learned the dreadful tale of the massacre of the Tribe Ossary many years before. The narrator was a renowned bard known, he was not hesitant in saying, as "Granard of the Silver Tongue, a joyfully welcomed visitor at every man's hearth in the length and breadth of Ireland." He told Duirmuid that he had learned all the facts of the tragedy and made them into a rune. Quietly, his eyes staring out across the water, Duirmuid asked Granard:

"Would you, for the sake of our exchange of oatcakes, sing for me a few of the stanzas? Those that tell of The Ossary returning from Waterford, his discovery of the slain, the destruction of his house."

And so Granard, an agreeable man, granted Duirmuid his wish. He heard how his father, accosted on the highroad to Carrick by an ancient crone, had been warned not to leave his castle that day for she, out ranging the bohireens and copses under the moon, had seen a red wolf abroad in the night snuffling at the gates of the outer bailey to Castle Ossary. "Go not far away, lest the Wolf of Menlo drench your house in blood," the old crone had shrieked. But Liam of Ossary, hugely impatient to get on to Waterford, had kicked the woman out of his path. Her curses on himself and all of his had blasted the ears of his followers. It was said that many of the more superstitious in his company had feared that they too might fall under the evil shadow of this curse on "Ossary and all his," and had deserted him then and there.

Granard waxed expansive. He chanted in rising and falling cadences, as was the manner of such runes of dire stress. The battle at the Ford of Cappoquin had been disastrous for the barons, he said. Sean and Corun, the two sons of Ossary, too hotheaded to heed the orders of the captains, had been slain early on in the fray. All day long the battle had veered from near victory to total defeat for the barons. When the deepening shadows of twilight came, retreat was their only resource. Liam of Ossary, in headlong flight with the handful of men left to him alive, battle-grimed and disheartened, entered, as sunrise gilded the beech and

aspen woods, the valley known as Reaches of Upper Ossary. As he rode up the hill to the portcullis a strange, unfamiliar silence struck him as ominous. No furious barking of hounds, no fanfare of welcoming trumpets from heralds stationed on the strong tower battlement. And then a dawn wind lazily riffling the grasses of the bog carried to the nostrils of the returning lord the stench of unburied carrion. Spurring his horse forward, Liam of Upper Ossary felt his weary eyes seared as if blasted when he saw carrion rooks in their black hundreds, rustling like an evil wind among the unburied and rotting corpses. With a terrible cry of foreboding of what he would find within, he fell senseless from his horse.

Granard stopped his chanting. Duirmuid sat silent, his chin sunk upon his breast, twirling a spear of ripe wheat between his fingers. He lifted his head. "The Saga of the Ossarys. God go with you, Granard; my debt to you is great. Just one more word. There was not a one left to speak, you say, save Ossary himself. What of him?"

Granard had risen and shouldered his leathern wallet, which was crammed, Duirmuid noticed, with food. "Ossary—he lived not long. His grief crushed him. He killed himself by falling on the point of his sword. God guard your steps, Old One and Lone." And he set off at a striding pace down the road. Old One! Duirmuid looked at his hands and the sallow skin of his arms. He felt the dryness of the hair of his head and his matted beard, gray as coney fur. His face he had not seen, even mirrored in water, since he could remember. So, he mused, I am an old man. I was only fourteen when I ceased to live. Old—old—I must get about my plan. No longer can it wait.

And so it came about that in the West of Ireland there walked the roads a bard of strange repute. He sang the saga of the "Ossary Massacree" with a fire and intensity of dramatic effects that no other bard could match. True, he was most old, livid-white of skin, nearly toothless, not goodly to look upon, being bent of frame and halting in gait. But his voice was golden-soft and his eyes blazed like the lurid rays of Beltane's Fire in the northern skies when he sang his rune to a hushed throng of nobles. Here, they would nod to one another and whisper, was the magic of true bardry.

One evening in late autumn the Lone One, as Duirmuid was mysteriously known by his own preferring, came to the gaunt, sable, pitch-daubed walls of Menlo Castle, set high and forbidding above the shallow chain-linked Lakes of Menlo. To many a man, no matter what his condition in life, this "palace" of the

Blakes was shunned as fearfully as if it were a haunt of plague, the black death itself. But the Lone One feared nothing. Never, no more. The Blakes had dealt him all the atrocity he would ever experience in life. He pulled the bell rope at a side postern gate and craved admittance as the ancient right of a bard off the roads, prepared to entertain all within.

An old serving man bent nearly double from the misery of crooked joints grudgingly opened the heavily-barred door, but only wide enough for Duirmuid to sidle through. By his hooded mantle and small willow-wood knee-harp his bardship was proclaimed.

"Go yer way up them stairs. Himself will have the say will ye sing yer songs er no." The old one pointed to a flight of narrow stone footholds that had been set ladderwise into the thick walls of roughhewn stone.

Cautiously Duirmuid mounted the damp stones and walked down a long, wind-swept corridor as empty of furniture as a crypt, and as bleak. Two men-at-arms, armed as if for battle, stood in front of an archway over which hung a curtain of deerhides crudely stitched together. "I am the Lone One," Duirmuid said in his soft, caressing voice. "I would see The Blake of Menlo. I would compose for him a saga of his deeds and the wonder of his lordly house."

The arras was drawn aside by one of the men, and at last Duirmuid stood only a few paces from Gavin Blake. For a moment the Lone One was stunned at the ancientness, the corroding of years that sat like a brooding vulture upon the crouched shoulders of this ruin of a man, his ancient enemy. Gavin Blake looked up from under craggy white eyebrows into the eyes of this bard of the roads, his own eyes glaring wildly from dark, skeletal sockets. He had seen many bards in other nearly-forgotten years when he had kept high court. The foods on his tables, his wines, his women, the entertainment of his guests had been the grandest in the land. But now, what could he enjoy of bardry or aught else, old, sick and deserted even by cronies whose pockets he had lined with gold, women he had hung with jewels, sons to whom he had given lands and power of place? Well, he would hear this old croaker out. His runes might induce sleep.

"Bard, what are ye called, and from where do ye come?" he asked.

"I am called the Lone One," Duirmuid said. "And I come from everywhere, and beyond. I come to chant you a rune of your great deeds."

At that moment serving men appeared and a table was laid in front of the stone dais on which was set the great oak chair, its seat and back covered with the skins of red foxes and gray wolves. Sunk deep amid these furs against the mounting cold of the night, harried ·by a stiff wind off the sea scudding across the chamber under ill-hung doors, Gavin Blake took his food alone. He bade Duirmuid sit on the edge of the dais.

"Now," he said, "chant me your song. My deeds, you said. Ha! my deeds have been many, and best forgotten. No matter, sing of what you will."

Duirmuid rose from his place on the dais edge. Save for two serving men moving in and out of the room he and Gavin were alone. He crossed his hands in the loose sleeves of his robe. He fingered the thong of stag gut, the kind he used to string his knee-harp, that he had coiled and hidden in his folded cuff. He waited until both serving men had left the room. Then in two swift strides he stood in front of Gavin Blake. "One of your deeds has ne'er been forgot," he said. "Foulest of all—the murder of my mother, the Lady Ailagh of Ossary. I am Duirmuid of Ossary."

Blake sat bolt upright in his chair. Grasping the arms he leaned forward as if better to see one whom he had thought dead these many years. "You were slain —that day—like all the Ossary save Liam. He slew himself—after." Then he sank back among the furs, gaping as if demented at the white-faced man before him.

Bending his tall thin body over the speechless Gavin with the lethal suddenness of an adder striking at its prey, Duirmuid whipped out of his sleeve the leather thong. With a loop of the gut he encircled Gavin's neck. The thong was pulled taut, twisted. There was no sound to attract the attention of the two servers standing deep in gossip in the shadows at the far end of the hall, save a low rattle of choked-off breath. Duirmuid stepped down from the dais. He gathered the folds of his long cloak about him and went away out of the dimly-lighted chamber, through the door whence he had come. Although he heard the voices of the men-at-arms who had been on guard in the corridor when he entered the Great Hall, he met no one. Descending the narrow, twisting stone stairs with all speed, he let himself out of the postern gate to become one with the shadows of the night.

Persons not familiar with the ways of the persistent Irish ghost might well believe the tragedy that befell the House of Upper Ossary so long ago would be recalled to mind only dimly if at all—an occurrence horrible, but fellow to many such deeds of bloodletting in the feuds that incarnadine the early history of the obstreperous Gael. But the Irish as a race, particularly the countrymen, to a surprising extent live with their legends, however ancient. They include tales of romance and horrid deeds alike, as part of the daily round.

I have heard many and various recountings of how one of the most restless ghosts I know of comes back almost nightly to stalk the roads of the West Country, mouthing and gibbering "black talk" of murder and revenge, as it appears Duirmuid of Ossary must have done during the long period when his mind was "away." I sat one evening with a farmer and his wife outside of their whitewashed stone coteen in the wild and beautiful reaches of "haunted Connemara," where the lagoons of pale-amber bog water mirror the bluest sky in the world, or the blackest storms. I listened to a tale told me in the soft, blurred speech of the glens, the like of this.

"I do be out in fair and foul weather carvin' turves ave peat in the bog ferninst," Bartly Cannonard said, motioning to the vast stretch of bog behind his shale-roofed coteen. "I see all and either, but none ave weirdry to match the Lone One, Duirmuid of the Sorrows, himself that was ave the Ossarys. One night not long since, I was gatherin' together me staves and turf-irons against runnin' from an old monster ave a storm brewin' with too much ardour fer me taste beyond the behind ave the Twelve Pins. As ye may know thim mountains, all twelve ave thim are a class ave incubator fer all the storms out ave Hell. I was just about to get away out ave that whin I heard a terrible screechin'. The tatarara came from over beyant the road to Mamm's Cross, and fer a minute I thought it was a woman in the depths ave distress. I was about to drop me gear and help the creature whatever, whin I see coming towards me, strutting on long pipe-stem legs the like ave a marsh heron on the jump, the old bard that I'd seen before miny's the time streelin' the bog roads shoutin' and keenin' to the winds about his afflictions. But this time, instead ave passin' me by with divil a nod nor glance, the auld omhadon made straight fer meself standing undecided-like on the top ave the sod bank borderin' the bog road."

At this point Cannonard speculatively pinched his windpipe between thumb and forefinger. He cleared his throat. "I noticed the bard held his two hands outstretched, limberin' a length ave leather thong that looked to me like a garrote. Before I had the time to utter a prayer er a curse, old Duirmuid had looped the thong around me throat. Fer a second I thought I was a deader. And thin, as the old bhoyo twisted the cord, I realized there was no more feelin' ave hurt than had it been a thread ave night mist that was driftin' in clouds across the Bog ave Inagleeah. In me agitation ave deliverance from, as I thought, meetin' death, I slipped back down the steep slope ave the bohireen. Whin I clambered up the side agin I heard Duirmuid ave Ossary's ghost still screechin' his woes, but he was not visible. All I could see was the perishin' gloom ave mist."

It is often told thus. The ghost of Duirmuid the Mad Bard, as he is sometimes called, ranges at all times the roads around the now ruined Castle of Menlo. In his lifetime, once he had regained his reason after the black years when his mind was a blank, he had one idea and that alone: to seek out and kill Gavin Blake. He chose the garrote as a means to do the deed. Perhaps Duirmuid died that night when his mission was accomplished. And, dying, his mind was pinned on a moment of time, the moment of his revenge. It is this moment that for more than seven centuries Duirmuid has relived in a kind of perpetual anniversary of exaltation in the way of ghosts.

Slippers That Waltz Till Dawn

GARRON TOWER, COUNTY ANTRIM, 1828

THIS IS a tale of moonlight, roses, love in June, gallant hussars, languishing naval ensigns, lovely women, a romantic castle; then—tragedy. At the time of the Battle of Waterloo the dramatic old pile of Garron Tower was a sumptuously appointed house. This had not always been so. When Sir Hildreth Starrat married the aged, eccentric Countess of Antrim for her fourth husband, the castle was scarcely fit for human habitation. The old pile of hugely-lewn stone blocks was drafty and rat-ridden. Damp and mildew from incessant fogs drifting in from the Irish Sea corroded the walls of high-vaulted rooms. Draggled tapestries sagged on walls of peeling paint or cracked plaster the like of gigantic cobwebs. But Sir Hildreth changed all that in short order. In record time this energetic man, who loved the grace of living, changed the castle into a beautiful residence hung with crystals and damask, and carpeted with shimmering rugs from the East. Not only the interior of Garron sprayed colour the like of a Roman candle; the long terraced gardens were planted so thickly with roses that Flora, gazing down from her cloud pavilion, was amazed and envious.

Obligingly, the countess died soon after the wedding, leaving Sir Hildreth a vastly rich man. At first her sudden death met with some adverse speculation. For, almost immediately after his marriage, Sir Hildreth had installed his ward, a niece, Lady Constantia Gainsford, at Garron, and during the few months the old countess lived, she had refused to see the girl. The atmosphere at the castle may be said to have been charged with electricity. Whether the exit of the countess was engineered by her husband or God has remained a moot point down the years.

99

In every way Lady Constantia was admirable. Her popularity in the village of Glenarm and the surrounding countryside was proverbial. Her beauty was of the fragile sort: silvery fair hair, gentian-blue eyes, and a rose-leaf complexion. A glance from her eyes devastated most males. Unfortunately, without meaning to, Lady Constantia inflamed the heart and rakehelly brain of her guardian to a point which set jangling all the strange quirks of his mind. Extremely handsome, a born flatterer, a voluptuary of the first water, Sir Hildreth had made a career of infatuating women to his eternal gain.

He was crowding fifty-five years when he gave the first ball at Garron Tower, to celebrate the engagement of Lady Constantia to young Lord Avonport, a dashing blood in the Irish Fusiliers, the crack Irish regiment of the period. From the first hint of a love affair between Avonport and Lady Constantia, her guardian had cast a jaundiced eye on the proceedings. Outwardly he appeared extremely pleased with the match, admirably suited on every count as the couple were. Inwardly he seethed with jealousy. Tasting his own bile day after day, the man became secretly a monster of revenge.

All was set for the festivities. A moon close to full silvered the standard rose trees and the latticing vines of climbing yellow roses which covered trellised arcades. The hope that the full of the moon would endure for the ball seemed certain. Mantuamakers from Belfast had for days worked feverishly on a series of gowns in which Lady Constantia would delight her guests, for the ball was only one of many entertainments planned by Sir Hildreth to launch his beloved ward on her engagement.

Everyone so fortunate as to be invited to the ball at Garron Tower arrived all during the day, decked in whatever costly finery each could manage. It was the period of peacocking for men and flaunting every jewel and plume in their wardrobes for fashionable women. Irish beaux and dandies still wore perukes dressed high, *en pompadour,* in the French and Italian style, far later in the nineteenth century than was the mode in England or on the Continent, according to a Dublin fashion magazine for men, delightfully called *The Beaux Quizzing Glass.*

Irish women had seized eagerly upon the fashion for immense Turkish turbans of gauze and light silk. These erections, sprouting a panache of plumes or aigrettes, had been introduced to the ballrooms of Dublin by Lady Blessington, a "glass of fashion" paramount, after her triumphs in the salons of Paris.

Brilliant uniforms, resplendent with strappings, gold lace, and the insignia of smart regiments, were worn by most of the young dancers in a ballroom at this time. A military or, to lesser extent, a naval career was the goal of the young aristocrats.

True to predictions of the weather-wise, a moon full to bursting hung in a blackberry-coloured sky on the evening of Sir Hildreth's ball for his ward. Fairy lights festooned the long stone balustraded terraces along the sea walk at the castle, which was etched against the sky with every window ablaze. The sound of music rose on the night breeze. Laughter and now and again a snatch of song issued from the wide, open terrace windows. Towards morning, when a faint finger of primrose dawn slit the eastern sky, the last gavotte was played. A few coaches belonging to guests who lived close by rumbled out the gates of Garron Demesne, the coachmen as sleepy as the occupants inside the cushioned box.

Sir Hildreth had been meticulously the grand host. But had one looked closely at his hooded eyes and noticed his withdrawn, watchful air, the realization that the man had some atrocious plan afoot would have come shockingly alive. The day after the ball the ladies slept long to repair the fatigues of continuous dancing. At lunch Sir Hildreth proposed some rough shooting in the savannas of bramble and larch a mile or so inland from the castle. A number of the young men, including Avonport, cheerfully agreed, for at Garron Demesne prime sport with guns was well known. A small body of water called Carnlough, near Glenarm, was a famous nesting place for wild geese.

Some ten guns set out with four beaters, and for an hour or so shots rang out at intervals. A good bag was laid out in rows of variegated plumage on a strip of turf near the lough edge. Harry Avonport was standing on a knoll close to a spinny of larch when a shot exploded so close behind him that he turned quickly, only to stop a second cartridge full in the heart. When his friends ran to the spot where he lay dead, bewilderment as to how this tragedy could have happened ran rife. One explanation, given by Sir Hildreth, was that a malcontent in the neighbourhood had twice taken a shot at Lady Constantia's guardian. Because Avonport was wearing a dark-green shooting jacket and broad-brimmed hat similar to his, Sir Hildreth ventured the shot had again been meant for him. This version, while within reason, was not fully accepted by the others of the party, although no one openly, at the time, entertained more than suspicion.

When Lady Constantia was told the news by her guardian, she was at first inconsolable. But so deep was the man's sympathy, so tender his solicitude through her days of mourning her fiancé, that the distraught girl finally agreed to go to Dublin for a season, staying with her aunt, Lady Carmichael. In a few months the resiliency of youth asserted itself. She became once again the creature of smiles and love of dancing she had always been.

During Lady Constantia's visit in Dublin a demented streak in Sir Hildreth's nature swept all reason before it. Singularly vicious revels were held at the castle. An ill-assorted group of bucks would coach up to Garron Tower from Dublin, Belfast, and as far south as Cork. A chancy lot they were, some accompanied by women of voluptuous charms but low breeding. Often at the height of these drunken orgies Sir Hildreth would curse the lot and drive them helter-skelter from his house. Then for weeks he would remain recluse. At night the terrified servants would hear the master ranging the corridors, shouting blasphemies at God and all the saints in the calendar.

One day he coached to Dublin, to appear smiling and urbane at Lady Carmichael's house in Merrion Square. He informed his ward he had come to take her home. At first Lady Constantia demurred. Garron Tower held upsetting memories for her. She appealed to her chaperone, who replied, "It is disagreeable, I know, for you to return to Garron Tower. But Sir Hildreth is not to be put off. He is your guardian and you are beholden to him. Put on as good a face as you can muster, and I dare say, what with his pleasure at having you home again, he will be prodigious kind to you. Indeed he already talks of another ball to celebrate your return." To a visitor who arrived to take a dish of tea with Lady Carmichael soon after this advice, she added, "For so young a girl, a perfect bundle of delicate sensibilities like Constantia, to be shut away at Garron with one of the prize lechers of Ireland gives me the vapours to even think on. I will never know what possessed my brother Rathdavin to appoint Sir Hildreth as guardian to his daughter. A monument to loose thinking on Rathdavin's part. Disaster will come of this state of affairs, mark my word." Lady Carmichael uncorked a small crystal vial of ammonia salts to point her remarks. A few sniffs and she continued, "Constantia has another suitor. Many flutter around so lovely a girl, of course. But a young naval ensign from Cork Harbour named Tancred leads the field. A nice boy and very devoted. The sooner she is married and away out of that mélée the better for us all."

So it turned out that Sir Hildreth and his ward journeyed north along the vile rutted roads of rural Ireland, with trunkloads of finery strapped on the roof. "My dear Constantia, we will be gay as starlings at the Tower this summer. I have planned all manner of diversions for you."

"Ah, Sir Hildreth," the pensive girl answered, "you are indeed prodigious kind. I hope the roses are all in bloom. I remember the ropes of roses twining the stair and balcony rails at my . . ." She stopped talking suddenly.

Quick to detect any hint of brooding, Sir Hildreth said, "We will have a Ball of Roses. Indeed a *bal masqué* in which the ladies dress to counterfeit roses. That should set the dowagers to cackling. Should you like a Rose Ball?"

Soon after Lady Constantia's return to Garron Tower her guardian took to making mysterious trips, to what destination she never knew. One morning before he started out, he came to the morning room where she was having first chocolate. "Constantia, what is the name of that young man who I hear paid such assiduous court to you in Dublin? I should like to ask him to the Ball of Roses next month."

Looking up from a letter which she had just started to read she smiled. "How odd you should ask that question at this minute. I have this letter from him. His name is Nevin Tancred. He is stationed at Cork Harbour. His ship is His Majesty's 'Cormorant.' I will invite him when I answer this letter."

Had the girl noticed particularly, she would have seen a wave of dark anger flood the aging face of her guardian. He turned on his heel to leave but stopped short in the doorway. "Are you engaged to him? Or about to be?"

A trilling laugh came from Constantia's lips. "No, no. He has not asked me. I find him agreeable. Perhaps sometime I might find him even more. He is witty, gay, and startlingly handsome." She returned eagerly to reading her letter.

A fortnight later Sir Hildreth came back from his visit to, as he said, Galway. "I bought two splendid stallions to add to my stud" was all he vouchsafed before shutting himself morosely away in a distant wing of the castle. For days Lady Constantia did not see him. A gossip living in the environs of Glenarm, monstrously taken with the rich widower of Garron Tower, was constantly turning up for a dish of tea, always primed to relate the latest news, preferably of scandalous nature. Not finding Sir Hildreth anywhere in evidence, Mrs. Bawn-Brackley cornered a footman to announce her to Lady Constantia. Over a dish of tea on the terrace she said, "Was it not sad about that handsome young ensign being drowned in such a mysterious way in Bantry Bay?"

Absently, for she was not listening very attentively to the woman's chatter, Lady Constantia asked, "Who was it? I had not heard."

"Well, you of all people should know. It was the Tancred boy who paid you such ardent court in Dublin last season."

Stunned, the girl listened to Mrs. Bawn-Brackley recount what she had heard. It seemed young Tancred had received a message on board his ship. It read that his father, who lived near Bantry Bay, had been taken seriously ill. He must come home at once. It was signed by his mother. Alarmed, he had not looked closely at the writing. He left Cork Harbour Naval Depot on a fast horse. From then on, all that anyone knew was that the horse had been found dead on the rocks below Curryglass Headland. So broken was the carcass it would seem the animal had fallen from great height. The next day the body of Nevin Tancred was found floating near Whiddy Island in Bantry Bay.

Even when alone and miserable in her room, Lady Constantia did not in any way connect her guardian with Tancred's accident. Being of guileless nature, the girl had accepted Sir Hildreth's account of buying horses in Galway as the truth. After a while the master of Garron Tower emerged from retirement and set out on a series of entertainments of a nature to please his ward. The notable charm which had ensnared the foolish hearts of so many women through his temperamental journey of life was now brought into full play. He swept many women off their feet by his attentions, including infatuated, garrulous Myrtle Bawn-Brackley, who was almost hysterical with excitement at the bare thought of becoming mistress of Garron Tower. But, as always, Sir Hildreth had a method in his campaign. He wished so to enthrall the countryside they would all be on his side in case of an emergency. For by now his jealousy for his ward had become paramount in his life. So in love was the man with this fragilely lovely girl that his life was a torment. Let a young man so much as take Lady Constantia for a stroll, in broad daylight or in evening shadows, and Sir Hildreth became a thunderhead on the landscape. Of course the girl sensed this obsession to some degree, but fended off any attentions on the part of her guardian as expertly as any Parisian cocotte.

Late in August, Sir Hildreth came upon his ward one day at the end of the terrace. She was engaged in threading ribbons through the eyelets of satin dancing shoes. "Well come upon you, my child. I have set the date for the Ball of Roses. The last night of August, when the roses are at their height. Always the second blooming of Garron roses is the most luxurious. Then the perfume is most heady. Which rose shall you impersonate?"

The girl was silent for a space of minutes. "I had not thought. The pale tea rose is my favorite. Must we have this ball? Are invitations already sent?"

"What is this?" Sir Hildreth put his hand under her chin. Lifting it he looked longingly into the clear blue eyes. "We must be gay and make this ball the most talked of. For at the ball I have a surprise for you and—"He turned towards the balustrade, gazing at a splendid view of the sea. "And a surprise for the country-side. Yes, even for Dublin and silly, dance-mad Cork. Oh, yes, I promise you it will be a vast surprise."

As Lady Constantia sat awhile on the terrace after Sir Hildreth had gone, she never for a moment even conceived that he would announce his intention to marry her, on the night of the ball. However ardent the man had at times appeared, she had put it down to his rather flamboyant, over-gallant nature. Yet, insidiously re-moving all obstacles, Sir Hildreth had been planning this matrimonial coup for years.

The night of the Rose Ball, Garron Tower rang with suppressed excitement. Among the guests who gathered in chattering groups on the terrace and in high-ceilinged rooms, the talk was of the latest dance, which was to be inaugurated that night. The Vienna Waltz. The craze for this whirling dance had swept all Europe like a conflagration of gaiety. Irish gentry were notoriously backward to accept new modes. The tone was first set by decorous Viceroys at the Castle in Dublin. Once the viceregal court had given a nod of approval, important hostesses eagerly followed.

Musicians from Dublin started tuning violins and harps. Late arrivals strolled through the castle admiring the fragrant decorations, for everywhere ingenuity in arranging legion species of roses was evident. Great swags of dark red and white Gloire de Valois roses hung from cornices. Standard rose trees in all shades of pink formed a dado in the ballroom. Terrace and garden walks led through tunnels of climbing roses. Added to this, the women had aped in satins and crackling taffetas the crisp petals of red, yellow, pink, and white roses. Many brilliant uniforms ap-peared among the throng, for a ship of the line, His Majesty's "Forward," had an-chored a few days before in the adjacent harbour of Carrickfergus. Shoals of fresh-faced young ensigns would sweep the ladies off their feet in the waltz. A cavalry regiment stationed at Glenarm added dash to the scene as tall officers, sabers clanking against sabretaches, strode about greeting friends. One officer in particu-lar stood out in the ballroom for his height and mane of red hair: Captain Alistair Strand, who had paid marked attention during the last few weeks to Lady Con-stantia.

Sir Hildreth started the first dance, a gavotte, with the ranking peeress present, the Duchess of Clandyboy, while fortunate Captain Strand led out Lady Constantia. For the second dance a waltz was played. More than a few of the guests did not know this dance, so the ones who did had an appreciable audience gathered around the walls. Little by little as the violinists' bows leapt in the fast tempo, eager dancers joined the whirling throng. Brooding on the sidelines stood Sir Hildreth, for the sight of Captain Strand, partnering Lady Constantia for the second time in succession, caused the red flare of jealousy to gleam hotly in his eyes.

Walking out onto the terrace Sir Hildreth realized he must cast his engagement surprise into the teeth of his guests just before the supper dance at midnight. In the meantime he would absent himself from the ballroom, else his rage at attentions showered on his ward would unsettle him to a point where he would make a bad showing as a prospective husband.

Never had Lady Constantia enjoyed herself so much. To Captain Strand she said, "I could waltz until dawn lights the sky. Indeed, if I do not dance three pair of satin slippers to shreds tonight, I shall not consider the ball a success."

Swinging his partner expertly in and out of the dancing couples Strand replied laughingly, "I once knew a girl in Edinburgh who danced four pair of slippers to ribbons. But she was never as light to swing as are you." When the dance was over he whispered, "Let us take a turn on the terrace. I know a bower at the end of the rose walk. I have a question to ask you, very secret. Here, through this window."

Sir Hildreth had not been able to stay away from the ballroom. His jealousy, inflamed now by heavy drinking, acted as a magnet to draw him back to the long, candlelit room. Just as Captain Strand and his partner slipped into the shadows of the terrace he caught sight of them. His rage mounted as he followed. Softly— do not let them know, he cautioned himself. Softly. Then he saw the captain take Lady Constantia in his arms. A scarcely audible question followed. A less audible but eager answer, and the two kissed long and passionately.

Swiftly through the dark channels of this eavesdropper's mind raced methods of revenge upon yet another suitor for Lady Constantia's hand. Obviously this time the affair was not youthful dalliance, as in the case of young Tancred. Well versed in all nuances of wooing, Sir Hildreth sensed deeply that his ward had answered her lover's proposal of marriage with a binding "Yes." Into his inflamed brain flashed an idea. Swift as lightning, and as deadly, it pointed the way. He knew clearly what he must do.

First he called to a lackey who was passing the niche where he stood concealed. "Watch her ladyship and when she is dancing with another than Captain Strand, the officer who is approaching with her now, let me know. I will be at the end of the corridor leading to the summerhouse." Turning, Sir Hildreth made off down the passage.

Blinded with rage at the sorry turn of events which had thwarted his so carefully laid plans, the man paced in demented state up and down a small reception room at the end of the corridor he had mentioned. This room, in a little-used wing of the castle, was private. At the moment all activity was in the rooms in the main block facing the sea. From a long box on a console Sir Hildreth took a slender rapier of Italian workmanship. Expertly he tested the point and blade. "This will be quick and silent," he nodded to his reflection in a mirror.

In the doorway appeared the lackey. "Your honour, sir, her ladyship is mountin' the stairs on her lone. May ye be wantin' me to take her a message, sir?"

"No," replied Sir Hildreth sharply. "Find Captain Strand, the officer I pointed out to you. Tell him Lady Constantia wishes him to attend her immediately in the little summerhouse at the end of this corridor. Show him the way, then return to your duties. Be quick about it."

But search as he would in every room, even out on the terrace, the lackey could not find Captain Strand. Meanwhile Lady Constantia, having procured another fan to replace one she had broken, descended the stairs. She almost danced along the corridor leading to the summerhouse, where she had asked Alistair Strand to meet her. Vaguely, she wondered why the hallway was so dark. Someone must have snuffed the candles which earlier in the evening had burned in every wall sconce. Hastening her steps, she was about to burst into a snatch of song Alistair had taught her. She was just abreast of an open doorway when a man suddenly appeared in the corridor before her. His eyes gleamed with madness as, with a swift lunge of a rapier, he ran the blade through her heart. Blinding jealousy, the dark passage, the sound of footsteps he expected to be Alistair Strand's, had so confused Sir Hildreth that he mistook his victim.

For a moment, as he bent over the dying girl, his senses reeled back to sanity. Then with a cry more animal than human, torn from his heart, Sir Hildreth fled the castle. In the morning the body of the master of Garron Tower was found hanging from a limb of an oak in the farthest reaches of the park. Today this tree is called Starrat's Reward.

Soon after the fatal stabbing of Lady Constantia Gainsford, persons living at Garron Tower told of varying ghostly manifestations within the gray walls. At night a lilting laugh is heard echoing through a corridor in the oldest wing, the one abutting on the rose garden in the park; and sometimes snatches of a barracks song, sung haltingly, as if the singer were not familiar with the melody. Whenever this song is heard a pair of tea-rose dancing slippers are seen to spin round and round in the ballroom. A woman who was a guest at the castle a few years ago told me she had seen this phenomenon occur at intervals all night. A pair of slippers dancing tirelessly until dawn. I asked her if the crossover ribbons of the slippers were laced and tied or swung freely. "Well, now you ask me, I cannot recall. I believe the ribbons were tied, as around an ankle, else I should have noticed especially," she replied. With this apparition a pervading scent of roses drifts through the rooms. No matter what the season, the heady scent of summer roses is strong.

Another dramatic version I have heard is that sometimes the disembodied slippers pause in their dancing, hesitate, then dance away down the long corridor towards the summerhouse. A shriek rings out, the slippers disappear. Then there spreads a pool of blood at the spot where Lady Constantia was stabbed. It has been found difficult to erase this gory spot from the tiles.

Potatoes and Babies

BALLYSHANNON, COUNTY DONEGAL, 1954

AN ENGLISHWOMAN of rather overwhelmingly gushing manner, addicted to gathering literary lions for her London "at home from five to seven" soirées, happened to be visiting in Dublin. Guest at an afternoon gathering of literary lights at a house in Merrion Square, Mrs. Rodney Vane-Tempest Newbury went overboard anent her admiration for Irish poetry, literature and the drama. Upon the entrance of a shy man of letters recently elevated to the "immortals" of the Abbey Theatre roster of playwrights, Mrs. Vane-Tempest Newbury impaled the man on the flash of her eye.

"Welcome—and well met, hero of the moment. I have just been telling Sir Duncan that Ireland's claim to fame is its literati. You do agree? Oh do—*do* say I am right."

A deprecatory cough, a bow from the waist, and Mr. Eustace Carboy replied: "Madam, Ireland's chief claim to fame is undoubtedly a duo, potatoes and babies. In apparently inexhaustible supply."

A chance visitor to any Irish country fair or weekly gathering of farmers and drovers held for the buying and selling of livestock and farm produce will agree with Mr. Carboy that the succulent tuber and the crowing infant do indeed loom large in the Irish scene. I have noticed particularly the multiplicity of babies. Often I have encountered a broad-hipped farmer's wife striding the road leading to whatever market village, pushing her barrow of potatoes, with two or three "childer" on foot, one or more sitting contentedly atop the wabbly sacks piled on the barrow and, more often than not, to judge by the ample curve of her belly, a child safe and snug "under the apron."

On a bright morning in August, happily one more link in an unusually long chain of sunny days, I set out from my house Ballykilleen for the Horse Fair held semiannually in the open market square, big and wind-swept as a parade ground, at Ballyshannon in County Donegal. This attraction is held largely for the benefit of farmers in need of a work horse and for tradesmen, shopkeepers in small villages where a horse and cart are needed to deliver purchases to outlying country houses. The Irish countryman is proverbially suspicious of the "hot-blooded" Thoroughbred, and so it is the "cold blood" horse that is always in demand and that is mainly offered for sale at Ballyshannon Fair. As Mary Moriarity, an old retainer at my Grandfather Reynolds' house Rathgannonstown, remarked coldly when asked if she would like to take a short spin in his claret-red Renault, the first motorcar of its kind in Ireland, "I'd not at all, thank yer honour, sir. I'd meet death at the crossroads surely in that divil's velocipede."

On this sparkling day with a light salt-laden breeze blowing inland from off the Aran Islands, I came into the county called Golden Donegal for its abundance of wheat which ripens early and strews the landscape with carpets of shimmering golden grain. Land holdings are small here, the terrain hilly, so that tip-tilted fields seen from the high-set headlands that saw-tooth the rocky coast line seem the like of gold-embroidered banners hung out on the mountain ridges to celebrate the summer festival of Demeter that she may revel in her golden harvest. As I mounted the rise of Bloody Foreland and looked off and away towards Derrybeg, the rays of a strong, hot noonday sun shattered into myriad golden sequins against the bending wheat-heads. A compelling sight surely—I was held by wonder, watching the foam-laced waves of the bold Atlantic lapping the edge of wheat fields that extend downhill as if to bathe in the sea.

When ranging the Irish counties in any direction, one is treated to a kind of extravaganza: beauty of landscape and, invariably, a sudden transformation of the variable elements. I could encompass a panorama of magnitude—land and sea, jagged promontories, secret bays and loughs tracing far inland. But it was three legend-haunted islands that stole the show. Because of the extraordinary clarity of the atmosphere, I could see, each as sharply cut as an intaglio jewel, the islands of Aran, Tory and Inishbofin, rock formations once used as lairs by ancient Scandia sea rovers and still called Danes' Castles. Suddenly, as so often happens in the West of Ireland, from a cerulean cloudless sky I noticed thunderheads piling up with astonishing rapidity, their colour intensified by the icy-white gleam on the wings of high-sailing gulls. The air was heavy with thunder; on

every side, where a few minutes ago all was so brilliantly blue and gold, I saw
the same sea and sky smoky gray-blue. The islands turned to huddled dun levia-
thans disappearing as if submerged beneath spears of indigo rain. In all the drear
of this sea-storm there remained only one slash of colour. On Inishbofin, touched
by a single ray of sunlight, appeared a ridge of livid yellow rocks. Two or three
pookawns, fishing boats said to be of Spanish origin, their red-ocher sails lateen-
rigged, ran with the wind, racing for the port of Rossnowlagh.

And through it all I sat high-placed on a headland, sun-hot and dry as if oc-
cupying a stage box during a particularly realistic performance of *The Tempest*. For
the past half-hour vendors of horses had been passing me on the ridge road leading
from Ballintra to Ballyshannon. I appeared to be the only person in the vicinity
even conscious that a monumental storm had brewed up in a jiffy from a perfectly
still and cloudless day. I doubted not at all that if I could have heard some of the
remarks directed towards me and my rapt attention to the storm by the hostler
lads minding the horses on their way to the fair, I would have seen myself as "a
class ave loony, God grant he's a stranger to these parts and 'ull be soon off an'
away."

When I arrived at Ballyshannon market square I found it crowded with humanity and divers domesticated animals; of babies in arms there was a super-
fluity. Babes on laps, some even strapped papoose-fashion to the backs of lean,
leathery, dark-visaged Mountainy women from the fastnesses of Errigal and Blue
Stack Mountains. Infants dozed in prams or yelled in discontent in empty baskets.
Others had been put to sleep under the big canvas umbrellas that serve as a sort
of marquee beneath which the market women display their wares. These wares
are potatoes—potatoes raw, boiled, or baked in their jackets in the hot ashes of a
portable peat fire. The spiraling blue smoke of sphagnum-moss turf always lends
a dreamy azure veiling to the spirited scene.

I walked around the square visiting the various pitches, such as a booth set
up under an awning for the sale of delicate violet or horizon-blue Belleek ware. I
"collected" a sketchy lunch, one might say on the hoof, by first asking a woman
who had huge rose-red hams set out on a trestle table to cut me a few thin slices.
"I will an' all, sir, for yer kind patronage, arragh yer the first to hunger after me
lovely little porker's haunch the day. I'll trim it thin as a virgin's sigh." Further
along the way I bought a few bannocks, the piping hot oatcakes in which one may
find hiding within the crust either currants, crumbled bacon or, if the bannock is
baked in one of the fishing-port villages, a few flakes of salted fish. A mug of cool

porter, a slab of Irish cheddar cheese, a shade too bland for my taste but acceptable for its golden smoothness, and I was replete and ready for the horse trading.

Horses were grouped about the square. I could tell by the tatarara of derisive shouts and imprecations from knots of prospective buyers that feelings were already running high. "Shut yer gob else ye utter unbeknownst a word derogatory to me luvely little mare Fair Ella. I'll have ye hear it from me lips that she's sensitive to yer bitter remark that she's not worth a tinker's plugged farthing." This sort of exchange of Irish pleasantries, verbal insult and injury to the sensitive feelings of man and beast, is part and parcel of a really stiff bit of horse-coping at country horse fairs.

While walking around the horse-pens made of sheep-hurdles set up in orderly rows with a "street" in between, I had noted a gray horse with a particularly handsome head. My eye is always attracted to a well-conditioned gray horse, whether of cold or hot blood. I said to myself, "That horse is no Thoroughbred to be sure, but a three-quarter-bred with some exceptionally good blood in him." I walked over to get a closer view.

Two men were standing within the pen. Somehow these two seemed strangely set apart from the raucous throng of buyers and sellers. They were, I noted, back-countrymen, for one man wore jacket and breeches of the maize-white bauneen tweed; the other's loose-fitting garments were of hand-woven, vegetable-dyed homespun—a raglan and shawl, a wide neck-scarf woven, cut and whipstitched by "herself" in a shadow-dark coteen in the remote, almost legendary Grianan of Aileach region—the Place of the Haunted Glen. Then I realized why these two men were withdrawn from their fellows. It is said that these dwellers in Grianan of Aileach "walk alone, they are not of us; they be not dead, though they be not wholly alive."

When and where or expressly why this tale of the shunners and the shunned originated, I have never been able to find out. Directly I ask anyone along the Donegal coast to give me a lead they either change the subject or disclaim any knowledge of the story, with a rejoinder such as "Whist—ye'd better leave all *in* it, *out* ave it. Arragh, it's a drear, dread lingerer in the mind. . . . Well, God's day to ye," and they are off about their business. Once at Ballyshannon Horse Fair I had an eerie experience after trying to learn more of this curiosity in the daily round.

It was a day of brilliant sunshine when everyone walking about the square cast his proper length of shadow. I noticed a woman, taller than ordinary, clothed all in black. She wore a voluminous hooded cloak; the cowl-like hood was pulled so far forward it completely obscured her face. She seemed extremely agitated, darting this way and that, one moment about to accost a stall vendor, the next extending a yellow, talon-fingered hand to clutch the arm of a passer-by, then pulling back as if conscious of having made a mistake in identity. Two or three times I saw that when she approached a man or woman they would immediately blanch and flee the scene in no uncertain manner. I wondered just what caused the black-cloaked woman's anxiety and the embarrassed, hasty withdrawal of persons claiming her attention. Then, just as I saw her disappear into an alley between tall stone houses, I was suddenly aware of two things: that I had not caught even a glimpse of her face, and the startling fact that her tall, black-cloaked figure cast no shadow on the cobbles.

Only once did I ever find even a partial explanation of this apparition. She is seen quite frequently, I learned, in the market square of Ballyshannon, hiding her face from view, casting no sign of shadow. And this is the story I heard from Michael Killigs of Ballyshannon. I took the words down on a leaf of my sketchbook.

"Long ago it was, whin meself was a sprat ave a youth, but very active with the gurls, I courted a bit here an' a bit there, ye take me meanin'? There was an old woman livin' beyond, to the east ave Dunkineely, an' she was thought to have a great store ave money. She had one daughter Maureen, pretty as a lily. She caught me eye, an' me all hot fer settlin' in snug on me own bit ave farm with a warm wife next me under the down quilt. But Maureen 'ud have none ave me. She whipped off an' married a great, loose-tongued gaum from the Glenties. A loony, be the by, who'd not know the front ave a woman from the back." Michael spat a monumental gob halfway across the quay where we were sitting, to emphasize his scorn of such congenital ignorance. "The auld mother died soon after the weddin'. Arragh she left the pair as poor as they were before. One night a man who had once tried to marry the Widdi' Caneeghan himself stopped by the daughter's coteen to ask a night's shelter from a torrent ave rain. After warmin' his bones wid a bowl ave scaldin' tea the fella' asked, 'And why are ye both so poor-showin? Did the auld woman leave ye nothin' er are ye as great misers as was herself?'

"The daughter answered, 'Not a shillin' nor a penny-piece did she leave.'

" 'An' she'd no word,' the man asked, 'nor no message to ye in her last breath?'

"Maureen's breast heaved with a great sigh, 'Not a word—she did not. Exceptin' only me promise that I'd not put the tooth ave a comb to the snarls ave her poll and she dead.'

" 'An' you heeded 'er?' asked the man.

" 'I did an' all, daughterly,' she said.

" 'Well, this is a grand turnout, entirely,' the man of the night let out a great roar ave delight. 'Tomorrow night let the two ave ye,'—dippin' his head towards the lout himself who'd not opened his gob fer fear—'go down to the graveyard. Dig up her coffin and look in her hair and just see what it is you'll find in it.'

"An' may I choke on me next breath if the twa ave thim didn't do as he said. Quietly they went down to dig among the relics. They dug up the Widdi' Caneeghan's coffin. They near died ave fright unwindin' the shroud. With the tines ave a fork they'd brought, the one comb in the house havin' lost near all its teeth, they combed through the widdi's hair and there in the roll ave 'er poll they found a tidy fortune."

Michael puffed out his chest the like of a pouter pigeon about to call to his mate, and in a carrying voice he pronounced, "Five hundred pounds in good notes and a small sack ave gold sovereigns!"

I praised Michael's memory for details and his prowess as a raconteur. Then I said, "I expect the Widow Caneeghan does not rest easy in her desecrated grave. Do you know anything about that?"

"I do, an' more," he said. "It is told there was heard from the graveyard a great screechin' fer nights after her daughter relieved the auld woman ave her gold that she thought she'd so artfully hidden. Then whin her daughter got shut ave her gaum-witted man an' bought a fine house in Ballyshannon clapped right on the market square, the widdi' took to prowlin' the town, night er day makes no matter, searchin' fer 'er ducats."

"Have you seen her in the town?" I asked.

"I have. In the town an' rangin' the roads demented-like, mutterin' to herself. She's only a black body now, ripped be the winds." There was a space of thoughtful silence, then Michael brought his mind back as from a far place. He shook his head wonderingly. "I saw her face often enough in life, but there's naught but a black hole under her hood in death."

Ten Peculiar Apparitions and Ghostly Manifestations

The Black Abbess of Carlingford Castle

CARLINGFORD LOUGH, COUNTY LOUTH, 1482

O N THE DAY that Plantagenet Harry of Monmouth, later Henry V. of England, was born at the Castle of Monmouth August 9, 1387, a woman named Elspeth Tradescant of Polporto Manor hard by Penzance in Cornwall gave birth to a daughter who was christened Henrietta Anna. As she grew tall and spare, into her "salad days," she was credited with being the greatest tomboy daredevil in the country, known to the countryside as "that Henny." Time passed and on reaching her late twenties Henny Tradescant announced one day at table that she was planning to become a freebooter or, if you liked, a pirate. This bald statement electrified her rather staid family, if not the neighbours or people of the countryside, anciently addicted to smuggling as "an old art of the Cornwallers," and regarding piracy as just another facet of their traditional "art."

And so, true to her word, Henny donned masculine long-hose and boots reaching far up her lean thighs and set herself the task of finding a ship not too large, lying low in the water, and of necessity swift as a swallow in flight so as to outrun a pursuer in a chase. Apparently Captain Henny, as the girl came to be known up and down the coasts of England, Wales, and Scotland, found just the ship she was looking for—"The Black Abbess," lately out of Bristol and known to be swift as a running wave.

There have been tales of many female pirates down the centuries, from tiny Manchu Yi Li Fang, who rose in importance from an abscure river pirate on the Yangtze to Supreme Imperial Concubine, "The Flower of the Palace of Han," during the last years of the Han Dynasty, to raucous, one-eyed Mary Rourk who, during the extensive trading between Spain and Galway in Western Ireland during the sixteenth century, reaped a rich harvest of damasks, brocades and tooled leather-work pirating Italian and Spanish ships in Atlantic waters, until her gullet was untimely ripped by the stiletto of a malcontent English member of her crew.

The chances are that in the ordinary course of events popular Harry of Monmouth, either as prince or King, would never have met Captain Henny Tradescant, save perhaps, had she ever been caught out pirating a ship in English waters, he might have chanced to ride past her corpse dangling from the end of a rope athwart a gibbet. But it is natural that the prince would have heard of Henny's notorious exploits, for she enjoyed, over a score of years, a wide celebrity. Then, during a storm off the coast of Scotland when "The Black Abbess" was running against the wind, plowing gunnel-deep through a raging sea, Henny's famous good luck altered in the time it takes a mountainous wave to snatch a man off a heaving deck and drown him like a rat in the sea. The man was Henny's lover, one Nevin O'Neill from County Tyrone, as black-visaged an Irish renegade as ever stopped a gasp of breath in a windpipe with the strength of his two hands, which was Nevin's favourite method of obliterating another's—to his mind—unnecessary life. But to Henny Tradescant the loss of her lover was the extinguishing forever of the warming flame of her heart. Never in her life had she cared a spit in the wind for any man who crossed her path until Nevin shipped as her next in command aboard "The Black Abbess." Of her crew, even those most hardened to ruthlessness, to cruelty as met daily in the life they led, were beset with a great wonder at the change of spirit that draped the heart of their captain like a pall of woe from the day of Nevin O'Neill's death. Now Henny carried a weight of deep grudge against life itself. It had treated her scurvily and she was through with it, or so she was convinced in her own mind.

One day she called the crew into her cabin. In itself this was not strange, for she had, since the start of her roving, called an "assemblage" into her presence whenever she had some particularly daring plan afoot. Henny sat in an armchair, her brooding eyes heavily hooded, pouched underneath now that she was so wild beset with sorrow. Indeed some of her men wondered at this sudden marking of age, since she had reached only thirty-two years. In a colourless voice, her manner drear, noticeably different from her habitual buoyancy, when every few sentences were punctuated by vibrant laughter, Captain Henny informed the crew that she was through with the sea from that out. She said that she would dispose of her ship as soon as she could find a berth somewhere in the Scilly Islands, as safe a harbourage for freebooters with a price on their heads as anywhere she knew, save the wild and remote Hebrides.

And so it came to pass. At this point in the story the coincidence that Henrietta Anna Tradescant and Henry Plantagenet, now Henry V of England, were born on the same day, becomes important. Henny had heard, from chance gossip circulating when her men had stealthily entered small fishing coves to obtain provisions, that King Henry was desperately in need of ships to carry himself and his vast army of men and horses to France. This was approximately the time when Henry had written that extraordinary letter, happily preserved, "To our Cousin and Adversary," King Charles VI of France, wherein he reminded his brother monarch of former peace between England and France and requested him to avoid a deluge of human blood by restoring Henry's minimum demands with the Princess Catherine of Valois, for whose hand negotiations had been proceeding. On the eve of the Battle of Agincourt, Henry wrote to the Dauphin: "Considering it hath pleased God to visit with infirmity our Cousin, your Father . . . we offer to decide this our quarrel with God's grace by combat between our person and yours."

This assuredly meant war. So Captain Henny dismissed her crew and they went, grumbling a bit at losing the prospect of cushy days of plundering shipping up and down the coasts, aboard "The Black Abbess"—"the grandest little beauty under riggin'," as the late Nevin O'Neill would have it. Henny sat for a long time in her big carved chair that had once felt the weight of a corpulent Spanish captain. She mused and she brooded. So—her young sovereign, gay at times but deadly serious now, needed ships. Good—she would provide him with one at least. "The Black Abbess." Of course she must alter the name of the ship, repaint her and change the rigging before running, with a newly-picked crew, into some seaport near Yarmouth or Rye.

With the sudden and complete disappearance of the fleet ship "Black Abbess" from the seas, her Captain Henny Tradescant, the most feared yet extravagantly admired adventurous woman pirate of medieval times, disappeared from the picture as if a sea serpent had swallowed her alive. On her last day aboard ship, while the vessel, totally obscured from the shore by a dense fog, rocked gently on the choppy sea a few miles off Yarmouth Old Port, Henny had done two things which she had never done before in her temperamental life. She wrote a letter to King Henry V and she wore upon her person a piece of jewelry. She pinned on her breast, under a brown leather doublet, a jeweled cross. This cross, barbaric in its splendour of design, was the only present ever given her by Nevin

O'Neill during all the years they had sailed together. During her younger life at Polporto Manor, Henny had learned to write. Her letter, laboriously written, in truth, its spelling individual to say the least, was nevertheless perfectly legible and made sense. It was to be entrusted to Dickon Rylands, a fresh-faced young sailor sprung from yeoman stock in Somerset, who desperately craved to join the royal expedition to France. As guileless a face, Henny thought, as the king would ever see. Brevity in speech amounted almost to a fetish with Henny. So her letter was brief. She acquainted the king with the facts that she shared his birthday, and that she had heard he wanted, above all things, ships. So she herewith presented him with her own ship "Sea Spray," painted in his colours of red and blue. She prayed that God would prosper his quest, for England and St. George. Henny signed no name. She simply stuck her right thumb in a pot of vermilion paint and pressed it to the parchment as a finial to her letter. What Henry of Monmouth made of all this we will never know. I dare say he was mightily pleased with the gift of a stout ship and at table drank the health of the mysterious giver.

It was the year 1460 when one evening in the winter dusk a woman pulled the bell wire at the postern of a religious house in the wild wastes of Northumberland—a small abbey in the wolds called St. Bonaventura's. The woman was noticeably tall and spare. Her girdled robe of black wool accented her slimness, and her cape, with its hood partially concealing her face and its folds sweeping out in the evening breeze, added an effect of unfurling wings. The nun who answered her summons took momentary fright when she saw the stranger, so grim was the expression on the white face, long and pointed of chin, shadowed by the protruding folds of the hood. The almost lipless mouth traced a hard line, but the deep blue eyes were kind, even though the nun perceived in them a look of deep sadness. The visitor said she wished seclusion for a few days. Soon she would be on her way.

Thus, after nearly thirty years, Henrietta Anna Tradescant, who had been far better known as Captain Henny, reappeared from wherever she had spent the intervening years after she had presented her ship, rechristened "Sea Spray," to Henry V.

During the week she spent in solitude at the remote abbey, Henny spoke to no one but the abbess, and that only to make a gift of money to the order. As Henny was leaving the firelit room in which the abbess received visitors, she parted her lips in a thin smile and said, "By your gray habit I shall remember you as the Gray Abbess of the Wolds. And you"—she looked down at the long black tabard covering her figure from chin to toe—"think of me as the Black Abbess. I was for long so identified."

After Henny had taken her departure, walking out along a ridge of the downs towards the sea, the Abbess of St. Bonaventura's stood looking into the fire. To herself she said, "What a strange, compelling woman. I wonder what is her story. Of a surety she has one." And then she wondered on. Wondered about the heavy gold cross that she had glimpsed for only a moment, as the woman who called herself the Black Abbess had arranged her habit so as not to trail in the ashes of the fireplace. In the firelight the green and crimson jewels had glinted and, it seemed, winked evilly. The abbess shook her head. How brilliantly the cross had blazed, and how quickly the woman had drawn her black tabard across her breast, as if she feared the jewel's being seen. Odd. Surely it had been too gaudy for a Saviour's Cross, too barbaric for her taste. She remembered having seen a similar one, crudely hammered from a single ingot of gold and set with rough-cut jewels, that had been brought back from Byzantium by a young Norman knight. The abbess returned to her candlelit desk and picked up her goose quill. But before setting down her household accounts she paused, reflecting. "That woman haunts my thoughts. Who, I wonder, may she be? Well, we are a hospice, however lonely and half-hidden in the wolds. All kinds of strangers come here. I have dealt with all manner of woes."

A few weeks after her stay at the Abbey of St. Bonaventura's, the Black Abbess (as we will call Henny Tradescant from here out, since it was the way she styled herself during her life in Ireland) stepped from a small rowboat at the water stairs leading up to the pointed arch which pierced the outer bailey of Carlingford Castle. Here the Black Abbess was to assume the duties of prioress to a group of women of noble family who, because of widowhood suffered through the constant warring of the times, or from the urgings of extreme, even fanatical piety, wished to retire from the world.

The first evening after her arrival at Carlingford Castle the Black Abbess walked along a path hewn from the rocks, indented here and there by silver-sanded coves. Her thoughts were bleak. To herself she told the truth. The reason she had come to this lonely castle fronting the bold shore of Carlingford Lough was to be near the sea. More than half of her life had been spent on the sea. She felt stifled inland; she craved like nothing else in life, deeply bereft of Nevin as she still felt, the smell of salt-rimed waves and solitude to watch the tides change under the moon. And then she always remembered it was the sea that had taken Nevin O'Neill; perhaps he would come to her again from the sea. She would watch and she would wait.

The years passed. In her high chamber in the seaward tower of the castle the Black Abbess would sit for hours on end, looking off and away, always out to sea. Long since, she had ceased to take any part in the life, quiet and secluded as it was, of the castle. One by one the women who, like herself, had sought the stillness that seems to take on added depth behind strongly-built stone walls in which to mourn or to pray, died off. One day, rousing a little from her lethargy, the Black Abbess realized that save for the nearly senile Lady of Renvyle and old Rona MacAnnamac, who waited upon her and tended the kitchen in the shiftless manner of old family servants, herself was the only inhabitant of this huge and sprawling castle.

One evening the Black Abbess had been more than usually restless. Unable to sit longer in her tower chamber, she sought first the small chapel that had been arranged by a former incumbent of the priory, one Lady Farrowly, for her private use. When Lady Farrowly had died a few years ago, all the gold and silver altar investiture had been removed by a distant relative. But the serene, gently-smiling madonna carved in cedar, brought from France at some time earlier, still occupied her accustomed niche above the altar.

It was while kneeling here at the feet of the madonna on this oppressively hot summer night that the Black Abbess first heard the voice of Nevin O'Neill calling to her across the years. Calling from the sea. Rising and falling in cadences soft as the susurrus of waves frilling with the incoming tide, the voice of Nevin called Henny to come to him. For a moment, her thoughts awry, the Black Abbess felt as if her limbs were paralyzed. Then, her hands reaching up, she unclasped the chain on which she wore the cross Nevin had given her. Slowly she rose to her feet and placed the cross in the outstretched hand of the madonna.

"Oh, Mother Mary, hear me. I pray to you it may be true, that his voice is no trick of the wind. Grant me this prayer. If I do not return, you will know in your infinite compassion that I have found him."

Running, as she had often done as a young girl to reach her ship and put out to the free life of the sea, the Black Abbess raced down the winding stone stairs and out along the causeway to the beach. For only a moment she hesitated as she saw the darkly gleaming figure of a tall man, broad of shoulder, his proudly-set head thrown back, his arms stretched out towards her in welcome.

She threw herself into his arms just as a gigantic wave crushed her beneath its weight of water.

The House of Plantagenet rose in glory, then fell monstrously to an end on Bosworth Field. Henry Tudor, Duke of Richmond, reigned, and then his amorous son Henry VIII. Then his daughter red-haired Elizabeth, the Virgin Queen, who loved the sea and ships, reigned long and gloriously. Too, she mightily loved jewels and gently-born long-limbed young men, fair-complexioned, with laughing eyes and bold wits. One day, hoping to raise his waning popularity with her subjects, she sent her favourite Robert Devereux, Earl of Essex, to Ireland with an army at his command.

"Go," she said. "Pierce those Irish bog mists and so put down these unregenerate Irish mongrels. They irk me; I would have done with them. Go, Robin—here is your chance; too long you have been fretting your mind and my temper to taste the honey of victory on your tongue."

But Essex's expedition was doomed from the start. He and his disgruntled army coughed themselves nearly to death with mist-fever engendered by the winter miasmas hovering over Irish bogs. When in desperation Essex made a "treasonous" truce with O'Neill, Earl of Tyrone, he was hailed back to Whitehall to feel the wrath of Elizabeth. Before he went to the Tower to await execution, Essex managed to send the queen a letter pleading his love, begging in return her loving mercy. The letter was wrapped around a large, rather crudely-wrought golden cross barbarically set with red and green jewels, gaudy, but of no great worth. In the letter Essex said that he had found the cross reposing, covered by ages of dust, in the outstretched hand of a madonna in the dark chapel of a castle he had stayed in while pursuing Tyrone.

Walkers of the roads in all kinds of wind and weather, those garrulous chroniclers of legends and ghostly lore, have related over and over down the years tales of a man and a woman seen walking along the rocky path or, sometimes, in close embrace on the sands of some secluded cove on the shores of Carlingford Lough. They seem to be wearing dark clothing of ancient cut. The woman's garment has the appearance of a medieval hooded cloak. Sometimes this pair are seen to mount the tumbled stones that once formed the water stairs of Carlingford Castle, presently a magnificently impressive ruin.

An Englishman visiting Ireland, whom I met in the nearby fishing village of Greenore, told me that one summer night about eleven o'clock he was returning by motorcar from a day spent at Downpatrick Races in County Down. His battery failed him in the midst of a sudden storm of wind and rain which had caused him to lose his way in the darkness. He found himself at the foot of the ramp on which one wing of Carlingford Castle is built. By this time the downpour was intense and the wind howled in from the sea, cold as Greenland blasts. He sought shelter in the lower part of the castle. Each time the lightning flashed he was more convinced that he was in a kind of chapel. There was a Gothic stone altar raised along one wall and behind it an empty niche in which he assumed there had once stood a figure of the Virgin. The night began to clear. He became aware that moonlight was brightening the small chamber. Something moved in the shadows. He was more than a little startled to see the figure of a tall woman in sweeping black robes standing beside the empty niche. Her eyes seemed to glow with a strangely blue radiance, although her lips in a pallid face were a colourless straight line. As he watched, more fascinated than afraid, he said, the woman was joined by a man, tall as herself, with a shock of tangled black hair and a cruelly handsome, deeply-lined face. The man, too, was attired in black, a garment cut straight, belted, and hanging to the knees. As if two persons could be so drawn to one another as to merge into one form, so these two did. With a motion of gliding, the dark figures passed under the arched doorway, merging into the shadows of the night.

The Winged Dagger of Braghee

BRAGHEEHOOLY CASTLE, COUNTY OFFALY, 1450

THIS ghost story is brief, sharp as a fatal sword-thrust. It is a kind of tattered, bloodstained shred of horror, as if threads had been ripped from the design of a tapestry and blown down the winds of time for men to marvel, yes, and to shudder that such cruelty lived as was in the shambling, deformed person of Rone the O'Hooly.

The medieval history of any land is rife with tales of bestial nobles, powerful overlords of vast lands or perhaps whole provinces. But when I cast my mind backwards, remembering all the stories I have read, from that of Ivan the Terrible stalking sword in hand through the crimson, purple, blue and orange-walled dungeons under his palace in St. Petersburg, wantonly slaying defenseless, chained prisoners, to that of Captain Bligh, whose domain of cruelty was the bridge and holystoned deck of his ship, I find no fellow to The O'Hooly of Braghee.

A contemporary chronicler brands him "a brutal, ferocious, barbarous, savage man." And although the mists of time obscure a great deal of The O'Hooly's life, the fragmentary documents that I have been able to patch together prove that his monstrousness, his sheer cerebral cruelty, took the most fascinating, blood-chilling turns imaginable.

The man first looms on the scene as a huge creature of surpassing ugliness of visage who "carried a great hump on his back the like of Atlas bearing the World." Bragheehooly Castle had been for centuries a massively-built, solitary keep. In 1450 The O'Hooly added curtain wings and a vast banqueting hall, the barrel-roof groined and raftered in the manner of the great refectory (once used as a church) that is part of the ancient jumble of roughly-hewn rock buildings on the Hill of Cashel, called by the poets the Irish Acropolis.

It would appear that the greater part of The O'Hooly's rancour, his deep and fiendish loathing for his fellow men, stemmed not so much from the knowledge that his person was repellent as from the fact that he was sterile and so no begetter of sons. No matter how many times he forced women to submit to his ardours, and he roweled them from every condition in life, he could father neither son nor daughter. The tales of Rone the O'Hooly and his brutish rages seem to me to reach the heights of terror in the story of how, before the eyes of half a hundred guests seated at his banquet table, he slew young Colum Blaney, a page at his court.

It was a custom of the times for the young sons of nobles to be, in a sense, "exchanged" from one household to another. In this way a boy of twelve to fifteen, by attendance on a lord or lady for a few years, would learn the manners and courtly deportment of a princely household, its intrigues as well, and, more often than not, its vices.

It was at a great banquet richly spread to celebrate The O'Hooly's return from a victorious border war that young Colum Blaney, aged fourteen years, but newly come to Braghee, ran most frightfully afoul of the master. The boy was carrying to the table a dish of wild boar, smoking hot and swimming in greasy sauce, when he tripped over a deerhound nuzzling for scraps of food at the feet of The O'Hooly and landed the platter a great douse over his master's face and bared chest. With a howl of rage and pain, The O'Hooly grasped the knife lying on the table in front of him and hurled it point-device at Colum who, in stark terror, had fled down the hall towards the door to the inner bailey courtyard. The knife whizzed through the air with a whining sound like that of a sudden squall of wind across choppy water; its point pierced the boy's neck just under one ear and sank to the hilt, the steel protruding from the other side of his throat.

Dreadful silence followed a single piercing shriek as the knife struck and Colum fell senseless, mortally wounded, among the blood-wetted rushes spread ankle-deep upon the stones of the banquet-hall floor. And then, as a woman guest, hot with anger and compassion, rose from her place at the board and started towards the dying boy, Rone O'Hooly let out a great bellow, the like of the Bull of Avoca. "Let be," he shouted, "all of ye! I have not finished with the clumsy gossoon yet."

He stepped down from the dais on which the High Table was placed. His lopsided height towering above a throng of warriors who at all times formed a guard of honour about their chieftain, Rone O'Hooly walked swiftly down the hall. He stooped and lifted the slender, limp body of Colum and hoisted it over his humped shoulder as a miller would a sack of millet. Save for the rumble of growling among the hounds intent only on scavenging scraps of food thrown onto the rushes, silence, nearly articulate in its intensity, reigned in the Great Hall.

Every eye in the room followed the limping stride of Rone O'Hooly as he strode over to the cavernous fireplace where logs of bog oak, cut that day to the length of eight feet or more, had been piled in the maw to form a pyramid. The logs thus tented over a bed-fire of peat turves were at full blaze, the flames writhing halfway up the cone of the circular chimney. Standing in front of the fire Rone O'Hooly grasped the body of Colum Blaney by the feet, then letting out a great windy laugh he called out in his boastful voice, "Here's how I hurl a stone sling. And always straight to the mark!" With that he swung the boy's body in an arc above his head, then let go the feet. Colum, still breathing alive, whipped through the air and fell among the flames. Women shrieked, and some fell back from their benches and lay on the rushes as if stoned. All hid their eyes from the sight of such insensate cruelty. Warriors turned their backs and with bent heads stumbled out under the archways into the cold night air.

Even in an age when kings, princes and chieftains, Christian or infidel, wielded the power of life or death over men within their households, this terrible deed of raging bravado on the part of The O'Hooly of Braghee sickened the vitals of all who heard the recounting. Old Brano Blaney of Castle Cloon in County

Louth, accompanied by his three sons and a troop of gallowglasses, set out on the hunt for The O'Hooly. But the chieftain was both powerful and wily, and it is told that for seven years he avoided meeting The Blaney in other than light skirmishes. Then one day retribution for his life of savage rapine and uncounted murdering caught up with Rone—it was a hideous and lonely death that clutched him by the throat and finished him off. It appears that at last the Blaney faction apprehended him as, with a small retinue of guards, he was riding along a narrow bog road one evening when the gaseous ground mists, so fearsome to encounter in the wastes of an Irish bog, trapped Rone O'Hooly. The Blaney men-at-arms created a diversion at one end of the bog road by shouting and beating upon bronze shields with sword hilts to ape the fury of an encounter between men in armour. The O'Hooly bade his guards ride on a way to see what was up. He would ride back along the road and await their return with news.

He spurred his horse to wheel about in the narrow confines of the road. The heavily-caparisoned Clonsilla stallion took fright at a swoop of rooks seeking shelter for the night in the stunted bog oaks bordering the roadway. Rearing on his haunches the horse threw Rone O'Hooly into the cold, brackish waters of a bog-pool. In less time than a man would count the fingers of his two hands and they mutilated, The O'Hooly was sucked down to his death in the morass of mud, lethal as quicksand.

The Castle of Bragheehooly has stood, massively towered, foursquare to the elements, down the centuries. Today it is less ruinous than many fortress keeps of its era. But always it has loomed against the sky a house of dread memories. The frenzied ghost of Colum Blaney is not the sole reminder of unspeakable events that have taken place within its buttressed walls, thickly matted with ivy, the leaves black as jet, forever quivering no matter how still the air. There are ghosts aplenty to haunt these riven walls. But countrymen or chance visitors to the locality who tell of hearing mysterious clamour and at times seeing the ghost of Colum Blaney, seem inclined to elevate the unhappy boy to the place of ghost-in-chief of the castle.

It appears that for half a century after the death of Rone O'Hooly by strangling in the muddy depths of a bog, the castle was used more as armoury and barracks by men-at-arms for the Tribe O'Hooly than as a dwelling place. The picture at this point clouds over until the end of the sixteenth century. One hears then that a man named Connel McAnerty, master stonemason from Sligo, who had made a modest fortune in carved stone architectural ornaments, lived with his family for a short time in one wing of the castle. But it seems that no one could endure the reek of carrion that often at night wreathed in smoky tendrils along the walls and the boldly-fashioned stone groinings of the banquet hall built by Rone O'Hooly.

The phenomenon, according to members of the large McAnerty family, never varied during their tenure of the castle. Without warning there would occur a whizzing sound as if some object was suddenly hurled through the air. A clear, agonized shriek followed on the instant. Then the barking of dogs, faint and far away. Then a thud would be heard, followed soon after by the odour, oddly sweet, sickening to the nostrils, of burning flesh.

One evening a young daughter of Connel McAnerty who was perpetually afflicted with ill health was found unaccountably dead, lying in front of the fireplace of the great hall. There were no marks of violence on the corpse. Indeed, a letter written by an elder brother describing the scene says, "We found Maria lying quite still, her eyes wide open, staring, the pupils large with the look of intense fright. What she could have seen in the summer twilight we are obliged only to surmise. Some terror assuredly for which this godforsaken house is notorious."

The McAnertys were the last family known to have lived at the castle. Now, derelict, the pile is left to the rigours of wind and weather and its hauntings. Brian Gogarty, a friend I had known in Trinity College, told me that he once spent a weekend at a country house not many miles away from the hulk of Bragheehooly Castle. On an evening in early autumn he decided to walk over to see this old castle of which he had read and heard such dire tales. A hunter's moon in full beauty rose about nine o'clock, just about the time that Gogarty came abreast of the dry moat once spanned by what was purportedly the longest drawbridge (of Norman construction) in all the Irish counties. Before his eyes stood the great keep, its lines strongly drawn in black and silver. I recall how he put it: "In this light, showing few scars, here rose at its best the arrogance of medieval masonry for defense."

Gogarty walked around the moat and was just preparing to climb a flight of crumbling stone steps leading to a kind of causeway when the night stillness was most unholily ripped by a strident scream, its suddenness and vibrance echoing against the range of dark hills that formed a crescent-shaped background to the castle towers. There, as he told it to me, "I saw the figure of a young boy in a red doublet, his legs bare, running as if pursued by demons along the parapet which seemed to be a sort of upper terrace to one of the castle wings. His yellow hair, worn long in the old Gaelic fashion, seemed to be smoking, for, as I watched, a kind of blue haze obscured the running figure. But not before I had seen that a long knife was thrust through his throat, while blood gushed like a freshet from his mouth."

"Yes," I nodded, "that is the way of it. Many's the time I have heard just this story." To myself I thought, this is, without doubt, the apparition that, suddenly made manifest to delicate Maria McAnerty, caused her heart to stop beating in her breast.

The Shriek of Slaney

CASTLEGREGORY, COUNTY KERRY, 1536

BENEATH the croghna-shrub-clad shoulders of Beenoskee and Stradbally Mountain rises an uncommonly high stone keep of early Gaelic fortress construction. From the crenelated battlements one may obtain a sweeping view of the sandy peninsula stretching out between Brandon and Tralee Bay to wave-torn Rough Point and those banshee-haunted islands, Magharees, better known to mariners as the Seven Hogs. Singularly high and narrow, the tower appears more pagan monolith than Christian castle where once dwelt a notorious turn-coat, a blow-hot-blow-cold political, a devious "maneuverer," as the Irish style this brand of gentry, one Gregory Hore of Castle Tower, and his beautiful Junoesque wife Slaney.

While the beauty of "Slaney of the Fair Girdle" was widely sung by the traveling bards, she was known to be as bad-tempered and willful of disposition as her person was radiantly lovely. On a day in winter when perishing winds blew to a climax around the castle walls, whirling at the same time down from Beenoskee and driving in from the bold Atlantic tides, word was brought to Gregory Hore that he must receive as a guest at his hearth that evening Lord Grey and his officers, who would stop the night en route to attack Dun an Oir at Smerwick Harbour.

Now to the fiercely patriotic Gaels, "the stink of my Lord Grey the Tudor's fart," or indeed even the mention of the deputy of Henry VIII, was anathema. While Gregory Hore, who loved the British, preened himself at the honour of providing hospitality for Grey, it was decidedly another story where the lovely Slaney was concerned. Forthwith, and in no uncertain terms, the mistress of Castle Tower categorically refused to allow Lord Grey or any officer in the British army to step a foot in her house. While loudly voicing her reasons, it is said that she sent servants into all the rooms to open windows and so admit the wintry blasts, and had them heave all turf and gathered firewood into the moat, so that if her husband overrode her wishes the halls would at least be the coldest comfort Lord Grey had ever received even in Ireland.

But surprisingly, Gregory Hore, usually the mildest-mannered of men as far as dealings with his beautiful wife and her opposite political sympathies were concerned, turned berserk. Loud, bitter words flew about the cold rooms, sharp as the dagger-point wings of the starlings flying in and out of the open windows seeking shelter from the icy, rain-laden winds. Gregory accosted his wife at a landing halfway up the staircase leading to her chamber, where she was prepared to lock herself away. The infuriated husband stabbed her to death as she shrieked her defiance to his adamant insistence that she receive the British deputy, and hurled her body down the stairwell. It is said that Gregory Hore calmly ordered servants to carry the broken body of the Lady Slaney to her chamber and, since it had been her last wish in life, lock her in. He then ordered all the windows closed and various pieces of furniture smashed against the granite chimney-breast in the living hall for firewood. A roaring fire was built and, as the flames leavened the chill of the room, he dispatched a mounted gallowglass to ride hell-for-leather to Tralee, where Lord Grey was at the moment housed, to acquaint him of the fact that Hore was impatiently waiting to receive the deputy and his officers at Castle Tower.

Each year, on the night of the anniversary of the stabbing by Gregory Hore of his wife Slaney, a nerve-racking scream—more of anger than of sudden pain—rings out in the stairwell of Castle Tower. Then, for three days, which is said to be the length of time Lord Grey enjoyed the hospitality of Gregory Hore, blood drips down the stone stairs. There is another thing of striking oddness. Centuries of blood dripping from the sill of a window high in the tower, which is thought to have been the chamber where the supposedly dead body of Slaney was carried by the servants, leads one to assume that she was far from dead. Perhaps she somehow managed to crawl to the narrow window and lean on the sill, but was too weak to cry for help. Perhaps the blood from her wounds ran a rivulet down the walls. However near the truth this conjecture may be, there is a dark stain on the stonework for all to see. Each year this stain freshens; it gleams wetly in the light of day, sticky to the touch. The rampageous, ever-present starlings are often observed to have what appears to be fresh blood upon their wings.

The Dreamer in the Tower

CREEBRICK CASTLE, MELLIFONT, COUNTY MEATH, 1140

AS I READ the early history of Ireland, its legends and bardry, there is, in the galaxy of "great women all, they might be queens"—such as Maeve, gloriously fair daughter of Eochaid, High King of Ireland; or Grania of the Tears, a legendary beauty of sad countenance, wandering her ways in the County of Meath—no name that so stirs my imagination to evoke the old romantic days of sound and fury, as richly resonant Dervorgilla. The name of this raven-haired beauty appears constantly in Irish literature; she is often referred to in songs of the early bards ranging the roads of the four extremities of the island, and in the works of the later poets and dramatists.

I have had scores of lonely keep towers pointed out to me in the way of "There ye are, sir. That auld monster ave a ruin toppin' the rise is where the gorgeous Dervorgilla was whipped out and away from the bed ave 'er own man be the bold Mac Murrough." I never challenge these largely erroneous historians —I make it a point to give my informants a free rein, for in this way I learn highly-coloured fragments of local history.

The romantically situated riparian Castle of Creebrick, reflecting its massive square tower in the reedy sedges of a small river near the ancient Cistercian Abbey of Mellifont, appears to have been the castle to which Dermott Mac Murrough took Queen Dervorgilla after the wild adventure of his carrying her off from the "palace place" of her husband The O'Rourk of Breffne during a torrential storm.

It was a quiet summer day when I last sauntered along the river bank across from the castle. I had walked over the meadows from Mellifont Abbey to sketch the tower. Sitting on a hillock of turf I ruminated upon its history, for Creebrick is purported to be the first fortress keep or castle to be built of dry-laid stone in the South of Ireland after the "palace places"—the timber and wattle "great halls" of the pagan kings and chieftains of tribes—had fallen into ruin from abandonment, the kings having found that the great days of feasting were past. At one time gargantuan banquets had been held in these "palace places" to mark ceremonies of births, weddings and deaths; festivals of games and trials of sports and battle prowess took place to mark the coming to manhood of the heirs to the kingdoms. But then predatory warrior chieftains had stirred out of the north and the western bogs, the like of Roe O'Flaherty of Menlo and Donal O'Neill, King of Tyrone; walls of massive masonry for protection against protracted siege had to be built in place of banquet halls of gilded wood.

Clouds of iridescent dragonflies skimmed above the swathes of white and rose-pink mallow spread as if for festival, a carpet of delicately fragrant flowers to encircle the base of Dervorgilla's Tower. I remembered that this whole region of the Boyne Valley of Meath is legend-haunted to the wide. The castles and the ancient raths, or sod-constructed forts, and the tumuli, the burial places of chieftains and kings, loom large in both history and song of Ireland's turbulent past. I will sketch briefly here the places and characters of one particular drama.

Spreading wide and deep on a rise of a meadow I had crossed on my way to Creebrick, lay grass-covered stone, all that remains now of a "palace place" or "high hall" of a pagan Irish king. I could trace long lines of these foundations radiating like the points of a star from a central hub or deep well. Constructed of "split and wholly round" logs of yew and oak, often the entire structure would be overlaid with sheets of metal. In Lady Gregory's book *Cuchulain of Muirthemne* there is a beautifully sensuous description of a king's house of this type.

"This now was the appearance of Cruachan, the Royal Hall of Aillel and of Maeve, that some called Cruachan of the Poets; there were seven divisions in the house, with couches in them from the hearth to the wall; a front of bronze to every division, and of red yew with carvings on it; and there were seven strips of bronze from the foundations to the roof of the house. The house was made of oak and the roof was covered with oak shingles; sixteen windows with glass were there and shutters with bronze on them, and a bar of bronze across every shutter. There was a raised place in the middle of the house for Aillel and Maeve, with silver fronts and strips of bronze around it and four bronze pillars on it, and a silver rod beside it, the way Aillel and Maeve could strike the middle beam and check their people. And outside the Royal House was the dun with the walls about it that were built by Brocc, son of Blar, and the great gate; and it is there the houses were for strangers to be lodged."

This dwelling, having such luxuries as glass in the windows, sheathings and strappings of silver and bronze, was far more rich in appointments and bodily comforts than were the later roughhewn fortress towers with cramped living quarters where man and beast dwelt in a huddle during siege.

The old Cistercian Abbey of Mellifont was the first religious house of a foreign order to be built in Ireland. It was founded in 1142 by Donogh O'Carroll, Lord of Oriel, at the instance of St. Malachy, who is known to have conducted there a school which was set up in an ancient barracks for gallowglasses or men-at-arms of Murtagh MacLaughlin of Ulster, King of the northern branch of the Hy Neill. It was from the stones of this school that Creebrick Castle and its massive outer wall was built.

The Lady Dervorgilla is said to have lived for years recluse in the Tower of Creebrick. At her death she was buried quietly with no pomp in the crypt of Mellifont Abbey. The voluptuous beauty of Dervorgilla is famous—her slumberous black eyes, her improbably long tresses of raven hair whose "coils enmeshed the souls of men," and her long, delicately-boned, snow-white hands. She was passionately worshiped and eulogized in her lifetime, and her memory is still kept forever green as the verdant green of Ireland itself.

Creebrick Castle is said to have been continuously inhabited from the time of its erection until the marauding soldiers of Oliver Cromwell, who is known to have used the tower briefly as headquarters, put it to the torch as a kind of last defiance prior to their defeat and hurried departure from Ireland in 1650. It was not until as late as 1780, and the tower a derelict haunt for countless rooks, that anyone told of seeing the ghost of "that dreamer," the local name for the woman recognized by her long black hair and gleaming white hands as Dervorgilla.

And then "that grand auld queen is after takin' a fancy to sittin' in a windi' ferninst," a farmer herding his swine along the river to market in Trim vouchsafed, motioning towards the tower battlements when I asked him what he knew of Dervorgilla's ghost. It seems the figure chooses to sit lone and still and dream away the hours in the highest window under the guards' walk facing Mellifont Abbey. Sometimes she is seen at twilight, head bowed upon her breast, her long, loose-hanging hair obscuring her face, but it is always noted and remarked upon that her white hands, the fingers moving restlessly braiding a pattern in longing, gleam with an unearthly light. These daylight appearances are rare, but two manifestations a fortnight apart were recorded by Oliver Goldsmith, an avid ghost-tracker who lived for a time in a small house in adjacent Slane.

It is in the still night watches when the river meadows are sheened with silver moonlight that the glorious beauty of Dervorgilla proudly sustains its ageless repute. Then she is seen sitting in her high window combing her waves of pitch-black hair with a silver comb. At such times her famous hands gleam whitely. Slowly, slowly—up, down—with long, sweeping strokes, her dreaming eyes turned towards the moon, Dervorgilla combs her hair. "The Helen of Ireland" relives her life in all its tumult of passion: her desertion by her paramour Dermott Mac Murrough, and the long lonely years of waiting, of deliberately immolating herself away from the eyes of men.

For as Henry Burkhead, a chronicler of ancient Irish lore, reminds us:

"No man ever looked upon the face of Dervorgilla but he lusted to lay his length upon her."

Fatal Foxgloves at Skreen Castle

TARA, COUNTY MEATH, 1740

SKREEN is a small castle set in the clearing of a wood. Its one soaring tower and the two-story crenelated wings flung out at right angles to the tower are so completely covered with ivy, its thick, burnished leaves brilliant as if lacquered, that the castle seems more a pavilion woven of woodland fronds and leafy branches than an abode where agonized shrieks disturb the night, murdering sleep as surely as Lilith Palmerston was murdered by a passion-crazed suitor in the year 1740.

The story leading up to the tragedy was largely told to me by a relative of Miss Palmerston, now living in the castle. Lilith Palmerston was a beautiful bluestocking who had been brought up in Dublin as ward of an elderly guardian, one Sir Bromley Casway. A prisoner to his wing chair from chronic gout, prey to prodigious discomfort, Sir Bromley demanded of his ward almost constant attention to his whims. Until his eyesight began to fail he had been an omnivorous reader. Books on travel to far places in the fabled East, to India in particular, were his favourite reading. So it turned out that his lovely ward, instead of taking her place as a belle at the cotillions held at the Castle where the Viceroy and his lady entertained on a lavish scale, or appearing in exquisite raiment at the soirées and balls held almost nightly during the season at the great houses fronting Merrion Square and St. Stephen's Green, must sit on a stool at the side of her invalid guardian and read to him from cover to cover the books that Sir

Bromley caused to be sent him from London, Berlin and Paris, the publishing centers of Europe.

By the time Lilith had reached her twenty-fifth year she had become nearly recluse. And a great shame it was, said her friends, for she was the loveliest sight imaginable, with her high-piled auburn curls, her bewitching heart-shaped face and her iris-blue eyes set slightly aslant under arched, nearly black eyebrows.

"But," her closest friend Mary Lorrier sighed, when describing her last visit to Lilith in Sir Bromley's big, drearily curtained house in Upper Merrion Street, "such a pity all that wit and beauty wasted on that selfish old curmudgeon. She has turned into a complete bluestocking I do assure you, Agatha dear. And talks nothing but bookishness. I declare I hear from her as truth that Sir Bromley intends shutting that great barracks of a house and taking up residence at Skreen Castle somewhere down in Meath." She paused while Lady Carmody refilled her tea cup. "It's a lone demesne, the roads in Meath are atrocious, the wheels of a coach bog down to the hubs, there's no society at all. I call it wicked."

Lady Carmody nodded her head. "I agree. No life at all for the most touted beauty in Dublin. But then she shuns society for her books. I am told she is writing a book herself. A sort of journal of her opinions, she said, though her opinions of what she did not clarify. Perhaps Lilith won't mind that hermitage Skreen, since, as she told me, she does not care to 'go out.' "

And so it came to pass that Sir Bromley Casway shut his house in Upper Merrion Street and retired to the densely-wooded banks of the Boyne Water in County Meath, accompanied only by his ward the lovely Lilith.

Once settled at the little Castle of Skreen, Lilith paid not so much attention to her books or any idea that she may have had of compiling a "journal" as to the garden which had been allowed to run riot during the years that Sir Bromley had seldom visited Skreen. Favourite with Lilith were the masses of tall foxgloves so variegated in colour. In the south counties of Ireland, foxgloves are a meadow or hedgerow plant which thrives exceedingly, bordering the bohireens, the paths through a wood or any spot where they can raise "glove"-strung stems, often to the height of six feet, to greet the sun. Mauve, rose, tawny-yellow, the blossoms, as delicately shaped as a mitten to fit the paw of a fox cub, display a powdering of dark wine-red or russet-brown spots. Lilith extravagantly admired these tall swaying flowery stalks. Often in the early morning hours when she walked along the river terraces and perhaps farther afield into the sun-latticed glades of beech and aspen trees, she would converse about flowers in general with old Tomas Garrity, Sir Bromley's gardener, who was forever telling her, "Arragh Miss, don't be after cuttin' down all me luvely flowers fer a bouquet. Why do ye not enjoy them in their natural grandeur at all?"

Lilith would laugh and say, "I know, Tomas, I know. As you so often tell me to enjoy, as it were, flowers on the hoof."

Then one day while walking along the river path in the direction of Tara, Lilith met for the first time her neighbour Phelim Sellers, and it was a dark day and a drear hour that she did that surely, for it would have been a better thing had she never clapped her eyes on him at all.

Sellers was a brutish man, of surly disposition, at odds with the world entire. He held his broad-shouldered, muscular body arrogantly taut, his head high, his fists clenched as if at the ready to ward off an expected blow. Although Sellers' manner to Lilith was courtly, she was a shade abrupt with him, eager to get away from the staring bloodshot eyes which, she thought to herself as she hurried back to the castle, had seemed to be mentally undressing her.

Before the advent of Sir Bromley and his ward at the Castle, Phelim Sellers had lived a closed-in life at Boyne House, built so near the river that its foundations actually overhung the sluggish waters. It was a big, ungainly house and it held a dark secret. Sellers' wife, a girl from Belfast, years younger than himself, he had treated savagely. One day a servant found her dead in her bed. The cause of Mary Sellers' death was a mystery and had through the years so remained.

And now it turned out that Phelim Sellers became a frequent visitor at Skreen Castle. Ostensibly he paid his visits to Sir Bromley, as partner in a game of whist to which the old man was addicted, but his eyes constantly followed the slender figure of Lilith as she moved about the room where her guardian habitually sat. Lilith was conscious of Phelim's regarding eyes, and because she had at their first meeting taken an instant and violent dislike to the man she felt an unease, a curious latent fear in his presence. As soon as she had poured tea for Sir Bromley and his guest she would make some excuse to leave them alone together. She often sought the lower river terrace where she had furnished, with chairs, scattered cushions and a writing table, the rustic summerhouse so pleasantly situated that on a summer day one might enjoy the river breezes.

It was on a day of stifling heat when she was sitting here engaged with her writing that Phelim Sellers, far gone in drink, she was instantly aware, strode suddenly into the summerhouse and forced his attentions upon her with such savagery that her screams of fury as she tried to beat him off brought to her aid the gardener Tomas and a young boy who had been fishing the river below.

Following this unfortunate encounter, Sellers disappeared from the Tara scene, and for a time Lilith saw no more of him. Perhaps a year had passed when one day she drove a gig into Moyvally to post some letters and make a few purchases. In a draper's shop she saw Phelim Sellers. He came up to her, made an elaborate bow, grasped her hand before she was quite aware of his intention, stripped the driving glove from her hand, and soundly kissed her fingers.

After this meeting Lilith begged Sir Bromley to allow her to visit friends in Dublin for a while. She made no pretense of hiding the fact that she feared the presence of Phelim Sellers in the neighbourhood. Her guardian listened silently. Then he said: "As you wish, Lilith. I will open the Dublin house for the winter. It is high time and more that you saw a little of society."

During the few days before the departure of Lilith and Sir Bromley for Dublin, Lilith busied herself with preparations for leaving. She neither saw nor heard anything of Sellers until the evening before they were to leave Skreen, when a maidservant came into the drawing room to light the candles. She motioned to Lilith to come out into the hall.

"That Mr. Sellers from Boyne House is lurking in the driveway. He stopped me on me way back from Tara to ask is it the truth we do be leavin' the morn fer Dublin. Did I do right at all, Miss, to answer 'im short-like that we are?"

"It was quite all right, Breena," Lilith said. "He would be bound to know we are leaving in any case, for we will pass his gates on our way."

About ten o'clock Lilith retired for the night. Just as she was falling asleep she was roused by what she thought was a footfall on the roof of the dining-room wing of the house, which lay directly underneath one of the windows of her room. She listened intently; then, persuaded that she was so tired as to be imagining things, she settled herself again for sleep. Suddenly the half-closed shutters of the open window opposite her bed were wrenched apart and a man sprang into the room. Before Lilith could cry out, he was upon her and bore her down flat upon the bed.

It was Tomas who found the body of Lilith when, early about his chores next morning, he opened the wicket gate leading to the lower terrace and the summerhouse. She lay sprawled on the path, her thin nightgown partly torn away. The fingers of her outstretched hands were clenched and bloody, as if, in a desperate fight to live, she had raked the face of her attacker. But the most curious thing of all was that handfuls of foxglove fronds had been ripped from their stalks and thrust down Lilith's throat with such force that she had died of strangulation.

Phelim Sellers was caught in Galway Old City as he was about to flee the country on a French packet ship. He was tried at Galway Winter Assizes, found guilty and hanged by the neck until he was dead, in the jailyard at Clew Barracks.

Persons living at Skreen Castle tell of hearing shrieks in the night and of seeing a woman in a white nightrail who clutches her throat as if fighting for breath. She runs stumbling along the path leading to the woods which surround Skreen Castle on three sides, and disappears into the shadows of the trees.

The Lament of Brian Healy

BRAY HEAD TOWER, VALENCIA ISLAND, COUNTY KERRY, 1050

IT HAS often been said that there are more public houses (called "licensed premises") strung out the like of a necklace of beads along the coast of County Kerry than are to be found in any other county in Ireland. These public houses range in condition from nearly windowless stone cabins, dark, damp, reeking of spilled whisky and porter, variously known as shebangs or pubeens, to such admirable, comfortably appointed taverns as the Tarred Rope Knot at Stradbally Strand or O'Ryan's Cosy Corner at Bolas Head. These pubs are frequented by fishermen and sailors from off the small, rusty coastal steamers that sail, hugging the Atlantic Coast, from Bloody Foreland in Donegal to Waterford Harbour. It is here that tall tales are heard—rambling accounts of some eerie experience the like that men who follow the sea, out in all kinds of weather, so frequently have. Old mariners will tell you that Valencia Island was, "way back in the years behind us," a giants' playground. On this ocean-borne plateau the old Gaelic gods and heroes used to gather for games. I have yet to hear a story-monger who does not credit every hero with giant stature, as, for example, "Man dear, he'd be twinty feet tall an' over, be the size ave the footprints ye can see fer yerself, left be Foileye the Bray Head giant on the rocks ferninst the auld tower."

I have often walked this high, rock-strewn, forever windy plateau, and indeed there are strange fossil-like indentations on many of the flattened shaly rocks that resemble, surely, the imprint of an immense human foot. I have even counted five splayed toes, and, by the look of one footprint, Foileye was deformed in the right foot.

But when I range the rocks of Valencia Island my chief interest is the Bray Head Tower that rises dark and forbidding as a finger of doom even against a cloudless summer sky, cradling memories of a father's inhuman cruelty to his demented son. The legend tells of the terrible fate suffered by Brian, the youthful son of warrior chieftain Desmond Healy of Kinsale Keep, a few miles down the coast, and his wife Oonagh of Derrynane. Oonagh was celebrated in pagan days throughout Ireland and beyond, for her stupendous beauty. "She walked all in a green-gold radiance that was of her own brightening," the bards sang of her.

It seems that one day Oonagh took her small son to the ancient druid tower of Bray, for near this place she had caused a bower to be erected, an airy lattice-work of flint shards. The bower was a retreat for Oonagh and her attendant ladies. Benches of carved chestnut wood and red cedar were arranged in a circle about a dais where a cushioned seat was placed. High sat Oonagh here, joining with her ladies in cutting out designs from silk to appliqué with gold and copper threads onto the arras and banners that decked the golden-roofed Warriors' Hall of her home place at Kinsale. Close by, the Keep of Bray, always a haunt for sea birds, attracted little Brian to amuse himself by skimming shards of flint at the darting sea gulls. One day in his eagerness he ran too close to the edge of the headland. He fell onto the rocks below. The spray from waves crashing against the headland had made a deep pool of water into which Brian fell head-long. Matted kelp and sea rushes broke the child's fall so that though badly bruised, he was not killed. It would have been far better if he had been so, for from that day out the boy's brain was awry—he knew not his mother nor his father, nor had he a smile for anyone at all.

As Brian grew in years and stature, he was given to fits of wild disorder. With any weapon handy he would attack whoever came near him when he was in this case. From the first days after Brian's fall from the Bray Headland, his father had gone about like a man accursed. A man big in his pride, Desmond Healy felt that the gods had deserted him and by their cruel trick of clouding the mind of his only son Brian had disgraced him before all men, friends or enemies alike.

Soon his wife Oonagh saw that Desmond had taken a great hate on his mad son and would not go near him. And then came the darkest time of all, the dreaded winter solstice, when the sky, weeping day and night, flooded the world. It was late one dismal evening when Desmond Healy, astride his great Spanish war horse Garronore, rode into the courtyard of his Keep of Kinsale. Drenched to his hide, Desmond flung himself off his horse, calling to a man-at-arms to rub the stallion dry and bed him down. For to Desmond Healy there were but two grandeurs in his life, his wife Oonagh and his magnificent barb Garronore.

But at that moment a series of wild cries rang through the keep. Well Desmond knew that this sort of disturbance presaged another fit of demented wildness from Brian. When these sudden attacks struck the boy he was usually promptly subdued by massive Ganby, one of Desmond's gallowglasses or spearmen who, ever since the mind of Brian had flown away, had kept constant watch over him. But tonight the wildness was different, for with the cunning of the insane Brian had tricked Ganby into absenting himself from the room where he spent his days. The boy had broken out and came leaping down the stairway the like of a hounded stag. Before Desmond could intervene, Brian had grabbed a spear left resting against the arch leading into the keep. With a cry of fury he hurled the weapon at his father. But his aim was chancy—the spear flew wide of its mark, to bury its bronze point in the throat of Garronore, severing the stallion's jugular vein.

For the space of three days Desmond Healy prowled about his halls speaking to no one. Oonagh, who tried to comfort him for the loss of his great horse, he bade be gone from him. "I must think—think—" he cried. "Think what I am to do with . . ." But he would not even utter his son's name.

Then the terrible deed was done. When Lady Oonagh lay deep in slumber in her arras-hung bed, Desmond left the keep by stealth. He was companioned only by Ganby, who carried over his shoulder the drugged form of Brian Healy wrapped in a black cloak tightly as in a shroud. The two men set out on foot along the sea road. A furious gale from out the west tore at their mantles as Desmond saw the light of a bull's-horn lantern swinging to mark the cove near Clonakilty where a boat was waiting. With wind tearing at the rigging, the sea waves mountainous with unrest, Desmond and Ganby set out for Valencia Island. Even in the best class of weather this is a goodly sail. But no rage of the elements could brook Desmond Healy's purpose.

And so it has been told and retold down the years how Desmond himself must have become demented, for a time at least. Once he and Ganby had arrived at the Tower of Bray he is said to have sent away the boatman and killed Ganby by the thrust of a dagger. He then placed the tightly-bound body of his son Brian in an alcove and with his own hands walled the boy up while still alive.

To this day men give Bray Head Tower a wide berth after nightfall. Even the herds of sheep cropping the short, salt-wind-toughened grass of the plateau run from the cries that are heard issuing from the tower. There is, too, a curious sound of singing—high, tremulous, a young voice, or so say those who claim to have heard it, as if a lament rising and falling in cadences of woe. This lament may go on for hours.

Julius Kenryan, a veterinary in Portmagee on the mainland shore facing the island, told me that he was called one day to Bray to tend a horse. After ministering to the animal, the day being fine, he walked up the turfed rocks to the top of the headland. When he peered in at the arched doorway of the tower, his attention was arrested by what sounded like the scraping of metal on masonry, as if someone was scraping the stones with a knife. He remembered hearing many's the time the story of the boy walled up alive in this tower. Kenryan entered the single room at its base. The sound came from above. He noticed a jut in the wall halfway up, the remnants of a stone stairway tracing an upward winding course to the top of the tower. The scratching was now louder, more frantic in haste. And then, said Mr. Kenryan, a despairing cry, as if wrung from the depths of abysmal grief, rose to echo against the mossy stone walls.

"I had had enough," Mr. Kenryan said. "I was convinced that I had heard the ghost of Brian Healy and—"

"And," I interrupted, "you were even more convinced when a few years ago, during a monumental storm of wind that lasted for nearly a week, some of the stonework of the tower became dislodged and fell out onto the turf." I stopped for a moment, watching his eyes widen, then continued. "And the nearly-turned-to-dust bones of a youth were littered all over the turf. Yes, I know all about it."

That particular form of the legend, showing proof of its assertions, is a great boon to all these talemongers, as the Kerry men are known in the pubs. The story is always good for a few drinks from a traveling stranger.

The Old Rock Creature

GLENSHESK, COUNTY ANTRIM, 1954

THOUGH I have journeyed to far places of the wide world many's the time, I can never remember having seen such variety of terrain or such changing moods of Nature in so relatively small an area as in the confines of the fabled Nine Glens of Antrim. On a day of wandering afoot I entered the first Glenarm through a dense tunnel of arched redbud oak trees, a continuation of the dark-ling wood surrounding the trumpet-vine-hung turrets of Rathlarn Castle. After perhaps a quarter of a mile of shadowed greenwood path I came out abruptly into bright glare of sun, a circular space as large as a military parade ground, spread thickly with wild asters and meadow-rose vines past flowering, the thorny sprays of the vine glowing redly with early autumn rose haws.

Glenarm is the gentlest in mood and the brightest of the glens. The ground dips into darkling Glencloy, where tall ferns rustle in the crisply cool October air. Glenariff lies small and pinched, haunted by the Dun Bull which slew Queen Raghilla's child and was in turn hunted down by her and slain with a bronze spear. Afar off I caught upon the evening air the reek of decay—Glen Bally-mon, where a stagnant lake lies still as death, and as black. The sun was near-ing the end of its arc when I entered, through a thicket of yellow alder trees, the twin glens, Glencorp and Glendun—"glens of the unknown"—linked together by a deep, gaseous ravine, where the silence bore down upon me more terrify-ing than clamour. And now the ground rose to embrace a small plateau, wind-racked Glentow, where tall, lightning-blasted trees riven black, or white as bleached bone, lean close together forever gossiping, telling and retelling old runes of the proud Gael. The ninth glen is Glentaise, squelchy with cat-tail stacked marshes.

Now I had come to the end of my traipsing. Down into a cave-like waste of heath I went—Glenshesk, the banshees' lair, where under the Great Black Stone of Shesk lie ten dead princesses. Once a year they rise and dance in the thin light of a new crescent moon, symbol of Artha, huntress in the Gaelic hierarchy of godhood, counterpart of Greek Artemis, goddess of the chase and of the moon. In song and legend it is told oft and always that these maidens were the ten daughters of King Barcc, a forest monarch who ruled all the northern reaches of Ireland in antique times. These princesses were Amazons in form and spirit, closely welded in their desire for celibacy, caring only for pursuits or games de-manding strength and cunning, and for roaming the forests in the chase. No matter how the old king their father, who expected soon to shuffle his coil, thundered that at least one of his daughters should wed and provide him with a grandson to rule in his stead, not one of them would heed his entreaties. Not one of them, they shouted in unison, would bed with a man. Each pronounced herself dedicated to chastity as a priestess of Artha of the Chase.

And so it turned out that in his high and kingly rage, old Barcc shut himself away in his red-painted hall. Of what use to him, a dying man, were ten daughters who gave him no sign of filial love, but scorned his wish that at least one of them should marry some young warrior and bear a man child to perpetuate the kingly house of Barcc? Well he knew that further pleas were useless. So he devised a plan. He waited until the full harvest moon had waned. He knew from old usage that on the night the infant moon, device and badge of Artha, lay like a luminous hunting bow in the sky, his ten priestess daughters would repair to the heath of drear Glenshesk. There on the black stone dedicated to the virgin goddess Artha his daughters would offer sacrifice of a doe, its hide rubbed all over with the powder of chalk. For only "white sacrifice" propitiated the jealous goddess Artha.

On the chosen night the ten daughters of Barcc, attired only in long white woolen cloaks of cloth woven on a silver loom by their own hands, and with silver leather sandals on their feet, repaired to Glenshesk. The grassy acres were but palely lighted under so young a moon. When the sacrifice had been completed it was Ava, the eldest princess, who stepped into the space before the bloodied altar stone to commence the ritual dance of propitiation to the goddess, an invocation to lend her favour during the year to their forest chase. By prearranged plan this was a signal for a band of assassins, who had hidden among the trees, to leap out into the clearing and slay each dancing maiden with a spear thrust through her heart, as they had been bade to do by King Barcc. As the crescent moon rode down the sky and the first finger of saffron-tinted dawn showed at the earth's edge off to the east, the great black altar stone was lifted to bury under it in a deep-dug grave the spear-pierced bodies of the ten defiant princesses.

As the slayers went out and away from Glenshesk there rose a great turmoil, a shrieking wind, as scythes of livid green lightning gashed the now storm-black sky. At the foot of the rock there suddenly appeared an ancient crone, a Warn Woman borne on the howling winds from her cranny in the Cliffs of Moher. Above the sound of the storm her voice rose like a shriek. "Daughters of Barcc, hear me under the earth. For such untimely death, so foully dealt, I will give you back one hour of life each year. On this very day come one year, when the new moon tilts in the sky, you will all rise from under the Stone of Shesk and dance as you were about to do tonight when slain." So saying the crone reached beneath her mantle, which for raggedness resembled the draggled plumage of some sea bird, and withdrew a billet of wood that shone dully with phosphorus. She hurled it at the altar and a blaze of green-blue fire encompassed the stone. As if by magic the storm howled away out to sea, the night grew clear and the sky was patterned with the brilliance of myriad stars.

It is said that at the beginning of October of every year there is to be seen an old woman of the roads going about her task of setting up a tarpaulin shelter, as the tinkers are ever wont to do, in the lee of the black rock. The creature will go about arranging her few pots and pans and will even forage for berries, nuts and roots; she may deftly snare a bird or two, or catch with furtive hands a slithering fish from the little stream that meanders lazily through the glen. But an odd class of thing it appears that when a week or more has passed and the moon shows at the quarter, then sometime in the night this old woman will stealthily slink away. Perhaps the next year the Old Rock Creature, as she is known locally, will be the same woman; perhaps she will be a different woman, a stranger to the region. No one knows and certainly no one particularly cares, for the woman never causes any disturbance.

The first time that I entered the glen it was September midmonth. I looked carefully at the Great Black Stone of Shesk, but save that its hugeness is awesome it is no different from countless other rocks strewing the nine glens. So I made a point of returning on the second day of the month of October. As I entered the glen I distinctly smelled smoke from a rank kind of tobacco. Presently I came out of a thicket of stunted bog oak onto a path leading to the great stone. There sat an old woman smoking one of those cobeen pipes, a mere three inches of pipe given mostly to a rough carved bowl, the kind that are fashioned by tinker men from the knots of an arbutus tree that grows in splendour around the Lakes of Killarney. The air being a bit sharp, the woman had wound herself in yards of a dun-gray homespun shawl, so that she looked like some particularly ugly giant larva about to issue from its cocoon. However, she favoured me with a toothless smile.

"God's day t' ye, yer honour, sir. Would ye be after havin' a twist er a curl ave tobaccy about ye? I'm that out I'm jist smokin' the smoke, ochone the day."

As I habitually smoke a pipe when tramping the countryside, I obliged by giving her a handful of my best Dublin Gold. This she sniffed and gave me a bleary-eyed wink of approval. "I'll be high in me grandeur whin I draw on this, be the Holy God, and no one t' see me wealth."

So, the ice broken conversationally, I set out to acquire a little knowledge. I first asked her name. "Thim"—she nodded her head towards Ballymoney, the nearest village to the glens—"calls me the Auld Rock Crathure. Same as all ave us that tind the altar here fer the dead." As I must have looked surprised, she continued, "Me name, if I've one at all, is Glanna—jist Glanna ave the roads." And then, by devious questioning, a word here and a word there, I learned a strange and to me wondrous story.

It seems that from time immemorial it has been a kind of unwritten law among the fraternity of tinkers and people of the roads that at the rise of a new moon each October a woman of their number must spend a few nights as attendant to the ceremonies that take place at the Great Stone of Shesk—a kind of handmaiden, I gathered, to the ten princesses risen from their common grave to breathe one hour of life, to dance their ritual invocation to Artha of the Chase, and then return to their tomb to lie, if not wholly dead, at least inanimate for another year.

I asked Glanna of the roads what were the duties of this sinecure and why it was nearly always a different woman who came here to officiate. To the first part of my question she paid no mind, other than to stare at me from her weak, pale-blue eyes. Then she said, "Whoever is walkin' the roads nearest t' the glen comes t' keep the vigil."

As the sun was far gone, with night approaching and a cold wind sprung up, I delivered, so to speak, my Parthian shot. "Have many persons other than yourself and the women of the roads seen the princesses rise from the dead to perform their dance?"

There was a stark silence. It was then I realized I had trod on sacred ground. Giving me no answer, the old woman Glanna started to rummage in a capacious tarpaulin sack which had been lying at her feet. Gravely she extracted a hunk of filthy-looking cold bacon and a thick slice of bread. She regarded them absently. Then she looked up at me, but her eyes now were blazing as with an inner wrath.

"No one comes here on *the night*." She spat out the last two words in full strength of a lusty voice. "No one who's any wisdom athwart thim wants t' see. It 'ud torture the eyes in yer head, t' the state ave the blindness ave a mole."

So—I had had my answer. This was akin to the Mysteries of Eleusis in ancient Greece, where an uninitiated observer in the temple was on discovery forthwith beaten to death by the women devotees. So having learned, if not entirely, yet more than a little of what I wanted to know, I prepared to depart. Presenting Glanna with my remaining Dublin Gold tobacco and a pound note for good measure, I turned to leave. She was, rather grimly, I thought, munching on the hunk of cold bacon.

"Good night," I said. "I hope you enjoy your supper."

She retorted a shade bitterly. "Well—I'm not at all, havin' no more teeth than the divil has conscience."

White Horse Shod with Silver

KILKEA CASTLE, COUNTY KILDARE, 1429

ANCIENT KILKEA might in very truth be called the Castle of Storms, for about its granite battlements the wild elements have raised storms aplenty. But none have been more ferocious than the storms of hate, flaring as prelude to murders, that were visited by brother upon brother and by husband upon wife. There were family feuds galore. In one instance three sons besieged their father and "roasted him to the crackle, as they had many a time seared a poled ox," according to an old chronicle.

Built in the massive style of a foursquare fortress keep, Kilkea boasts three hexagonal and two round towers; its granite walls are five to seven feet thick, with only a few windows larger than in the original building first erected by the famous warrior Hugh de Lacy for Walter de Ridlesford, who received the Barony of Kilkea as his portion for aiding the Anglo-Normans in their conquest of Ireland. The granddaughter of de Ridlesford married Maurice Fitzgerald, third Baron of Offaly, and the castle became one of the numerous Geraldine strongholds scattered, some ruined, some occupied as residences, in most of the south, east and west counties today. And all of them, I might add, haunted to the last corbel with an exciting and formidable assortment of ghosts.

Sacked by the Irish in an attack on the English Pale in 1426, Kilkea was later restored, enlarged and made habitable—a dwelling worthy of the "proud, fighting Fitzgeralds," a race whom Elizabeth I reviled in a fury of exasperation when she learned that a Fitzgerald had not only ambushed her favourite Essex in a lonely bog, so that he had to pay extortionate ransom for his freedom, but had also, at five different points simultaneously, sacked and massacred English families within the Pale.

"These Fitzgeralds," the Queen stormed, "were they suckled on blood, born clothed in armour, sword in hand, full-panoplied like so many Athenas?" To Essex she wrote, "Hunt out and slay every bearer of the cursed name Fitzgerald."

Amid all the tales of parricide, gory deeds of treachery and an apparently congenital disregard of the rights of their fellow men, a rather prim and certainly vastly disapproving Miss Kelty, the village postmistress, seems to have hit the nail squarely on the head when she answered me, and I asking her a few questions regarding some of the Kilkea ghosts,

"Ye'll be advised be meself to give the lot ave thim the back ave yer hand. I hear this an' I hear that, and I mind me own bib. No matter—I'll say the truth ave it fer once. Grand though they are, big and mouthy in their pride, that family is well known fer ostentatious behaviour."

The castle has its magic legend as well, in the story of the eleventh earl, the "Wizard," who practiced his black art in a tower room. This circular aviary where he worked his spells and incantations, surrounded by bright-plumaged birds brought to him from tropical jungles, is still shown to visitors. Thither the Wizard rides with his enchanted knights once in every seven years, rides breakneck from the Rath of Mullaghmast across the Curragh Plains, returning to the castle at dawn. The earl's ghostly horse is white, shod with silver shoes. His septennial ride will be repeated until these silver shoes have quite worn away. But I have a feeling that the massive towers of Castle Kilkea will have crumbled away long before it can be said "Fitzgerald rides no more."

Conflagration on Christmas Eve

CURRAGH CHASE, ADARE, COUNTY LIMERICK, 1935

WELL I remember stopping in Dublin for the 1935 Christmas holidays. Certainly I shall never forget the "stop press" edition of the *Dublin Times* early on the morning after Christmas. The headlines, two inches high and set in the blackest letters that printer's ink can produce, read:

CURRAGH CHASE, ADARE, BURNED TO THE GROUND ON CHRISTMAS EVE. TOTAL DESTRUCTION FOR THE WANT OF ADEQUATE WATER SUPPLY.

The burning of far too many of our fine Irish country mansions has come about for precisely this reason. I felt a deep sense of loss for a beautiful and friendly house when I read the account of the disaster, for I had stayed many times at the Chase and have always been highly entertained by the immense accumulation of memorabilia, including an outstanding collection of sword-arms, over five hundred pieces ranging from crude early Scottish claymores to indescribably delicate Florentine stilettos and French rapiers. One poignard indeed had a hollow blade. This orifice could be filled with six drops, no more, of poison swift to deal death and leave no trace, such as was once distilled secretly for use by the Medici and Valois. There was a circular library at Curragh Chase devoted only to poetry. Here were scrolls of Greek verse written in vermilion juice of pomegranate on white lambskin. From India there were folios of extremely erotic "divan" poetry, the capital letters set with precious jewels. And when I mention poetry in connection with this house, thereby hangs a tale.

Curragh Chase was an imposing late-Georgian mansion, incorporating far older portions, which stood on the edge of a reed-grown river in one of the most remote and romantic settings conceivable. I believe there are no houses, other than a lodge or two, nearer to the demesne gates than four miles away. "Bosom'd high in tufted trees serene," the house was surrounded by dense and luxuriant woods with, in the distance, the clear outlines of purple mountains. Long ago a grim, turreted castle stood on the site. This was the abode for centuries of the De Vere family, through the marriage in 1573 of one Henry Hunt with Jane de Vere, a younger daughter of Aubrey de Vere, son of John, Earl of Oxford. This branch of the family (for the Hunts only assumed the name of De Vere two and a half centuries after this union) have always considered themselves the rightful claimants of this illustrious earldom.

Curragh Chase has long been a sanctuary for poets of the romantic school. Sir Aubrey de Vere (1814–1902) wrote reams of poetry in the elaborate romantic vein, his *Duke of Mercia* and *Mary Tudor* being celebrated for redundant phrasing. Aubrey, his younger son, was an iconoclast. He wrote of his father, "My parent scorns to use in conversation or his alleged poetry a two-syllable word. If he is at loss to find one of six syllables he will manufacture a frightener of ten."

Aubrey was himself heralded as a "great Catholic poet" by his contemporaries, Patmore, Hopkins and Tennyson. The latter frequently visited Curragh Chase. During one of his summer visits he was, according to Aubrey, "stricken silly with love." The outcome was that Tennyson wrote that absurd poem *Clara, Lady Vere de Vere.* Tennyson is said to have returned to the house one night at a late hour. He told a tall tale of having heard a tremendous splashing in the artificial lake which was achieved in the first Sir Aubrey's day by partially damming up the river reaches in the lower park. The poet said that on close inspection he had seen the mystic arm of the Lady of the Lake grasping Excalibur. He was told that oddly enough he was not the first person to have seen the flashing white arm as, ringed in tiny wavelets, it thrust above the water.

A few days after the fatal fire at Curragh Chase I drove out to see what, if anything, of the house remained standing. Only four tall, flame-blackened chimneys loomed like charred tree trunks against a dismal gray winter sky. But in the village of Adare I heard what had occurred to start the fire. It seems that Mrs. Stephen de Vere, widow of the last of the De Veres, had invited a number of relatives and friends to make up a Christmas party. Shortly after teatime a rising wind had soughed through the trees in the park, and by the time dinner was announced a gale of tempest volume rattled every casement window in the walls. Indeed the force of the wind was so violent that branches were wrenched from the oak and beech trees near the house, to be hurled against the front door and onto the tiles. A table covered with a square of brocaded velvet had been set in the drawing room. On this table were two silver candelabra, each one branching at least a dozen candles. Gaily-wrapped Christmas presents from the hostess to her guests and from one guest to another were arranged on the table around a silver bowl which would later be filled with a whisky and lemon punch.

One of the male guests went over to a window. He pulled back the heavy damask curtain and peered out into the storm-tossed woods. This window faced the lake where Lord Tennyson had claimed to have seen the white arm of the Lady of the Lake. Suddenly the watcher at the window was frozen with horror, as, above the wind, rose a cry of acute anguish and of such force that even above the storm other occupants of the room heard it distinctly. They saw a figure of a woman, redly aglow as if sheathed in flames, rise from the churning waters of the lake and point, with arm outstretched, towards Curragh Chase. Then, with another cry even more horrible in its quavering intensity, the figure sank back into the fog-clouded waters of the lake.

It was at that very instant that the wind rose to hurricane force. A huge limb was torn from a beech tree near the front of the house. The limb crashed through one of the drawing-room windows, knocking over the table on which stood the lighted candelabra. Great gusts of wind swept through the lower rooms of the house. In an instant the place was a roaring furnace of wind-whipped flames.

A few months after the total destruction of Curragh Chase, the brick of the foundations and of the standing chimneys was sold to a salvager of such relics and carted away. Nothing then remained of the edifice that from the highroad, embowered in its ancient trees, had presented a façade of such classic dignity.

Silence. The changing seasons and the long years took hold of the De Vere heritage. Then curious stories began to be told and retold in the pubs, at the crossroad livestock fairs, and when housewives gathered at the wells in small villages lying round about the vast park of Curragh Chase. Men told of passing the gate-lodge of the demesne and witnessing sights "ave the divil's contriving." One drover was startled with "a class ave fright that grabbed me be the throat" when there, upside down in "that spot ave ornimintal wather," he had seen the reflection of many-windowed Curragh Chase. And so down the years the stories persisted. There were variations on the main theme, as always happens in like cases. But it was the reflection of the house, glowing redly as if enveloped in flames, that most of the persons claimed they had seen.

A Mrs. Lanier, who lived in a sort of half-ruined hunting lodge that had been built by one of the Hunt-De Vere family on a small holding a few miles outside the actual demesne walls, told me that one Christmas Eve she was driving a pony-trap back from Adare. Because the animal had cast a shoe she had to walk him, so she was far later returning home than was her wont. Just as the road steepened and she came out upon a rise of ground, her pony shied violently. At that moment, the night being still and overcast, she heard a terrible scream from the rhododendron brake below. Then it was that, for an instant only, she saw the figure of a woman enveloped in flames rise from the reedy sedges of the lake. In the livid glow Mrs. Lanier saw the apparition raise her arm and point towards the spot where once Curragh Chase had stood. As the figure, gleaming brightly in red and golden light, sank hissing back into the lake, the image of classic Curragh Chase rode serenely upon its ivy-grown foundations.

Only for an instant, Mrs. Lanier said, the house shimmered whitely, like a moonlit pavilion in mirage. Then, as if one had touched a match to a tissue-paper house, the pedimented façade grew red, then turned to black and gray, crumpling into ashes. The night was again dark and still. Mrs. Lanier quieted her restive pony and drove on her way.

Dunmahon Castle Lifts Its Gory Head

BLACKROCK, COUNTY WICKLOW, 1641

FREQUENTLY when I am near the seacoast of the lovely undulating County of Wicklow, identified from afar off by the grass-turfed conical heights of Sugar Loaf Mountain, a kind of aerial grazing ground for thousands of sheep, I stop for a time under the ivy-hung walls of grim Dunmahon Castle. The very ivy, thriving dark green at the root, proverbially turns as black as the prickly foliage of funereal yew, once its tendrils grasp the masonry to climb the walls of this pile which is haunted to its last crenelation by memories of deeds of shameful treachery.

Like all these solitary towers rising from Irish soil, there is for me in Dunmahon Castle a fascination that urges me on to delve into its past history; to explore, in a sense, deeper into its dungeons—for it is the dungeons, hewn from living rock embracing three levels, that still reverberate to the anguished cries of the massacred.

Dunmahon Castle, about three miles west of Blackrock, is a tall, square-turreted tower in a fair state of preservation, built about 1180 by the Geraldines as one of their "guardian keep of our demesne" watchtowers and a quartering place for gallowglasses.

At this time the Fitzgerald earls held vast territories amounting to petty kingdoms that embraced half the South of Ireland. Little is known—or at least recorded—about Dunmahon until the advent of the terrible Charles Townley, who "affronted every man who saw his mean and shambling self." This man, who occupied sundry shady offices under the Parliamentary regime, first used the dungeons of Dunmahon to extract confessions from rebellious Irish prisoners. Many a belligerent captive held his tongue to his undoing. He was then tortured by means of wrist irons. These instruments, stained with dark red-brown smears, corroded with rust, may still be seen spiked into the dank river-seeping walls of the second tier of dungeon cells. The method employed was to pull the unfortunate wretch under torture down to the ground by the wrist irons, against the pressure of a garrote which slowly choked him to death.

While the constant depredations of Townley and his henchmen are notorious, it was the massacre of over two hundred worshipers invited by Townley to hear Mass in the castle bailey and slain to the last soul by Parliamentary soldiers hidden from view until the elevation of the Host, that so exceeded all bounds of human behaviour as to be excoriated as "anathema" by the Pontiff in Rome. "They died on their knees from the fear to rise, a prayer to God and a curse for the monster Townley mouthing at cross purposes on their tongues," as one contemporary historian described the scene.

Apparently undisturbed by this atrocious bath of blood perpetrated within its walls, the castle was afterwards occupied by the Townley family. But the Dread Women of Moher, the Gaelic Fates, those persecuting harpies of Irish legend who never let up on the damned, dealt many's the fatal blow to succeeding generations of Townleys. All manner of misfortune followed them, including a great rarity of nature. In 1814 Roderick Townley was struck down by the only case of leprosy recorded in Ireland.

In the village of Dunmahon there is an old restlessness still hovering. The dark streets at night are remarkably empty of life. A few scurrying cats dart out from the shadows, long and enveloping, cast by the high, steep-roofed, stone houses with walls blank from closely-shuttered windows. Particularly is this wary seclusion apparent on the night of Pentecost. Then the villagers sit silent in their houses, hands clasped in prayer, for this is the anniversary of the Massacre at Mass. Apprehensively they wait. Soon there is the low murmur of tongues pronouncing the articles of devotion. On a rising note, chanting fills the air. At the instant when the light silver bells ring to mark the elevation of the Host, there rasps the clash of steel, then pandemonium breaks out as wild cries of incredulity and despair echo across the river. It is said that persons out on the river road that crosses an ancient arched bridge leading to the castle bailey have seen dark figures of men and women gain the battlements, and that behind them swords flash and curses ride upon the air. Then the pursued wretches fling themselves off the tower to escape the assassins of Charles Townley, only to meet death by sinking from mortal sight in the black waters of the deep-flowing river below the walls.

The Diffident Earl of Mara

STORM CLOUDS massed and broke away, torn ragged in the path of a high, raging wind. The leaden sky was intermittently pierced by spears of sun to pattern in gold light and harsh dark shadows the rutted road which hugs the seacoast from Dublin to Newtown-Swords. Along this road a heavy four-horse coach pitched from side to side, careening against the wind, its yellow wheels sinking nearly to the hubs in miniature gullies and puddles formed where waves had dashed over the rocks which were loosely piled into a kind of wall to thwart the bold Irish Sea. But the sole occupant of this vehicle, a lean man of singularly arresting presence and sharply-limned features, appeared totally unaware of any discomfort as the horses battled against the rising wind, the coachman exerting prodigious skill to keep the coach upright on this perilous road.

The man inside the coach would from time to time peer out of a window. Then, his darting eyes conveying satisfaction that this was the right road, he would sink back on the claret-coloured rep cushions and abstractedly tap long yellowed fingers on the etched-silver snuffbox which formed the top of his ebony walking stick, while nodding and listening to the wind playing familiar to the eldritch screaming of innumerable sea gulls. A look of careful calculation veiled the eyes of the "diffident" Earl of Mara, as, along with a good many other so-briquets, Johnny Mara was known to his intimates. Had any one of his rake-helly cronies in Dublin seen the look in the eyes of this unpredictable man, he would have instantly sensed it was worth a wager for guineas that some eccentric gesture was abrewing under the elegantly-tilted black beaver tricorn heavily laced and tasseled in gold galloon. This faraway, half-closed-eyelid look habitually presaged some prank devised by Mara to shock public opinion in general, but in particular to regale the *haut ton* of Dublin, always avid for bizarre novelties in conduct to add zest to the daily round of cards, cockfighting, eternally risking bets for this or that hazard, or performing and discussing prodigious feats of love. In the devising and performance of the most fantastic whims this aristocrat, "handsome as Satan and devious as Pan," to give Lord Mara a compliment tossed about in the card rooms of Merrion Square, was without equal.

Suddenly the earl roused from his cogitations and rapped sharply with his cane on the roof of the coach to attract the attention of his coachman. Lumberingly the coach jerked to a halt. A half-frozen footman who had been clinging to the strap-jump high up between the back wheels of the coach opened the door and let down a flight of folding steps. Mara ignored these; as lightly as a dog fox clears a frosty wall he leapt down onto the hard road. The earl wrapped his caped greatcoat of gray frieze about his lean body and walked over to stand on a rock outcropped higher than its fellows at the edge of the sea.

He saw, spread out in a dun-coloured panorama of rocks and fitfully-lighted water, a wide, flat strip of reedy marshes extending into the sea. A kind of causeway, half submerged now, was, even at low tide, scarcely wide enough for a donkey cart or a man-drawn peat barrow. At the end of this natural jetty, perhaps a quarter of a mile from shore, rose an ungainly huddle of bare rocks, curiously humped as if some prehistoric mammal was just rising from the darkling water, shaking thousands of raucous sea gulls from his serrated hide. The earl nodded thoughtfully and in a characteristic gesture lipped the silver top of his cane. He talked his thoughts to the sea wind, scarcely hearing the words himself, so drowned out they were by gulls screaming. "Yes—this is the place, surely. This is just as it was in the dream." He turned to look inland, intoning, "Yes—directly in front of the old Castle of Swords. Just as it was in the dream. Everything there except the house gleaming in the moonlight." He smiled wryly as a zany gull nearly swooped his tricorn off his head. The din and screeching of a multitudinous assemblage of gulls alighting on and restlessly taking off from the trident-pronged pinnacles of rock nearly cracked his eardrums. Not in the least daunted, Mara continued to fling his thoughts verbally down the wind. "The house I build will be perishing damp—and draughty. Many a petticoat will fly up in the gales, and obviously I will have to silence those gulls. How?" He turned and looked towards the shivering groom and his coachman sitting motionless as an image on the box, petrified with cold. The earl struck sparks from a stone with the ferule of his cane. "Look alive. Both of you." Turning, with one foot on the steps of the coach he took a last look at the rocks now almost hidden by mist and the shadows of fast-descending night. He described an arc with his cane in the sweeping way a conqueror declares victory in battle. "I know how to drive those lost souls forever wailing in torment away from my house. Oh yes, I know what to do." He prodded the coachman in the rump. "Come, drive me back to Dublin. Drive like hell."

On the return journey, even more tortuous than before because of the furious pace of the whipped horses, the Earl of Mara slept fitfully on his claret rep cushions. Again he dreamed of how beautiful on nights of a full moon would be Mara House, pointed up in silver light and black shadow. It was a short dream, but vivid. In some ways it is a pity he did not dream further into the future.

Forty-five years before this gale-buffeted coach lumbered from Dublin to Newtown-Swords and back again, the man dozing inside, who dreamed of a moonlit house set foursquare to the elements on a bleak rock jutting sheer from the sea, was born in a remote castle in the backlands of County Roscommon. This bellowing scrap of man-child was born posthumously, full-panoplied as Twelfth Earl of Mara, Lord Ferriter and Glan. Later, in the castle chapel he was christened John Manderville Killraven Cloyne. And the pompous Bishop of Conrally intoned, "May the light of God's mercy mantle your shoulders eternally and his blessings strew your path."

Small John was the twelfth Earl of Mara to be born posthumously. It was not only a family habit, it was the fulfillment of a family curse. Six weeks before the new earl's birth his father the eleventh earl had died by assassination, his brain pulped in his cracked skull by blows from a heavy cudgel in the hands of a demented tinker. The earl had been waylaid on the road from Kincorb to Ballyhaunis, indeed at the very gates of his Castle Blanard, as he returned from an evening canter. It was never revealed just what class of argument took place between the earl and Rab Bello the tinker, who was well known in the neighbouring counties as a bully "of a ragin' madness habitual." However, this murder added one more calamity to a long roster of such that had been inflicted on the Cloynes of Castle Blanard. The event of an Earl of Mara meeting death variously, but always violently, a few weeks or months before the birth of an heir followed the long-drawn-out pattern of an ancient curse. It had become a byword among the superstitious country people around Ballyblanard that their landlord was "the sire ave a curse," while in the more cynical Dublin clubs it was "the posthumous Earls of Mara."

Johnny Mara, as the earl was known to his intimates to the last day of his life, grew to young manhood ranging the wide demesne of Blanard and farther afield to the fascinating fishing ports of Galway and Sligo. His mother, Lady Mara, was indifferent to any particular education for her son, saying, "He is a Cloyne and a Fitzarden. Surely he will turn out all right. I give him the best tutors obtainable." Then she was off and away, occupied with junketings up to Dublin and rather mysterious visits to Paris and fashionable Italian watering places. The quality and changing array of these tutors became, as the years passed, a joke in the countryside. The tutors might be moderately carefree young men when they arrived at Castle Blanard, but when they left they were harassed individuals, aged before their time.

Early on in his life Johnny Mara embarked on his career of prankster. His talents gathered volume with years of practice, until in the regency of the Prince of Wales, later George IV, a series of pamphlets were written by Richard Brinsley Sheridan describing in elaborate detail some of the young lord's more lurid escapades. Extraordinary for inventiveness, these "charades" designed by his countryman absolutely fascinated Sheridan. When Mara tried a sample in a Dublin playhouse against an actor he abhorred, by coming on the stage at the same time as the actor, dressed and made up identically and mouthing the actor's lines in gibberish, the victim sued him and won a public apology from behind the footlights, as well as a fair sum of money.

Perhaps his first elaborately conceived "experiment," as Johnny Mara always called the escapades which so often turned into imbroglios, was practiced on the ninth in line of his tutors. This unfortunate individual was Liam Curran, a graduate of Trinity College in Dublin. It appears that on his arrival at Blanard he was incontinently disliked by Johnny Mara. One day at lunch Johnny learned that Curran was to celebrate his thirtieth birthday in a few days' time. Mara asked the tutor what he would like in the way of a present. Curran answered, "A short holiday, my lord, if you would be so kind. I wish to visit my betrothed in Dundalk." This request was readily granted. Immediately Johnny Mara set about inventing an "experiment" that would make the arrival of Liam Curran at the house of his bespoke Miss Flurry memorable, if a shade outrageous. With the aid of two cronies, a class of hangers-on who seemed always on tap to aid and abet him, Johnny Mara, then in his fifteenth year, ambushed young Curran as he was about to set out for Dundalk. First the tutor was stripped to the buff, his body was painted in peppermint-stick stripes with red dye, and then he was trussed like a fowl. In this predicament he was thrust into a wooden chest, known in Ireland as a dowry or marriage-portion chest, that had been dragged down from the attics of Blanard. Small holes had been drilled in the sides of the chest so there was no fear that the suitor would perish of asphyxiation before he arrived at Dundalk. The chest was then loaded on the top of a heavy coach. Bright ribbons such as are tied to a bridal coach at Irish country weddings streamed from dowry chest and hubcaps. The coach was driven at breakneck speed through a startled countryside by Johnny Mara himself, resplendent in cockaded coachman's hat and many-caped coat. With what mingled feelings Miss Flurry received and opened her present of a dowry chest, only to find that it contained the stark-naked, brightly-emblazoned form of her intended husband, is left to conjecture.

From this time out the countryside rang with cries of indignation or gales of amused laughter over the shenanigans of the ebullient earl. But a day of reckoning was at hand. In his eighteenth year Johnny Mara shot his bolt "beyond the beyond," as far as the County Roscommon was concerned. Because the road from Mallarany Strand passing the gates of Blanard was dark as pitch on a moonless night, Johnny Mara decided to light his way home from sampling porter in Mallarany pubeens by setting fire to stooks of wheat drying in fields bordering the highroad. It was a windy night and sparks blown from the blazing stooks set fire to the thatch roofs of a clutch of coteens, causing the death of two children trapped in one of the gutted houses. This "experiment," ending in fatality, enraged the country people of Roscommon and beyond to such a pitch of fury against Johnny Mara that it was thought wise by his factor that the unruly youth quit his demesne for a time. It was settled that he join his mother at Montecatini in the hills of Tuscany. It was while here, lying doggo but bored to the wide and ripe for "unholiness," for which he had lately been denounced by his parish priest, that the impressionable young earl contracted a desire for the intimate favours of Italian women. This craving was to be paramount in his amorous attachments throughout his life.

One golden autumn day, Johnny Mara arrived back in Dublin, sophisticated beyond all reason, his mind a glittering filigree of all the fashionable Continental vices so eagerly sampled by rakish young gentlemen of his time. The

Grand Tour of Europe had whetted and full-rounded Johnny Mara's appetite for "experiments." During this period of the eighteenth century, Dublin was wide open to a cult of obstreperous young bloods known as Pinking Dindies. Foppishly dressed, fluttering with gewgaws and fal-lals, these "Pinkers" strolled in St. Stephen's Green, Merrion Square, down the hill of Grafton Street and so through the smart but smelly purlieus of Ashton Quay and Smock Alley where the playhouses were situate, affecting nonchalance but surreptitiously ripping the attire of passers-by with needle-pointed swords. Johnny Mara joined the Pinking Dindies, but for him to join anything was tantamount to being leader of whatever. A downy bird, a born exhibitionist, was the Earl of Mara. He habitually made his immediate vicinity crackle with incident.

Among the Dublin rakes the earl set the style for extravagance in male attire. His tricorns were grandly plumed. His laces at neck and wrists glinted with sequins and gilt threads as dictated in the salons of Paris and the *ridottos* of Venice. His pinking sword, with which to puncture the buttocks of unwary ladies and rip open the flies of the satin or balbriggan breeches of their escorts, was an ell in length, with a point honed to draw blood by the gentlest pressure. When the amusement of pinking innocents abroad palled, newly-opened lottery booths swept like a tidal wave throughout the city. "Unhallowed dens of chance and ruin," the furious clergy cried from the pulpits. Johnny Mara set up lottery booths along Ashton Quay and Abbey Street under a dozen different aliases. Wagering amounted to frenzy. Dubliners, from verminous pub-crawlers to coroneted peers, wagered varying amounts on anything, from how many fleabites a man would show on his skin after spending a night with a doxy at Old Mother Sin and Sorrow's shebang, to how many hairs a blindfold man could grasp in his fist from the tail of a horse cantering past him.

But it was as leader of the Hell-fire Club, in league with his shadow Lord Clontibbertt, called "that impersonation of whisky," that Johnny Mara shone most brightly. It was as arbiter of this club, with its rigid rules and regulations compiled by him, that the earl earned the sobriquet the "diffident" Earl of Mara. It was his air of vagueness, of a mind forever ranging far places, his elaborate detachment, and to many his infuriating arrogance, that caused Mrs. Delany, exhaustive chronicler of Dublin high life in the spacious days of the Georgian period, to label him "possessor of a thousand graces but no single friend to admire them." In this sweeping statement the doughty Mary Granville Delany was wide of the mark. Women of all classes frantically admired him, and many loved Johnny Mara to their bitter sorrow.

While the Hell-fire Club was being built, perched like a forbidding Noah's Ark on top of Mount Pellier among the Dublin Mountains, Johnny Mara leased a hunting lodge from a raffish crony, one Wickham O'Brody, whose unpowdered mop of red hair appeared a veritable conflagration, causing him to be known as the Flaming Wick. At Mount Pellier Lodge the earl inaugurated a style of entertainment that was later to cause the ill-starred Hell-fire Club literally to go up in smoke (a blackened stone hulk may still be seen on the barren mountain top from the squares of Dublin) when barrels of tar on the roof were set alight as a beacon to welcome Johnny, the Hell-fire Boy Extraordinary, back from foreign parts. Heavy drinking, blasphemous oaths, the pursuit of Venus, and playing cards for high stakes was the curriculum which flourished, turning night into day, on the crest of Mount Pellier. It is said that amusing themselves with monumental orgies led the members to perform the iniquitous Black Mass. The "ladies of the town"—and Dublin town is just below the mountain—flourished, their charms in demand as never before. But it was an Italian adventuress, a notorious beauty called Emilia Ruccini, who reigned for a time over the uninhibited household of Johnny Mara. Her tenure, ending in a wildly-staged melodrama from which she ran out into the night, wrapped only in the red damask bed hangings, put "one more nail in the coffin of scandal" as Dubliners said.

So the years of profligacy for Johnny Mara waxed and waned. He made frequent trips to the Continent. His mother died in Venice, willing him her magnificent collection of Fitzarden jewels. One Italian mistress followed another. And then—the deluge. The hitherto uncapturable earl fell headlong in love. This time it was with a singer named Reza Buonamonte, a Veronese whom he heard sing at Teatro Antico in Verona.

Reza was the cool, restrained, *Madonna de la Luna* type, the "dusky Veronese blonde" one sees in the northern provinces of Italy. A golden beauty, in direct contrast to the fiery, voluptuous, black- or auburn-haired termagants the predatory earl had hitherto sought out for dalliance. But while Reza Buonamonte granted her favours to Johnny Mara in Verona, she refused to come to Ireland unless marriage to him was her reward. To her lover this married state was not only undesirable but downright inconceivable. He flung himself off to

Ireland, disconsolate but firm in purpose never to marry. That would be tanta-mount, he said, "to losing my life siring a posthumous Earl of Mara."

Then one night he dreamed his dream. He was standing on a bold shore. Waves of the Irish Sea crashed against the old rock known locally as Swords Headland. Behind him in the moonlight, gaunt and disheveled, loomed the dere-lict hulk of the bloodstained old Castle of Swords, built when Dublin was an armed camp of the Cromartys athwart the River Liffey, called Hurdle-at-the-Ford. But before him on the headland, perched, airy as a sea gull about to take flight, a white house—porticoed, pillared, as lovely in proportion as Milltown's classic Russborough or Leinster's Palladian Carton. He was aware of two things more: The gulls were quiet, nesting among the rocks or skimming silently in the moon-silvered air. And leaning over a ramp-like terrace facing the sea, beckon-ing to him, was the smiling image of Reza Buonamonte. Suddenly there was the eerie screeching of lost souls in torment, as sea gulls proverbially are said to be, and the bright, high-sailing moon was smothered by a storm-wrack of black clouds. In a cold sweat Johnny Mara woke up.

From that moment his mind was made up. He would go out to see the spot that had been so vivid in his dream. Not since he was a small boy had he been near the Castle of Swords. All his "experiments" were now tossed aside. He had a *plan*. A plan he felt sure would work out as he wished it.

The building of Mara House on one of the three pinnacles of Swords Head-land caused all Dublin, and the curious from many another Irish county, to flock by passing strange means of conveyance, from donkey-back to the viceroy's lacquered coach harnessing six ebony horses, to view the greatest folly of the century. But the house, built of blocks of gleaming white Connemara stone, Pal-ladian in style, rose unhindered on its wind-swept eminence. Workmen care-fully dovetailing the huge stone blocks were disturbed for a time, and the frosty whiteness of carved cornices fouled, by the droppings of flocks of gulls—gulls by the thousands, screaming protest to the usurpers of their sea-girt domain. A few times as the men were quitting work at dusk one of them would point to a dark, brooding figure of a shawled woman who seemed to prowl the Sea Road or wade among the reeds at the foot of the rock. "Oh, an old Warn Woman. Arragh, their like is a crucifixion. May the curses they deal out rebound on themselves."

When, at various times during his boyhood, Johnny Mara had sought an explanation as to why the Cloyne males were persecuted by an all too potent curse, he had been fobbed off with this way of it: "No one knows why. A Cloyne, some say, in ancient days ran crosswise to an old Warn Woman from out the Kyles of Ra. Let it rest." The women of Ra, Johnny well knew, were a race given to prophecy of doom. They were held in worse dread by the superstitious country people than those harpies the Wild Women of Moher.

Against all odds, the building of Mara House continued. Then, as if on cue, all clamour ceased. No gull came near the rock, save sometimes at sunset a lone bird would circle high above the portico that was slowly taking shape, rising proudly to face the far reaches of the sea. But the "people of the roads, himself and herself," weary of walking but forever en route, would maunder on, and they lying at night in the dark ditches, "That rock was given be Lir ni Og the Sea God as a breedin' ground fer thim gulls. A lost soul in torment, ivery one ave thim." Tinkers, and the fey bogtrotters, the newsmongers of Ireland, thinned their lips and crinkled far-seeing eyes, muttering, "No good 'ull come to the wicked earl. He'll folla' his breed to the grave draped in horror."

But Mara House rose unhindered. When finished it was a beautiful, gleaming, temple-like abode which brought a sparkle of proud ownership to the gray eyes of Johnny Mara. "My finest 'experiment,' " he mused. "A fitting house to entertain the fair Buonamonte."

The earl waited only long enough to see the first fire of peat turves lighted on the black-slate hearth of the great chamber facing the sea. Then he posted hell-for-leather into Dublin, thence by packet boat to France. From there he wore out relays of post horses over tortuous spring roads, to Milan, and so to Verona.

The day Johnny Mara brought his Veronese bride to the white-and-gold grandeur of Mara House it was by water, not by the rutted old coach road out of Dublin. His friend the British viceroy had loaned him the official barge with its complement of twelve oarsmen in crimson-and-gold livery. "I must do this presentation journey in Venetian style," the earl said to Lord Sellbridge. "Your emblazoned barge is the nearest thing to a gondola Ireland affords."

From the first sight of her high-set Palladian house, Reza Mara was enchanted. The days that followed passed more quickly and in greater happiness for them both than Johnny Mara, thinking it over in the night watches, voluptuous Reza lying in his arms, could ever have believed would be his portion. No longer was he the rakehelly prankster. In fact he appeared to shun his former companions. He and his countess seldom appeared in Dublin save for a ball or rout at Dublin Castle, where Reza was inordinately admired.

One night the earl and his wife were idling on the terrace facing the sea, for they never tired of these walks in the moonlight. It was a quiet night. No sound came from the calm sea and no hint of wind intruded. Oddly quiet, the night—too quiet, Johnny Mara thought. There was something ominous here; he sensed a cold foreboding in the deadness of the night air. He gripped Reza's arm more tightly, thinking, well, at least the gulls had departed. He had not needed to resort to his planned "experiment" of wholesale slaughter by gunshot or poisoned food-scraps. Suddenly, widespread white wings skimmed noiselessly down from the luminous sky. One wing brushed Reza's cheek, and as quickly the gull was away again into the night. With a sharp cry, more of surprise than fear, Reza raised her hand to her cheek. "What is it?" her husband asked. "Are you hurt?" Slowly Reza sank into his arms. "No—I don't know," she murmured through pale lips, the words scarcely audible. "It was like a swordcut, but there is no blood." And then she fainted.

The doctor summoned from Newtown-Swords was mystified. What manner of hurt it was that made the countess lie still as death, hardly breathing, he could not fathom. For one thing, he had learned that the Countess of Mara was with child. By the majority of husbands this news of prospective fatherhood would have been differently received than by Johnny Mara. To a man of the Cloyne breed the doctor's words were as a black signature of death across his brain. Hands covering his face, the earl moaned. "No—no—do not say that. It is my death warrant."

From that night out the gulls started coming back to the Rock of Swords. At first only a few birds, their white wing-quills tipped in black, wheeled in circles around the portico of Mara House. The susurrus of rigid wings and a plaintive mewing were the only sounds. One day succeeded another, but the countess did not rally from the trance into which she had sunk at the touch of the gull's wing on her cheek. Daily the flocks of gulls grew in number. Night and day the whirr of wings seemed to heighten the racked nerves, the utter weariness bred of monotony of sound, that came to all within the gull-haunted house. At night the wild screaming would rise to pandemonium more dreadful than the cry of the banshee in the dark Glens of Mourne.

Johnny Mara, half-demented with grief at the continued illness of his wife and the inactivity of prowling his beleaguered house, tried to devise some scheme to rid himself of this torment of gulls. He called the few menservants left in the house and bade them get out his guns and join him on the terrace. He then stationed them on the rocky ledges, ordering the men to shoot down every gull within range. Save for a few score mangled victims littering the rocks as the sun set, the men might as well have held their fire. Then, desperate beyond reasoning, the earl tried scattering poisoned food among the rock crevasses. He bought baskets of small fish from nearby fishing villages, drenched these with instant poison and set the baskets along the terrace balustrades. But all to no avail. It was as if the gulls instinctively sensed no kindness here, only treachery, as they hovered over the food but never swooped to touch it.

A fortnight of purgatory passed, during which Johnny Mara aged to grayness and the wrinkled features of a very old man. Then one day the countess rallied. Soon she was able to sit up, even to walk to the window on her husband's arm. Her eyes filled with tears as she looked down to behold the befouled columns of the once-lovely portico, the terraces and the little Temple of Love where they had watched the moon rise on the first evenings when she had come here as a bride, only a few months ago. She shuddered, nauseated, for the air reeked with the odour of bird manure and the white stone walls were hideously stained and crusted as if with corroding mould. Lord Mara assured his wife that as soon as she could travel he would take her away from this bedeviled house. Reza shook her head. "I have horrible dreams. Always the gulls. Like a chorus of Furies the birds seem to shriek at me, 'Out—out—away from our rock. We will drive you out.'" She sighed. "No guns nor poisons will prevail against those damned souls that have breasted the ocean winds for uncounted years. I am convinced they will kill us." But her husband tried soothingly to calm her fears. "Soon," he said, "we will leave. I will take you to Italy."

One night when the earl was at his wits' end with waiting and watching for Reza to gain enough strength to travel, he saw from an upstairs window the figure of a tall, gaunt woman, shawled in black, standing at the end of the causeway where the Newtown-Swords road forked in front of the ruined gates of Castle Swords. He peered out more closely to see who this woman might be. As he watched, she raised a skeleton-thin arm and pointed to the window where he stood. The night was moonless, but myriad stars shone icily in the sky. Yet even this white star-shine did not reveal the features of the woman's face. Johnny Mara felt chilled to the bone, for under the dark cavern of shawl there *was* no face.

For a space of minutes he stood at the window undecided. Was this the shawled Warn Woman of the ancient Cloyne curse? Too often in his life he had heard of her. No—it must be some tinker, perhaps with a message for him. The starlight and the shadowy hood concealing the head had played him tricks. Then anger rose in his mind. He listened. The night was quiet. He went hurriedly into the room where his wife sat reading. "Reza," he said, "it is prodigious quiet tonight. Perhaps the gulls *have* gone, defeated, worn out with disgruntlement that we have not run to cover on the mainland." He laughed. Bending over, he kissed her lips. She smiled up at his thin face where distraction had etched sharp lines. "Perhaps," she said. "Not even lost souls of the sea in their wrath can break an Irishman's spirit. I could have told them that." Then Johnny Mara kissed his wife again and went out of the room and down the staircase. He caught up a cloak that lay on a chair beside the door and went out onto the terrace. He went down the steps and started to cross the causeway.

As he stood in the open gateway with only the immense dome of sky above him and the sombre sea lapping round, the quiet night split asunder. What was that? The flurry of a thousand wings. The gulls struck like a giant scythe of white feathers. In the space of seconds his cloak was ripped to ribbons. His flesh was stabbed by countless bloodied beaks. Beaks as sharp as sabers pierced his eyes. Screaming as wildly as the vengeful gulls, he went down beneath an inundation of white wings.

Thus died the twelfth Earl of Mara, savagely, tortured beyond all imagining. In the welter of clamour and blood a dark, hooded figure folded her shawl more closely about spare shoulders. Gliding through the reedy sedges offshore, the shadow became one with the night.

A few days after the horrific death of Johnny Mara, the viceregal couple, Lord and Lady Sellbridge, appeared at Swords and took Reza to Dublin in their coach. On Christmas Day the Countess of Mara gave birth to the thirteenth Earl of Mara in a shuttered room at Cloyne House in Dawson Street. Straw had been scattered on the cobbles in front of the house to deaden the sound of horses' hoofs and coach wheels. Passers-by in front of the portal would salute each other and converse in the way of "Another posthumous earl for the Cloynes of Blanard." The answer might be, "How long has this curse to run? A frightening thing to be born Earl of Mara."

Today, anyone driving along the Sea Road leading out of Newtown-Swords to Malahide, and they looking off and away towards the Rock of Swords, must attend their sight closely to trace out the scarred ruin, merely a shell, of the once-noble Mara House. The elaborately carved cornices and window architraves of the derelict mansion have been scurvily treated down the years, as much by the elements as by the gulls. The blackened walls and fallen columns appear to be part of the craggy, living rock that at times seems to undulate with a life of its own due to legions of gray, black and white sea gulls forever restlessly mewing, for even in their nesting this class of bird is never still—like the ancient mountains of Ireland mantled by cloud shadows there is in them an unease; as the old ones say, "Ochone and duoa. They weary their rest." At all times the rock, devoid of habitation, is a kind of sanctuary. Various sea birds flock here to nest and breed, a timeless ritual of nature ever the ancient case.

Ask questions of any fisherman who casts his nets and lines in the waves that lap the Rock of Swords, concerning this unhallowed relic of a profligate earl's ambitious dreams. You will be treated to wondrous tall tales that, to me at least, have largely the ring of truth. For the keen-eyed fishermen of the Irish seas put up "wid no blather," they see what they see and tell it to you simply, as they have seen it.

I sometimes go out seaward in a dory with a fisherman whom I have chanced to meet on the quay at Malahide Strand or other. I find that from this vantage point, by seeing with plenty of perspective the ancient, ivy-hung walls of the Keep of Swords or Ballyronan Tower, I can paint with added ease and no onlookers to irk me while I work. One day not long since, I went out with Roney Curry of Malahide, who is regarded hereabouts as the *doyen* of fishermen, having fished these waters from the age of five years to seventy-two. What Roney does not know about the hauntings "apparitional," as he terms them, that are credited to take place on the rock from which rises the hulk of Mara House, I'll wager no one else does. I needled him with all sorts of questions, the like of "Roney, when did you last see your apparitional incident, and what was it?"

Roney, from his seat in the stern sheets, deftly played out a trawl line. "It 'ud be ridin' me hard ye are the morn. Me memory's a bit chancy, what wid late hours kept, scroungin' these perishin' fish from the sea and no help to ease me labor." He spat a great gob into the sea, the eternal punctuation of the Irish countryman, I have observed. "There—it was a few nights ferninst. I rode the swell too close to that auld rock fer comfort, sped in landwards be an undertow. Me mind was split in twain what wid tryin' to keep me dory top side up and me curiosity roused be that black woman stridin' along the crest ave the rock. I do be after seein' 'er many's the time before, but me hair still lifts me cap aloft at the sight ave 'er nevertheless."

To hurry him on to the point of his story, I broke in on his speech.

"Roney, is she the Warn Woman who cursed the Cloynes, do you think, or some woman of the roads chancing the causeway, scouting for gulls' eggs?"

"Divil a bit a tinker," he answered sharply. "That's the girl she is, the Warn, and a terrible class ave dread to behold at any time, night er day. Her standin' there in the screechin' gale, 'er black cloak writhin' about her skeleton, 'cause she's no more body nor that, and if a ray ave light touches the shada' under 'er shawl, yer eyes moan in yer head from fright, fer there's no more features there than 'ud be glimpsed on the flabby white belly ave a fish."

At another time I heard from a landsman, a carter plying the roads about Newtown-Swords by day and night. He told me that on a night of bright moonlight he had seen the nesting gulls on the rock suddenly stirred to protest by what appeared to him a huge black bird that descended among them, its wings trailing like scarves more than flapping in the act of flight. Pandemonium reigned as the frenzied figure of a man in a red coat ran crazily about the flat terraced portion of the rock. Then, as his shrieks rose even above the din of the gulls, the man was inundated by the mass of moonlight-silvered wings of the ravening sea birds. The carter said the uproar, accompanied with some sort of indescribable odour of fear, had so frightened his horse that it had run away, galloping wildly down the Sea Road, to be found next evening quietly grazing in a farmer's field ten miles away. "That smell ave dread on the night air, that was before as clear as a May mornin', was as strong as the reek ave rotten hides in that tannery (he pointed away down the road towards Aberny) ave auld Corby's."

A man in Dublin entertained me vastly at dinner one night in the Georgian dining room of the Kildare Street Club. Knowing that I am ever interested in ghostly lore, he asked me, "Do you know that old Hell-fire and Brimstone Johnny Mara does not spend his entire time while dodging Purgatory where he belongs, being pecked to flinders by gulls on the terrace of his ruined house? Oh, no—I have seen him myself. I live next door to Cloyne House in Dawson Street. It is the premises of an assurance company now. Wearing, in the height of fashion of his time, the white satin smallclothes and crimson-velvet, gold-laced, skirted coat of court attire when attending viceregal functions at the Castle." He raised a glass of Burgundy, admiring its ruby fire. "For a fellow who all his life was a prince of foppery, he presents a woefully disheveled appearance, for all his splendour is stained and tattered. Habitually he wanders in and out of the room where it is pretty well established that his son, the thirteenth earl, was born in the inevitable posthumous tradition."

As I walked up the hill of Grafton Street towards St. Stephen's Green after dinner, I pondered awhile upon the fantastically cruel fate of the perhaps stubborn and arrogant, but, I wager, extraordinarily entertaining Earl of Mara. In between his horrendous bouts with the Warn Woman flicking her familiars, the gulls of Swords Rock falling upon him to his undoing, he tries in vain to get a glimpse of his son born in the Cloyne town house in Dawson Street. I am convinced this urge arises from the fact that the mother of this boy was the one great love of Lothario Johnny Mara's tempestuous life.

The Astounding Luck
of Maeve Greatly

GLANRULLA HOUSE, COUNTY WEXFORD, 1856

THIS is a story of good luck attending a small, rather frail, shy and plain little girl named Maeve Greatly, through her life long. And a long life it was, surely. For Maeve Greatly McIllvery lived to be ninety-six years of age. She was, as well, hale, hearty and possessed of all her faculties to the last, as are many Irish countrywomen who are born and bred to stand up to the four winds of Heaven and ask no quarter.

Saving the fact that Maeve Greatly lived the last twenty years of her life in a tall, narrow, old Georgian house in Upper Merrion Street in Dublin (where she was taken by her husband, Shamas McIllvery, the barrister), she spent long periods of time at the house of her birth.

"Glanrulla, that auld ancient pile," is the way the Wexford people refer to the rambling, ivy-covered stone house which flings its strong, friendly, arm-like wings along a shaded reach of the River Slaney at Ferrycarrig in the County of Wexford. Today the house shelters in its crypt the body of Mrs. McIllvery, who, as retiring little Maeve Greatly, caused Slievnamon, the Beautiful Woman of the Mountain, to lavish such oceans of good luck upon her as have blessed few persons in this unsure world.

"Auld Glanrulla" itself has a unique history. Along one wall of the kitchen garden there run deep, cylindrical wells or "tuns" which were very probably dug as cisterns by the Danes during their long tenure as invaders and conquerors of the south coast of Ireland. Long passages and cellars extend like the spokes of a wheel, some under the oldest wing of the house, where there is a vast, draughty "treasure room." This damp, cave-like vault played a fantastic part in the luck of little Maeve Greatly.

Glanrulla House had been lived in by the Greatly family for three generations only. Great-grandfather Timothy Greatly had amassed a fair-sized fortune in coasting a small fleet of tanners' ships and coal-laden barges filled with the take of Welsh coal mines. Feeling that his modest brick farmhouse, hard by the village of Ballyhack, was no longer large enough for the grander life he envisaged, Timothy scouted around for a more imposing house in which to seat his family—a family of four stalwart sons, growing even stronger physically, if not mentally, as they approached manhood. The sagacious eye of Timothy Greatly spied out quiet old Glanrulla, dreaming away the years, reflecting its murmurous ivy walls and rankly growing greenery in the silently flowing River Slaney.

The last tenants of Glanrulla had been off and away for absentee landlords, for many years. The family of O'Lanay, original builders of the house, had been unheard of in the countryside since just after the departure of Oliver Cromwell from the Waterford, Wexford and Cork coasts. Some old tales had it that the family were slain, down to the last obscure cadet, for a treacherous plot against the Roundhead leader. In any case they appear to have gone forever after.

Timothy Greatly lived only a short time to enjoy his newly-acquired property. It took all the strength of his four giants of sons to clear the wrack and ruin of tangled savanna which had, in the warm, wet climate of County Wexford, all but pulled down the walls of Glanrulla. In time, all was swept and garnished until the fine old demesne was the talk of the countryside for order and the heartening hospitality of loud laughter and the most richly laden table in the county.

Timothy Greatly died and was succeeded by his eldest son, Rory. After a vastly happy marriage with a neighbouring landowner's daughter, Rory Greatly died, having fathered three sons, one less than his sire, but all strapping fellows. Succeeding to the demesne of Glanrulla came Tomas, Rory's eldest and most bull-like son, who cursed and bellowed up and down the highroads and bohireens of Wexford and surrounding counties until he was known far and wide as "Glanrulla's Nuisance." At horse fairs, Saturday markets, money exchanges and similar meeting places of the country farmers and landowners, the approach, loudly heralded by curses and bellowings, of Tomas Greatly was a signal for the mass exodus of the assembled throng. Usually, Tomas had the bull-pens, or pitch where mares and geldings were assembled, all to himself. Few cared to become embroiled in argument with the Master of Glanrulla, as he wished to be called.

It was a dour day for stridently masculine Tomas Greatly when his wife, Bella, gave birth to a frighteningly small girl child, in the high-posted, heavily curtained bed of the West chamber at Glanrulla house.

"Me first born," ranted Tomas in mounting and dangerous rage, "be the Holy, a puling brat of a girl ye could put to hide in a pocket purse and never find 'er after." Up and down the long, winding corridors of the old house by the river, ranged its master, roaring his lament: "Where is the fine son, like me father and his before 'im had, that is me due? A scalding trick to play on as warm a man as walks in Wexford."

Yes—Glanrulla's Nuisance was in full spate. Very slowly, it seemed to all about her who watched, did scrawny, whimpering little Maeve—as the shyly romantic mother called her child, after the ancient Gaelic Queen—prosper at all. Until her third year, she was all huge gray eyes, an abnormally large skull and sparse, sandy hair.

Tomas Greatly said quite openly, garlanded by curses, that he hated the child. Bella, for the first time since her marriage, became cold and implacable wherever Maeve was the issue. Bella stood up to tall, beefy, outrageous Tomas, and spiked his wishes at every turn. Tomas often said he could, and would some day, beat his wife to a pulp. Silently she clasped shivering Maeve to her skirts and defied her belligerent husband until he would slam out of her room, postponing the "beating to a pulp" until another day.

As the years strung out, Bella Greatly gave birth to no more offspring. Glanrulla became a house divided against itself. A sad state for a fine, friendly place which, from the day that old Timothy Greatly took possession until the advent of his loud-mouthed grandson Tomas, had echoed only the laughter and singing of the high-spirited sons of the house, and become the very symbol of hospitality for all the South of Ireland.

Then, one day of brutal, driving rain, all this sorry state of affairs changed. Not suddenly. Not from darkness to the bright of day, in one swift stride. Slowly, subtly, did the tenor of grumbling old Glanrulla change; but change it did. One might venture that on a demented March day in the year 1856, the keystone of luck was set high and truly in the main arch of the entrance gate to the courtyard at Glanrulla. It was set well and firmly by no other hand than spindly little Maeve Greatly, who would have died from shyness, had she had the remotest idea that she was destined to become the most powerful member of her family—a very ruler, when she chose, in the long years ahead of her. The family of Tomas Greatly became a formidable one, as well, in the ensuing years; for, after a long lapse, Bella Greatly rivaled Ceres herself in fertility. She bore four sons and three daughters to enhance the name of Greatly. Such signal performance and good will towards Tomas even had the unbelievable effect of somewhat quieting his roarings.

On that day in March, it was announced at breakfast (as were all things at Glanrulla), as a sort of manifesto, that Tomas would require the presence of his wife at his agent's office in the nearby market town of Enniscorthy. Her signature was required on an article pertaining to her dower rights. Bella remarked a shade bitterly that of all days of the year, this was the last one she would choose for driving the thirty miles to Enniscorthy. Nevertheless, she put a huge waterproofed cape over her carriage-wrap, and went out to wait in the covered porch for the barouche to pull round from the stables. Bella bade good-by to Maeve, who stood shivering from the cold blasts of wet wind that scudded through the porch, as much as from the ever-constant dread of being in her father's presence. As the carriage turned out of the gates letting onto the river road, Bella remarked to Tomas: "Would anyone, except ourselves who know for a fact, believe that Maeve is going on nine years old? She's that little and destroyed with shyness, one would say she is scarce five years old. Something must be done soon about her schooling. I will write to the Mother Superior at the Abbey School at Dunbrody and find out if they'll consider taking Maeve. I've a great dread on me what will become of the child." As it turned out, that was one fear of Bella Greatly's that was groundless.

After her father and mother had passed out of sight in the swirling mist and drenching clouds of rain which blanketed the river road to Enniscorthy, Maeve turned away from the library window. A long day stretched ahead of her. She was alone in the house except for Mary Darty and her silly daughter, Froli, the parlour maid. She would see little of them this day, for they would scarcely stir from the kitchen and the everlasting cups of "black amber" tea, with which both the cook and her daughter consoled themselves on cold raw days the like of this one.

When lunchtime came, Maeve could fend for herself for food. A well-stocked buffet table at one end of the dining room was always laden with cold joints, cheeses, both dark and white breads, pickles and currant or gooseberry tarts, against the mighty hunger which assailed the brawny Tomas at all hours. One had only to look at the worn spot in the carpet, shaped a little like the map of Ireland itself, which had been trodden thin by his countless trips to the buffet. A tiresome number of Tomas's most peace-shattering manifestoes had been delivered to unhappy Bella and indirectly, Maeve, while Tomas, a heavily piled plate of food in his left hand, walked back and forth in front of the long table, brandishing his food-scattering fork to emphasize his demands. But it was only ten o'clock in the morning. Far too soon to think of lunch. Maeve started to wander about the silent house.

As the dark morning wore on, Maeve went up to the schoolroom on the third floor of the "new wing," which had been built when Charles Stuart had arrived in England from exile in France, to start that period of elegant pleasures, the Restoration. This room was the only quiet world Maeve had ever known. Her father never came here. Her dolls sat unmolested in a long row in front of the fireplace, each with a teacup set before her. Actually, it was yesterday's tea party. They seemed contented, all ten of them. Maeve was restless and felt like wandering. The tea party could go on. Maeve climbed the attic stairs to a tower room where in summer she played "captured princess." Generally, it was a favourite spot. But today the wind howled ceaselessly and shook the tiny glass windows in a frightening manner. Maeve backed hastily down the narrow ladder stairs, and decided on the warm library as the best place to spend the rest of the day. As she passed the front window, she paused to look out into the park, but all she saw was writhing branches and water sloshing everywhere. Slowly she became aware that someone was beating against the storm, making lunges into the teeth of the wind, but making very slow progress. A tree crashed down across the carriage drive, barely missing the stranger. Suddenly, as if given strength by intense fright, the man darted forward onto the porch.

Somehow, Maeve never knew afterwards whatever gave her courage, she rushed to the front door and flung it wide on its hinges. There, cowering in terror from his narrow escape from the falling tree, as well as the misery of his cold, drenched garments, was an old man. At a glance Maeve saw how desperately poor his rags were, not even, the thought flicked through her mind, the "Lordly rags" the gypsies and tinkers were forever talking so proudly of. Just miserable old rags, through the rents of which she could see his blue-white flesh.

Small as Maeve was, there lay deep in her frightened heart a fillip of the courage and power of quick decision which had enabled her great-grandfather, Timothy Greatly, to best his competitors, grasp what he wanted from the world and acquire Glanrulla House. In a split second, Maeve decided what she would do. Half carrying the man, who seemed only a little alive, Maeve Greatly, with her rickety legs, seemed about to founder under the weight of her burden. She helped the man to a couch before the dining-room fire and, having seen her mother do the same many times when Aunt Callie from Cork had one of her "weakenings," Maeve poured a good portion from the brandy decanter down the man's throat. It appeared to work miracles. The drenched stranger sat up presently and smiled. It was a rather toothless smile, but heartening to Maeve, who had nearly died of fright that the patient would die right in the dining room —and then whatever would she say to her father? Far from dying, however, the man's eyes began to strike bits of sharp, blue fire. He laughed, a long, rolling laugh, deep in his withered throat. "Ah, the saints be praised. If this isn't the royal joke of all time. Me, Loney Brannock, dragged in be me ragged coat tails through the door ave his high pomposity, Tomas Greatly, who regales himself as Master of the demesne. The place that should be rights be mine. Instead, I walk the roads, exposed to the four winds of Granog, and me half naked." The man laughed again as if relishing highly the position in which he found himself. Looking up brightly at the small puzzled child, he said, "If I take it rightly, ye'd be the daughter of Tomas Greatly. What's yer name?" Scarcely able to speak, Maeve answered: "Yes, I am Master Greatly's daughter. My name is Maeve."

The old man nodded thoughtfully. "Maeve is it now? Sure yer very unlike the image I have carried of Maeve of Meath all these years on the roads. Yer that spindly. But ye've a good heart, ye've compassion, considered excess baggage be most ave the gentry these days, but no matter. Give me yer hand, Maeve Greatly, for I wish to draw the bit ave a tracery on yer palm. Come on, girl, don't be afraid." Oddly, Maeve was not afraid. Maeve Greatly, who would run from her own shadow on occasion, stood very straight and moved over to stand beside the old man's knee. Holding out her right hand, palm upwards, Maeve watched intently while Loney Brannock traced with a scraggy forefinger a five-petaled flower in her small pink palm. "Now, ye'll never have cause to regret yer friendliness to Loney Brannock when he needed it. The luck ave Slievnamon, who sleeps on the far-off mountain, will follow and watch over ye all the days ave yer life. Now, girl, skip over and get me a slice ave that fine red ham I see winkin' at me from the board beyond."

Maeve plied her new friend with ham and with thick cuts from a prime beef joint. Slices of yellow cheese slid down Loney's throat in a bewildering manner. A whole jam tart dissolved behind Loney's thin, munching lips in the time it took Maeve to eat one narrow wedge of an apple turnover. The brandy decanter came in for hard usage and was soon empty. The eyes of Loney brightened meanwhile, and his sunken cheeks turned to a bright crimson hue. Then came the crowning touch. All innocence, it seemed, Loney looked at Maeve: "Could ye now fit me out with a suit ave yer enormous father's clothes? They'll look a bit grotesque on me, for I'm only half as big. But no matter, I'll wind the slack about me ribs fer extra warmth. And the bare thought ave what a shindig he'll put on when he finds out, will hearten me slumbers fer years to come." Noticing that Maeve looked a bit startled at the mention of her father's shindig, Loney hastened to add: "Don't have a fear fer yourself. Yer luck will hold. Ye'd not want me to go out in this perishin' cold and wet with me old coat like a sieve, now would ye? Run upstairs and get me a fine, warm suit."

After Loney Brannock went his way, all but capering, Maeve watched him disappear down the drive. She stood in the middle of the library, looking intently at the palm of her right hand. Nothing whatever showed where Loney had traced the five-pointed flower. But a strange calm seemed to have invaded Maeve's frightened little heart. She knew that when her father learned that she had fed an old tinker at his table and given him a suit of his clothes, as well as an ulster, a pair of shoes and Aunt Callie's huge umbrella that she used when walking into Ferrycarrig on wet days, he would roar like a wild bull. But she did not care. For the first time in her life, Maeve Greatly felt no fear of her father.

The rest of the day, Maeve Greatly sat in a big chair beside the library fire and just thought. Then, just as the darkness of the long day merged into a greater blackness that was night, Froli Darty brought in the lighted lamps. "Well, Miss Maeve, ye've been as quiet as a graven image the length ave the day. Me mother and I thought ye were asleep. Ah, I hear the carriage turning in at the gate. Here'll be yer father and mother."

After wraps had been removed, and Maeve had watched her father puz-

zling over the empty brandy decanter, she told them. The tatarara set up by
Tomas was a classic. The food and drink, taken by his old enemy, Loney Brannock, was nothing to the loss of the suit and the Belfast Cape, as he called his
lost overcoat. "So—me charity-minded daughter takes in an old rat off the roads,
a man who tried to do me out of me inheritance on a trumped-up charge, and
because of his falseness lost every penny he ever owned and took to the roads,
and the drink. Don't be misled, me fine Lady Bountiful, ye've no tinker there,
but the greatest rogue in ten counties."

Tomas, with the hide and perception of a rhinoceros, never noticed, of course,
but Bella was secretly very pleased at the way Maeve sat all through her father's
tirade. She never cringed, as had hitherto been her wont. In fact, she did not seem
to hear him at all.

A few weeks after this event, the first manifestation of what was later to be
known as "the luck of Maeve Greatly" took place. Bella had written to the Abbey
School at Dunbrody as she had told Tomas she would, asking the Head to place
her daughter as a resident student as soon as possible. Word had come back that
there was not a vacancy, nor would there be for a long time. Bella was disappointed. Now the search for a suitable school must start all over again. A few
mornings later, a letter lay on Maeve's breakfast plate. It was addressed to Mistress Maeve Greatly, Glanrulla House, Ferrycarrig, County Wexford. Undeni-
ably hers, though Maeve had never received a letter in her life. When opened,
the letter stated that an expected student from Dublin had decided at the last
moment to go to a different school. The Mother Superior would now be happy
to welcome Maeve Greatly to Abbey School. As Maeve handed the letter to her
mother she started, and listened. "What is it?" asked Bella.

"I thought I heard someone laugh, softly, sort of pleased."

"Nonsense," said her mother. "Now we must make plans."

One day, just before the Christmas holiday, Maeve's greatest friend at Abbey School said to her: "Maeve, I've awfully bad news. I cannot return here
after the holiday. My father has lost his money. So it is good-by."

"No," Maeve said suddenly. "I will not have it that way. You will come
back. That is what I want."

On Christmas morning, a letter again lay at Maeve's plate. It was from her
friend, Moira Clarry, in Cork. Calmly, as if she knew what the letter said, Maeve

opened it. A smile spread over her face. When Bella asked what it had to say, Maeve answered: "Moira finds things not as bad at home as they feared. She will return to school when I do." Bella noticed that Maeve turned her head ever so slightly, and smiling, nodded as if to someone standing beside her.

It was during this Christmas holiday that Tomas Greatly made a statement one evening at high tea, the after-effect of which changed his manner towards his strangely quiet daughter, for the length of his life. Flinging into the library on this day, leaving a trail of river mud in his wake, Tomas poured a stiff tumbler of whisky and announced to Bella: "Dredgers in the river bottoms close to the ferry have just sprung the body of old Loney Brannock from the tangled roots along the bank. So that crafty old dodger, in me best suit of clothes, came to his rightful end at the last." Turning to Maeve he continued: "All your high-handed charity went for naught."

The intense look in his daughter's gray eyes, and the set expression of her pointed jaw, held Tomas spellbound as Maeve said, in a scarcely audible voice, "Yes—I knew he was dead. He must have drowned a few weeks after he was here in this room. Loney comes often now." Rising from the low stool on which she had been sitting gazing into the fire, Maeve went slowly from the room, closing the door behind her, and mounted the stairs. Tomas and Bella looked long into each other's eyes.

From this day out, Maeve Greatly changed in a bewildering manner. She seemed to grow up, to become a young lady of poise and assurance in a power singularly her own. At eighteen years of age, she was described in a society journal as "tall and graceful, with large expressive gray eyes and a coronet of red-gold hair." Her manner was reserved, and carried a latent authority which no one ever failed to observe and respect. As the years passed there were many manifestations of "the luck of Maeve Greatly," which became a household word. After the Abbey school, Maeve went to the Musical College in Dublin. It was there that she met young Shamas McIllvery, who was at that time a law student at College Green.

Ten years passed, Maeve was thirty years old and settled very comfortably at Glanrulla with her mother, her boisterous family of brothers and sisters, her horses and the many dogs she always harboured. Tomas Greatly had died two years before and left Maeve his heiress and in full charge.

On the morning of her thirtieth birthday, Maeve came down to breakfast to find a letter lying on her plate. It was postmarked Cork Harbour. The letter was from Shamas McIllvery, who was stopping with friends at Ballycotton for the Cóbh Regatta. Queen Victoria was on board the "Royal Albert," which was anchored in Cóbh Harbour for Regatta Week. It would all be very gala. Would Maeve and her mother be his guests for the week?

Maeve enjoyed herself during these exciting Regatta days, as never before in her life. As the train from Cóbh (or, as they had called the old seaport town in honor of Her Majesty, Queenstown) pulled into Dublin station, Maeve slowly turned the engagement ring round and round upon her finger. It had a ruby and a pearl. Her luck had held again, just when she was beginning to fear that the tall young Shamas she had met years ago in Dublin had forgotten her.

And so it went through the years. There were never any "miracles," actually (as old Mary Darty insisted on calling Maeve's turns of good fortune), but any issue that mattered, any event or circumstance to which Maeve McIllvery put her mind, came to a successful conclusion. Usually success was heralded by a letter on her breakfast plate, and a soft chuckle of laughter drifting over her shoulder.

When I was taken to call on Mrs. McIllvery in Dublin in 1937, I went with a mutual friend to the tall brick house in Upper Merrion Street about three o'clock in the afternoon of a bright October day. Tea was set early because of Mrs. McIllvery's great age—she was eighty-nine years old then. Seated in a large wing chair of dark wine leather, Maeve Greatly McIllvery was a remarkable figure. Spare but upright, her frosty-white hair nearly hidden beneath a cap of Carrick-macross lace, the wide gray eyes of the little girl who had found courage to pull dripping old Loney Brannock through the porch door of Glanrulla over half a century ago, still sparkled brightly. I felt they had never missed so much as a golden mote swirling in front of them down the years. I asked Mrs. McIllvery if she would tell me what it was that took place in the ancient rabbit-warren cellars beneath Glanrulla when she was a child. "I remember it perfectly," she said. "It was the day before I was to leave Glanrulla for the Abbey School. I had a very adventurous puppy. When I tried to fetch him into the house against the coming of night, he eluded me and hid in the old cellars. As I went into what had been the old treasure room, I carefully propped the door of heavy oak, so I could get out again. As I searched, suddenly the puppy, still wanting to play, ran past me, knocking the prop from the heavy door, which banged to in my face. I was terrified. Far up above me, the family could hear no amount of screaming I might do. It was cold as charity in these musty passages where water from the river had seeped for centuries. Nearly petrified with fright, I suddenly heard a soft, pleasant laugh, and the door in front of me, which I never expected to pass alive, swung open, and I dashed through and up into the kitchen and the enveloping arms of Mary Darty. It was a long time before I told anyone of this, fearing I would not be believed."

In many ways the greatest stroke of luck Maeve Greatly ever had came at the very last of her long life. On Christmas morning, 1943, a letter lay on Mrs. McIllvery's breakfast tray telling her that her great-grandson, Dominic McIllvery (who had been listed as missing in action for two years), was found to be well and safe, having escaped from the Germans in Italy. Mrs. McIllvery died in her Dublin house in 1944. Now, one wonders, will the woman whose name became a byword for good luck in Ireland, and remained so for nearly a century, come back on Christmas mornings to Glanrulla, or the house in Upper Merrion Street or wherever her beloved Dominic may be, to watch over him? If I know her caliber, Maeve will want to see personally if the boy is well looked after and happy. Maeve has said she will manifest herself. Dominic believes her.

Goddess on her rock

Lilylight of the Blasket Isles

GREAT BLASKET ISLAND, 1816

O F ALL the scattered groups of islands crouched near or far against the hurled might of bold Atlantic breakers off the western coast of Ireland, none more deserves the appellation "legendary isles" than the treeless, rusty-green, turf-rimmed clutch of five distinct rock formations called the Great Blaskets.

I well remember one wind-racked day in early autumn when I came upon a dust-begrimed man of the roads, fantastically wrinkled of visage, and he resting his ancient weariness from eternally traveling "to nowhere and beyond" against an escarpment of rock, a fragment of the prehistoric burial ground of Phoenician mariners who once voyaged for plunder along this cove-indented coastline. I "broke the quiet of the day" with the old one and offered him tobacco for his black cobeen pipe cunningly carved from a single whorl of bog arbutus wood. He replied by first spitting, at a chosen target of rock shard, a gob of improbable size—the immemorial prelude to conversation affected by the tinkers of Ireland.

"Ye'd be wonderin', sor, if there'd be a soul left alive on thim perishin' rocks after the wind an' the sea's got shut ave torturin' thim." He looked me up and down, then pointed to a curragh, a large class of tarred canvas and ash-wood craft, that waited at the jetty of Dunquin Quay below. "Would ye be after trippin' it over to the Great One?" He motioned seaward, meaning, I was aware, the largest of the islands.

I informed him that with so rough a sea running I had no intention of tak-

181

ing an unnecessary jaunt in a wallowing curragh this day, but that I had often done so to visit a cousin who, for a summer holiday, had once taken a cottage at the small fishing village of Moreara.

The tinker slitted his murky, slate-black eyes and murmured more to the wind than to me, "Arragh—it's wary ye'd be—ever wary an' withdrawn from thim haunted Blaskets. The Danish woman witch, she as scourged the Great One in the auld days, still ranges the Bellow Rocks." As if quite unaware that he was voicing his thoughts aloud, the tinker looked at me obliquely, then shifted his stare towards the islands. In a moment he raised his voice to a conversational tone. "I'm off on me way. Sure, the Blaskets 'ull love ye the one minute an' introduce ye to Death himself the next. A dark delusion, the clutch ave thim entirely."

After the tinker had gone on his way I sat for a while atop a hillock of turf and thought back on all I had heard, fragmentary at best, of "the Danish woman" Kara, a shipwrecked stranger who dwelt on the Great One in the seventeenth century. She purports to have been a witch. For her enormities—the seduction of overyoung Blasket males, and the bringing of plague on her libidinous person to the islands, Kara was stoned nearly to death, then bound with ropes and hurled while still alive into a blowhole, her body to be dragged down, down, by subterranean currents—down, down, down—to the farthest fathoms of the sea.

Night was descending. Purple clouds hung low over the blunt Headland of Moreara. I thought of the silent world of the Blaskets, so significantly eerie in old sagas and bardry and even holding an impact of mystery in more recent song. Each island, though they vary greatly in size, seems cut to the same pattern: low-lying, tapering from a blunted headland to shaly beach. So many names these islands bear. The Silver Lizards, because of being so often viewed through sheets of silver rain. The Golden Barges, for being illuminated by the sun overhead finally winning the battle with rain and mist to shine out hot and gild every needle rock carved into fragile lace by the persistent sea. I believe it is when I see the Blaskets at late evening, the headlands swathed in sable clouds edged with silver from a rising moon, that I feel most the eternal mystery that crowns this ageless archipelago, quiet and serene in itself yet set in so turbulent a sea.

I noticed clouds were blowing up, sweeping seaward from the direction of the Slieve Mish Mountains, those seaboard cradles of swift, destructive wind-squalls that forever harry the Clare and Kerry coast. I must be away out of that, for this spot was a very altar of the swirling winds to offer a mortal as sacrifice. Suddenly all storm-sound ceased. For a moment a kind of vacuum of foreboding quiet reigned. Then I heard a high-pitched cry. Was it exultation or distress? The sound came from the sea. Far out, as if performing some pagan ceremonial rite, a form drifted this way and that, headed in the general direction of the islands. A sudden ray of sunlight piercing the dark pall of clouds picked out the figure of a reed-slender girl. Her feet scarcely touched the frothed crests of wind-tossed waves. Her arms were held high above her head and her hands seemed to be ruffling a great mane of lint-white hair, the long tresses writhing like pale fire. The dancing ghost of Lilylight of the Blasket Isles, a very Hecate of the storms. Suddenly the sun was enveloped in black thunderheads, and myself was enveloped in a world of wind and spear-sharp pelts of rain.

The story of Lilylight is of a weirdness somehow associated with the antique myths depicting the trials and tribulations of water-nymphs and dryads of the forests. Because of frequent raids by Danish and Norwegian pirates on the once heavily-populated Blasket Islands, where as late as the fifteenth century a ship-building industry throve, the prevailing complexion of the inhabitants has always been fair. In many cases young boys and girls display pale, "watered-down" blue eyes and the flaxen or "lint-white" hair of the Norse legendary heroes. More often than not both eyes and hair darken somewhat as they grow older, but the Scandinavian fairness so frequently encountered in the people of Waterford, Cork, and Limerick, once the Danelaw Hold of Scandinavian usurpers, prevails.

Of such cast of fairness at its most delicate paleness was a girl known to posterity as Lilylight, who lived with her aged grandmother in a tiny coteen near Moreara Cove in the early years of the nineteenth century. This grandam of Lilylight's, Mare Fellerhan, was of passing devout turn of mind. Her thoughts dwelt continuously on immortality and the delights thereof, which could be enjoyed only if, while on earth, a body conducted herself precisely as the priest said a Christian should live. So from the moment her granddaughter was laid in her lap by a recently widowered son, bereaved Dame Fellerhan resolved that as this girl child grew in years herself would instruct her in the paths leading to sainthood. Ultimately her granddaughter should become a nun.

As the years passed and the girl grew in inches, Dame Fellerhan would sit contentedly watching the child playing with the rainbow-coloured sea shells she collected on the shaly beach or found piled in heaps in the coves, the usual after-math of a heavy storm when Atlantic combers had rolled into the myriad inlets that honeycombed the island.

"Light in motion as a lily on a stalk, she is." The musing woman would nod appraisingly to a neighbour passing by on the lane in front of the coteen who had paused for a few words of gossip. But to the neighbour it was no gossip but the eternal subject of "Me granddaughter does this, me granddaughter does that." Ever and always she must listen to the like of, "Light and lovely with that odd white mop ave hers. Light as a dawn lily that I give her to lay at the feet ave the Blessed Mother Mary of Us All at Easter Sunda'."

Light as a lily. Lilylight became the only name by which the girl was ever to be known.

But as she grew tall, slim and straight to the age of fifteen, Lilylight appeared to have no call for the devout life. Indeed she loped away from Mass wary as a coney of a trap. Although her grandmother would have cut her tongue out rather than let on that she was monstrously disappointed in the result of her years of patient care and pious instruction, she could not help noticing that Lily-light did not seem to listen to what she said about the repose of spirit to be found in the cloistered life. In all truth Lilylight was not as bright in intellect as she should be at her age. Her mind was wandering, if not actually "away." "The divil fly away with the thought entirely," said gossip Mindy Tesseroe. It was Mindy's son Rory, in her eyes "a great grand lather ave a boy," who had done more than his share of chasing Lilylight into the cart-track ditches and had been thrashed for it by his da. Mindy was loud in proclaiming to anyone who would listen, either voluntarily or from being helplessly cornered, "Be the Holy, that silly, lightheaded Lilylight had better clutch her mind, what there is ave it, be the tail er it 'ull whip away from 'er entirely." In high anger she would add a last screech: "An' the way she casts thim twa watery eyes ave 'er, pale as a ghost's they are, at me boy Rory to his destruction in followin' 'er into the bohireens fer a roll an' split-me, arragh I'll have 'er Lilylights if this goes on."

But to be fair and honest in the face of these accusations, it was no thought of Lilylight's to raise the pecker of lust in any of the Blasket youths. She had a kindly, responsive nature, always eager to please. As many a simple-minded girl has been before her, indeed many not so simple-minded at all, she was con-genitally unable to say no to any direct proposal from a young man, no matter who.

Soon the dalliance of lads in the assorted Blaskets became a local scandal. Even well and truly married women found that the usual ardour of their stalwart fishermen spouses seemed, in the conjugal bed, the candles snuffed, the wife all eagerness, uncommonly to cool. A certain lassitude by day seemed to descend on the male population of the Blaskets. The truth was that Lilylight had taken to an original, if curiously rousing, sport of running through the rocky labyrinthine caves of the island at night, naked to the buff, her nimbus of moonlight-silver hair identifying her nymph-like figure to the various males lying in wait, as if she had flung a luminous banner of the island's famed dawn lilies across her shoulders.

As it turned out there appeared at the fuchsia-hung coteen of pious Dame Fellerhan one morning a throng of island women not only highly irate and articulate, but indeed desperate. This nightly romp, the last escapade of her granddaughter—they forebore to use the rather virginal-sounding name of Lilylight even in derision—must stop. She must leave the island. Mindy Tesseroe flung down the gauntlet of no quarter. "An' mind ye now. We want no argy-bargy from yer saintly self. Out the streeler goes, next morn's morn. Before she makes this island the bawdy-hole ave the world, to the world's scorn."

Dame Fellerhan needs must bow her white linen-coifed head, greatly shamed, to the inevitable. She gazed mournfully at the determined women. "Ye've won the day. I'm beat. I'll send Lilylight to the mainland into service. There's plenty ave great houses there cravin' fer housemaids. I hear rumours ave it all the time."

And so it came about that Lilylight in her sixteenth year, slimly lovely, ethereal in her paleness yet somehow vibrant and alluring, left her natal island to step foot on the mainland of Ireland for the first time in her life. The chancy sea lying between Moreara Port and Dingle Bay had been unnaturally quiet. Only a light ground swell prevailed. Four husky and unashamedly randy young fishermen who in port fought for places to row Lilylight across "the strip," as this part of the seaway from Great Blasket was known, had each demanded a favour from this girl simply dressed in palest blue, somehow shy, with the gentle, provocative smile and, when asked a pertinent question by a lusty young male, the vastly accommodating way of her.

On the quay Lilylight bid each of her aquatic cavaliers a smiling good-by. She picked up her modest portmanteau, which had traveled only once before and then to Rosslare Strand on her grandmother Fellerhan's wedding journey.

A Mrs. Delancy, one of the more kindly-disposed of the Fellerhan neighbours, had given Lilylight a letter to one Honoria Hanaray, wife of a publican in the High Street of Dingle. Lilylight took a chaise from the port to the door of the Crown and Anchor pub. Here she produced the letter for the publican's wife. Before she had had time to catch her breath from so much lusty ardour pleasurably received in the stern sheets of the fishing smack which had delivered her to the hospitable shores of County Kerry, Lilylight felt the hands of Honoria Hanaray tying the cambric strings of an apron about her waist and she was marked, as if by a burned-in brand, as "in service."

But her tenure at the popular Crown and Anchor, a predominately nautical hangout for sailors or ship-chandler apprentices of every condition, was of short duration. Although she did not serve at the bar, nor in the populous bar-parlour, but acted as bedroom maid above stairs, many's the fellow who spotted this gleaming fair girl and in search of her invaded premises from which he was promptly evicted by a forceful Honoria.

One day, through no fault of her own, Lilylight when quietly about her sweeping was waylaid on the stairs by a huge, bewhiskered ship captain unsteady on his feet from too much drink taken. Lilylight, taken unawares, did a valiant battle of fists. In fighting the brute off, she slipped and the two went crashing down the stairs. No bones were broken, but quick-swelling bruises were taken by both victims. When the tatarara caused by this accident had somewhat settled down, Honoria and her husband decided that it was time and more for Lilyiight to move on to pastures new and, perhaps, for her greener.

Oddly enough, on the very day that Lilylight again lifted her portmanteau to enter a post chaise that would let her down in Adare, where she had been offered the post of barmaid at the Limerick Arms, according to an old Kerry adage "Fate lifted a finger and brushed aside the curtain of what might have been," thereby altering to a degree exorbitant the entire fabric of the girl's life.

It chanced that at this precise moment there entered the picture Liart Malloy, not only butler but far more, major-domo extraordinary in the household of Lord Grantham at Moycullen in the County Galway. Now Liart was brother of Honoria Hanaray, and after a few days spent among the markets in Limerick and Cork buying hams and flitches of peat-smoked bacon, which he undertook semiannually as a duty attendant on his exalted position at Moycullen, he proposed to spend a night under his sister's roof en route to the remote and wearisomely quiet demesne of his employer. He took in at a glance the tall, slender, pastel blue-habited loveliness of Lilylight, her face shadowed becomingly beneath a poke bonnet of burnt straw strewn with red poppies, a gift from Honoria, ever indulgent albeit decorous of lightness in female conduct under her own roof. On hearing that Lilylight was leaving for a new position, Liart hastily invented a tale that if the young lady was so disposed he could offer her a place at Moycullen as laundry maid; a place but lately vacated by the sudden marriage —he coughed discreetly—of its incumbent. "A flighty, unappreciative-of-favours piece was Letty"; he smiled into the rather vacant, pale-blue eyes of Lilylight, and doubted if this piece would be any less fluttersome than Letty.

The advent of Lilylight at table in the staff dining hall at spacious Moycullen House caused little interest. True, the women members of a staff numbering some twenty persons openly discussed the extreme fairness of her long silky hair, which she wore parted in the middle, the braids done up in a pointed Grecian knot. But for work hours she hid its curiously glazed fairness under a frilled white mull mobcap. The menservants, under the coldly piercing eye of Malloy, nodded a casual greeting to Lilylight and privately appraised her softly-curved, slim figure so pliant with the litheness of good health. Too, each fellow speculated on the vacantness of her expressionless pale-blue eyes, and wondered how long he would have to wait his turn in her bed. Of course this would not occur until after Malloy had taken his sporting rights as The Head below stairs. For it never entered the minds of these footmen and hobbledehoy "boots" and pages that Lilylight would be any more stiff for a fling on her back than lamented Letty, who had been most favourful to the least of them.

In the ordinary way Lilylight would have served them all as her usual obliging self. But as it turned out, after a few nights spent as bedfellow of easily-satisfied Malloy, there was so much confusion and extra work suddenly athwart Moycullen that every one of the staff was far too tired when bedtime came to care for any diversion other than the blessing of sleep. The return from London of the heir to Moycullen Demesne was the direct cause of this turmoil of turning out the great rooms of the Georgian house, of polishing the panes of forty tall windows that faced the Lough of Corrib, and of decking with swags of laurel and bog myrtle, the violet-blue flower that in Galway is so greatly favoured as the star of good fortune, the broad staircase that wound upwards from the Great Hall to the rotunda five stories in height.

Captain Lord Roderick Farrow, only son of the tenth Earl of Grantham, was arriving on a hurriedly-obtained leave of short duration from his regiment.

At the age of twenty-six Roderick was one of the youngest officers chosen by his kinsman on the distaff side, the Duke of Wellington, to be his personal secretary. It was this return to visit his parents at Moycullen, for only three days before he would be off in the service of the Iron Duke who had just been appointed ambassador to Paris, that had bred "a kind ave fermentation in the daily round," as it was described by Mrs. Tracy Killballon, the perpetually shortwinded and "persecuted be averdupoise" housekeeper.

The day of Roderick's arrival at Galway Spanish Quay by packet boat out of Bristol was of a radiance with a light, heat-tempering breeze referred to as "God's grandest." Lord and Lady Grantham drove to Galway in an open barouche harnessing four smart dappled-gray Cleveland cobs, two postilions up. This equipage of maroon lacquer paintwork with yellow wheels was a vastly admired treasure of the neighbourhood. A man in the throng of quay hangers-on exclaimed, "Its like is only excelled be the chariot ave the king himself." The earl seemed a sombre figure in his dull black, but Lady Grantham, attired in a silver-gray pelisse lavishly bordered with bands of ermine, filled the eye. Her high-crowned poke bonnet, flaunting a waving forest of emerald-green ostrich plumes, was fashioned in a style then all the rage, called the "Blessington Bobber" after the millinery affected by the reigning London beauty, Lady Blessington. When driving in Rotten Row she continuously "bobbed" her head to the passing parade as if she were royalty. A few cheers broke the afternoon stillness as the noble party drove onto the planking of the quay, for here was great grandeur. The display of wealth and pageantry is dear to the hearts of Irish villagers.

The packet boat "Bristol Rover" duly arrived. Captain Lord Roderick Farrow walked with swinging military stride down the gangway, and the cheering swelled in volume. For a moment he disappeared partially from view, submerged under his mother's kisses, satins, plumes and furs. Then he waved to the crowd, and with the postilions cracking their long-lashed whips the Moycullen contingent set off at a canter towards the tall Italian iron grille gates of Moycullen Demesne.

The sun was just setting, its last rays burnishing to gold the lake waters and the far purple-black reaches of the Partry Mountains, when the barouche reached the gates. Now at a gallop the cobs passed smartly through, and after a drive of one mile to the inch, drew up at the foot of the granite steps leading in sweeping curves to the pedimented entrance of Roderick's home. Lined up on both sides of the wide terrace in front of the door were the household and park staff, carefully instructed by Malloy and Mrs. Killballon just how to greet the young master. Each member was to curtsy or to bow, according to sex, and each one was to look no higher than his lordship's waist when saying in unison "God's grace to ye through a long life."

But Lilylight was struck completely mute by the sight of the most beautiful male creature she had ever laid her eyes on. She not only failed to curtsy like all the other maids and keep her eyes on the level of the black-leather, silver-mounted belt of Lord Roderick's uniform, but she looked him straight in the eye and he into hers. For at the moment that he was smiling a greeting to his well-wishers, his eyes just happened to rest upon her pale face with its curious, wide-staring, nearly colourless eyes. If he noted her particularly, she was never to know. In a moment the tall young man had passed into the house with his father and mother. That Lilylight got a good dressing-down from Mrs. Killballon for disobedience did not signify a whit. She rushed off to her little room next to the laundry and threw herself on her bed. The vision of what she had just seen was so clear it seemed as if the image of Lord Roderick, resplendent in his Guards uniform of crimson and black, the jacket looped and frogged in shimmering gold cords and braided lace, was painted in swift brilliant strokes on the lids of her tightly-closed eyes.

Like all the Farrows, Roderick walked tall and lithely. He bore his small head erect; his luxuriant raven-black hair he wore rather long after the prevailing fashion, allowing tousled front locks to fall at will in the so greatly admired Byronic style. His straight features were "neat" more than handsome, as he had often been told by his unsparing messmates. His smile was cool and his manner boyish yet rigidly self-contained. In short, by anyone less struck dumb with infatuation than Lilylight, Captain Lord Roderick Farrow was considered in the social circles in which he moved as only an ordinarily good-looking young man of no great personality, excessively prideful both of his rank and of his position as secretary to his mother's cousin, the Iron Duke of Wellington.

The three days of Roderick's visit home were passed by himself and friends gathered at Moycullen for festivity, in a kind of whirlwind of picnics on the lough and a large dancing party where a French enchantress visiting in the neighbourhood dazzled Roderick by teaching him a swiftly-executed Cossack polka. An equestrian meeting of marked originality was held in the park. Contestants, mounted on hunters and armed with bows and arrows, rode in circles around a grass mound on which had been set up an archery butt with a revolving target.

During this activity Lilylight moved about her duties in the laundry with all the animation of a somnambulist. "The Lily's more moony than iver," Timmy the boots told Michael the carrier, who brought the postbag from the village each evening. Men, as such, had never actually been more than a passing interest to Lilylight. A sensation here, another of more or less excitement there. But this was different. Here was a pattern of young manhood that had completely bowled the girl over. In short, here was a star at which she might gaze whenever it rose in her orbit, unadmonished by Malloy or Mrs. Killballon. A radiant being on whom she might even, though he noticed her not at all, lavish her affections. The wondrous beauty of idolatrous love that happens to mortals only once in a lifetime had come to simple-minded Lilylight of the Blaskets.

Roderick had brought to his mother a portrait of himself painted in London by Sir Thomas Lawrence who, along with Sir Joshua Reynolds and Sir Thomas Raeburn, ranked high as a fashionable portrait painter of the day. It was not a large picture, perhaps a yard high, but it depicted Lord Roderick in smiling mood wearing full-dress regimentals, his legs straight, chest out, as if the young captain were about to salute a superior officer. His head was thrown back in a stance of careless ease typical of the proud Farron males.

Lord Roderick, his visit ended, departed from Moycullen for London late at night after a dinner party. Lilylight was still helping the scullery maids wash up in the back scullery when he left the house. It was not until a few days after his departure, when Lilylight had been sent by Mrs. Killballon to bear some freshly-laundered lawn sleeve-ruffles up to the bedchamber where the countess lay recovering from a migraine induced, or so she said, by so much unwonted gaiety at Moycullen, that the girl saw for the first time the Lawrence portrait of Lord Roderick. It hung on a panel of the ivory wall at the foot of the stairs. Hanging just at this spot, close to a Chippendale highboy which cast a shadow, the picture was poorly lighted, so that on her way upstairs to deliver the countess' ruffles Lilylight did not notice it. But on descending the staircase she dawdled as always, in no hurry to get back to her work at the ironing table. A ray of sunlight entering from the high-arched Palladian window on the stair landing stabbed the shadows, to point up in relief the scarlet of the uniform worn by the figure in the painting. Colour always caught Lilylight's eye. For a moment she hesitated on the stairs, recognition flooding her mind. Then she did a curious thing for one of so placid a nature. She uttered a shriek choked off by a racking

LILYLIGHT OF THE BLASKET ISLES · 191

sob, then her senses darkened over. Malloy, coming out of Lord Grantham's room, found her lying in a dead faint on the landing of the stairs.

From that day out, an even greater stillness of manner settled over Lily-light. She scarcely ever spoke. She ate so little at meals that Mrs. Killballon "read her the riot act sharpenin' the edge ave me anger on her stubbornness," as she told Malloy, who had long since had his fill of Lilylight and her dullness and now let her strictly alone. The weeks and the months passed. Lilylight per-formed her duties satisfactorily enough, but she moved always like one whose next step was likely to be her last. Many a time she was caught in the hall stand-ing stilly in front of the portrait of Lord Roderick, her hands clasped over her heart. One day when she should have been at her ironing board pleating a starched fichu for her ladyship, Malloy came upon her in the hall.

"Arragh, me white-faced saint. This is beyond enough. Her ladyship screechin' the place down fer her fal-lals an' yerself moonin' about after a painted image ave a fella' who'd not know ye was alive did he trip over ye. Away out ave this an' below stairs where ye belong," and he struck her a blow across her thin shoulders that rocked her back.

The day that news arrived at Moycullen House that the Duke of Welling-ton had agreed to take command of the allies against Napoleon Bonaparte was a demented one of thrashing wind and torrents of rain. It rained for days, a pro-longed storm of such violence as had not been endured in this region within the memory of a living man. And so it seemed that rain and tempest wind set the stage for the tragedy that was to follow so soon on the announcement that Well-ington had maneuvered to meet Napoleon in what the allies hoped would be a last decisive battle on Belgian soil.

Five days after the epic Battle of Waterloo, word was brought to Lord Grantham that his son and heir, Captain Lord Roderick Patrick Vail More-wood Wellesley Farrow, had been shot through the heart by a French grenadier while delivering to Wellington a report of Napoleon's position. His body had been recovered from a thicket at the foot of the hill from which the Duke was directing his generals. Together with all his personal effects, the body of Lord Roderick was expected to arrive at Galway Spanish Quay within ten days. Or as soon as His Grace of Wellington could personally arrange for space on a packet leaving Le Havre. Noticing Lord Grantham wince as he mentioned the delay, the messenger shook his head and added, "You must understand, your lordship, there are so many British and Irish dead—over two hundred officers all told, besides unknown numbers of the ranks—to be shipped back, and so few ships at this time."

That night in the servants' hall when the dread news of the death of "the young master" was announced by Malloy, Lilylight sat as if turned to stone. The quietness that had settled upon her during these last months since Lord Roderick's departure seemed now, on the instant, to crystallize. After sitting bolt upright, stunned for a few moments, she started to sway backwards and forwards in the age-old way of Irish women keening in desperate grief—keening their hearts out in a low wail that seems to listeners a sound more animal than human. With every eye upon her, Lilylight straightened her back. As she rose from her stool she was heard to murmur dully, "Then I'll see 'im no more. Never —never no more."

In actual time it was over a fortnight before word was received at Moy-cullen one dark rain-sodden morning that a packet boat from France, bearing black streamers of mourning from its mast, had passed Gorumna Island at the head of Killkeirnan Bay at dawn. The ship had signaled that she would put in at Spiddal Port. With the sea running smooth under the slanting rain, with luck attending, she should drop anchor about noon.

Word of this arrival and of the alteration of port of entry spread like a con-flagration through the village near the gates of the Great House. From cellars to attic of the house itself, and to the stables beyond, a drear moaning arose. When Lilylight heard Malloy expatiating on all the work attendant on the huge fu-neral that would take place in a few days after the arrival of the casket, she grabbed her shawl from off its hook near the back courtyard door and rushed out into the rain-swept mist. That flash of livid pale face under her green Con-nemara homespun shawl clutched over her head was the last anyone at Moy-cullen ever saw of this strange girl who had for three years lived with them but decidedly not *of* them, inciting in no one affection or more than passing notice —a silent wraith moving in their midst.

Clutching her shawl tightly about her emaciated shoulders against the rain, Lilylight ran headlong through the underbrush of the park, swiftly as she had often seen a frenzied doe plunge forward unheeding direction when pursued by rapidly gaining hounds. But Lilylight vaguely knew her direction. Spiddal lay to the west of Knock. Once she gained the Knock Pass she knew her way. Mist drifting in from the sea hindered her progress. Once on a rise of meadow she asked a small girl minding a gaggle of gray geese if Knock lay near or far.

"There 'ud be it—in the vale." The child pointed to the west. Now Lilylight knew her way.

Once she had reached the sodden turf lane that marches with the quay at Spiddal Port she sat down on a porter keg to await what would transpire. She had no way of gauging the time, not knowing how long she had been on her way across country. Owing to the foul condition of the weather few persons were about. A few stevedores and pub-crawlers, hearing that a ship from France was unaccountably docking here, had come out hugging sackings about their thin and dingy garments, hoping to cadge a few pence by helping the regular porters to unload whatever cargo the "froggies'" ship was laden with.

Lilylight had not been waiting long when she heard the clop-clop-clop of horses' hoofs. It was the ancient black leather-hooded traveling coach from Moycullen. As it passed her she caught momentary sight within of black-garbed Lord Grantham and Malloy. Behind the coach a team of farm horses drew a farm wain which, in the ancient way traditional for a deceased country squire, would bear back to Moycullen the casket containing the body of Lord Roderick. All this she saw, but its implications failed to register on the shuttered mind of Lilylight, and her unmindful as she was of the water that sopped her bared head from which the shawl had slipped down to her shoulders.

Presently she heard a bell clanging, heard voices shouting in a language unfamiliar to her, answered by shouts in the clipped speech of Connaught. Dully she heard the screech of tarred rope as it caught hold and tautened on the timber davits of the quay. Suddenly Lilylight leapt to her feet and darted towards the ship. Amid the confusion of landing and of stevedores going aboard to seek out cargo, no one noticed the shawled figure of a young girl darting along the deck in search of the casket that bore within its narrow walls the body of him whom she loved above all beings on earth.

She came to it at last; she knew it instantly by its shape and size though it was obscured under roped-down tarpaulin for protection against the rain. But what caught her eye above all was a kind of bundle, large, square in shape, wrapped in some sort of black canvas that gave off the odour of oil or tar. There was lettering in white on top of the bundle, but as Lilylight could not read this meant nothing to her. But from the depths of her consciousness there rose the thought that whatever this bundle contained, it had once belonged to Lord Roderick. Quickly, as a famished animal will snatch at food and be off and away, in the droop of an eyelash Lilylight grasped the bundle with both hands. It was bulky and heavy as if it contained something of metal, but she slipped it under her shawl. The porters had just located the coffin but had not seen her movement. She sped past the men and up the gangway. Then it was only a moment of breathless hurry until frail, anguished yet exultant Lilylight melted away into the heavy wreaths of mist that by this time had shrouded the lonely little port of Spiddal.

If Lilylight had been silent, withdrawn, during her last days at Moycullen, she was quiet and unheeding of words or ways nearly to the point of nonexistence during the months following her unexpected return to her grandmother's coteen under the rocky headland of Moreara on Great Blasket. No one ever found out how she had proceeded to Ballydongan lying on the heel of Coulagh Bay far down the coast in County Cork. Here it was that a Galway hooker manned by three fisherman brothers had seen her standing lone and forlorn on the rocks, gazing off towards Dursey Island. One fellow had called out to her, "Are ye lone an' lost?" She had nodded assent. Then one morning she had walked in on Dame Fellerhan, who in surprise had nearly ruined her throat swallowing a bowl of scalding tea.

Lilylight, who now had a perpetual faint smile as if of some secret triumph, though her face was worn and thin of cheek, pale as a tallow-dip candle, would absent herself from the coteen for days at a time. Her grandmother was so old now that she scarcely noticed whether Lilylight was about the place or away. Only the cow protested her absence at milking time. For when Lilylight was at home she most ably performed the simple chores that had heretofore been done by Nimby Hearno, a gossoon or "low boy" of twelve years.

Now Nimby was a quick-witted, perceptive and particularly agile lad who spent his spare time clambering over the rocks exploring every cranny of the rock-face of Moreara Headland in search of succulent gulls' eggs. These he would either sell in the village square or perhaps, for a midday meal, boil a clutch of them in water heated at the communal stone ovens or "hearths" where loaves of bread were baking over red-and-purple embers of peat.

One day when Lilylight had not been seen in Moreara for three or four days, Nimby decided on pastures new in his searching for eggs. He had seen from the water, when out rowing, a cave set not too high from a shaly shelf cove, and he reasoned that it could be easily reached by a short clamber over a disused goat path which followed the rock-face for perhaps a quarter of a mile. All worked as Nimby had planned. He found the goat path. He skirted half of Moreara Head and was just about to let himself down to enter the cave mouth when he heard the sound of singing. Not loud singing—low and mournful, though it carried even above the distant thunder of breakers dominating the scene in their eternal assault on the base of Moreara Cliffs. Then, listening, Nimby thought it sounded like the crooning he had heard his mother use to bring sleep to close the eyes of his rampageous baby brother Paddy. Soft crooning—or was it keening, the like of the three women in black shawls? Those "auld rooks" he had called them often enough, as they followed the coffin in the island funerals, they being paid in shillings for their wailing in mock grief. Lightly, so as not to frighten whoever the singer might be, Nimby let himself down onto an outcropping of rock projecting at the side of the cave. Bending over cautiously, he looked into the cave from an angle above its rocky floor. The sight he saw was a surprise and a puzzler enough.

Lilylight sat on her haunches as if at devotions before a crudely-arranged altar. On a mound of stone festooned with wet seaweed, glistening in the stray sunlight piercing the mouth of the rock-shadowed cave, was a kind of image fashioned from crossed pieces of driftwood, the upright timber surmounted by an oval stone about the size of a human cranium. Soldiers had come to the island at various times. Nimby recognized the uniform of a British officer when he saw it. But it was the feathered hat surmounting this stone head, and all the richness of scarlet coat hung with gold cords, the highly-polished riding boots with little gold tassels dangling in front of the tops, the sword, its hilt hung with golden tassels too, that fascinated the mind of small Nimby to the extent that he nearly lost his balance. Instead, he gripped the rock ledge harder, craned his neck farther, and looked into the cave once more, long enough to take in the scene in detail so as to catalogue each article of red and gold and to be certain sure that the devotee in front of this to his mind fearsome altar, was really Lilylight. So strange she looked, her eyes staring in fixed intensity, her lips mumbling eerie sounds, half wail but, Nimby realized, more of keening. Then he scrambled up the rock and was off like a gust of sea wind to tell in Moreara of his discovery— to relate with flourish just *where* that loony Lilylight spent her time when "off rangin'" and, better still, *how* she spent it.

That night after the moon had risen, Lilylight, unaware of Nimby's discovery of her shrine, returned to Moreara. As she passed through the market place she sensed even through the barrier of her habitual somnolent calm that there was uncommon activity about. At any other time, at this hour the village would be lying dormant until the first flush of dawn called out the "dayers," fishermen who would meet the "nighters" returning with their catch. Suddenly one youth to whom in long past days she had given her favours, but whom since her return from Moycullen she had successfully repulsed, started shouting: "The Lily's a loony! Where'd ye get that gewgaw uniform Nimby saw? Was it at the Salt Hill Carnival in Galway? A red coat an' a cocky hat an' all an' all. Well, all ave us buckos 'ull take a jaunt the morn's morn and see fer ourselves what the bhoyo Nimby saw." He went into great guffaws of laughter that were echoed by a few of his drinking companions who came to stand behind him in the pub door.

Jockser Mullany, a tall gangling youth of singular ugliness, with a walleye and a broken nose, called out, "I've had ye up the mast miny's the time. Yer thin as a rake be now, but after we've finished wid ye, we'll burn the lot ave trash that Nimby says ye've cluttered yer cave wid."

During this brutal harangue Lilylight had stood in the middle of the small market square as if struck immobile in her tracks. Then, like a swift blow from an evil hand, the enormity of what she had heard flooded her numbed consciousness. The contents of the waterproofed parcel which she had filched from its place on top of Lord Roderick's casket—his dress uniform, his sword, and a number of leather boxes, repository for jeweled orders conferred upon him for outstanding bravery—all these she had secreted in her cave. She had built up a crude effigy of her beloved. This was her only life, her days and nights spent in devotions to his memory. And now these scaldeens with rough tongues, these beasts who reeked randily as mountain goats, would defile her shrine. Lilylight darted across the cobbled square, straight over to where Jockser Mullany, the ugly one, stood. He was still convulsed by his own pronouncement of his forthcoming revenge, and she spat full in his opened mouth. Before he could recover from his surprise and wreak havoc on her, Lilylight sped into the night and never paused in her flight until she reached the declivity where started the old goat path. Now carefully picking her way, tortuous to the uninitiated but familiar to her since childhood, Lilylight slowed her pace. Her mind darted swift as a dragonfly among mallows, seeking out every detail of what she knew that she must do.

The next morning dawned clear as the peal of the bells in the monastery of Mount Melleray. About mid-morning a curragh, rowed effortlessly in the un-naturally calm sea by four stalwarts, rounded the Scurry Needles, which rose as protective guardians, sharp spears of sea-gnawed stone, at either side of the tiny cove in front of Lilylight's cave. Three of the rowers were they who had so vilely baited Lilylight in the market square. But one was a giant of a fellow, one Casso Felter from Little Blasket, far-famed for his agility in climbing sheer, apparently unscalable rock-face. All the fellows were equipped with climbing tackle, for they planned a great sport today. That sullen streeler Lilylight would get run out of the village later, time enough after they had had their bonfire to cleanse the cave.

But however roused their spirits had been from a few rounds of drink taken at Cleary's Pub that morning before starting out, each man returned to Moreara as subdued in spirit as if he had been poleaxed. What each climber had seen struck him dumb with awe. Lilylight sat on the floor of the cave, her body propped up in the cleft of a rock. She had arrayed herself in the red coat, belted and sashed, of Lord Roderick's Guards uniform. On her head she had set his shako, now fallen slightly askew. She had removed the white feather panache, which she held in the stiff fingers of one hand. The manner of her death had been the ancient hero's way of a warrior taking his own life on the battlefield rather than suffer capture. She had fallen upon her sword. So thin she was that the blade had pierced her heart to protrude through the white flesh under her shoulder blade.

Mariners of disparate nationalities who sail the seas that lap the long western coast of Ireland—and this is a frequented waterway—tell tales of seeing the ghost of Lilylight of the Blaskets in the night hours under the moon, or often she appears suddenly as a wraith in the mist of morning, drifting lightly, her bare waxen-white feet scarcely touching the waves. As with all stories of apparitions, different men tell different tales of just how the ghost appears.

A Mr. Ashby whom I met in Oranmore, a village near Galway Old City, told me that he was returning one evening from a day's rough shooting over the demesne of Dunsandle House. The property marches with that of now burned-out Moycullen. Darkness was descending rapidly and he was a shade worried that he had missed the particular bohireen that would act as a guide so that he might reach the highway leading into Oranmore. He heard behind him the sound of wailing, sharp on the wind, high-pitched, also breathless, as if a woman in some distress was nearly foundering from running over the trappy terrain of the rank-grassed fields. He turned to see running towards him a tall, improbably thin figure. A woman who stumbled over the ground, her mouth open, almost grimacing as if in agony, her eyes—which in the fading light appeared to be opaque, even sightless—fixed straight ahead in a somnambulistic stare. My informant said that he had seen the same look in the eyes of a sister who was addicted to sleepwalking to the extremity that a fall from a balcony while in this condition had caused her death. What had most startled and highly interested the man was the woman's oddly unsuitable apparel. She wore, over a pale-blue dress with skirt cut loose and flowing in the style of an older day, the red, gold-laced coat of an officer in a British regiment. But this garment, too, was of a style long outmoded in military circles. Her long, lint-white hair flowed out behind her from under a kind of turban composed as nearly as he could tell from a British officer's sash. On the figure came, until, as if a cold clammy wraith of mist had for a moment enveloped him, the ghost of Lilylight passed right through Mr. Ashby and ran stumbling and wailing on her way.

Again I was told by a Mrs. Carstairs living in Knock that she saw, one starry night when she was returning from Galway, the scarlet-coated ghost of Lilylight pass by, this time not *through,* her. She was just alighting at the gate leading to her house in Cole Square when she noticed a woman running breathlessly towards her. Mrs. Carstairs' eyes were immediately attracted by the red military coat worn by the agitated figure. She was about to speak, offering help if needed, when her blood congealed in her veins with horror to see that the hands of the woman, which Mrs. Carstairs had thought were simply crossed on her breast, were in reality clutching, as if driving it through her heart, a sword. As the apparition floated more than walked past her, Mrs. Carstairs said, she saw that the pointed blade of the sword protruded for the length of more than a foot from a point just under the shoulder blade.

Mrs. Carstairs told me as well that there is a hillock near Knock where no shepherd nor goose-girl nor boy will ever graze their flocks. The grass grows green and juicy there—the famed "goose-grass" with blossoms full of seeds that lag geese dote upon. This is apparently the hill where, on the morning that Lilylight bolted from Moycullen to meet the French packet at Spiddal, she stopped to inquire the way to Knock from a small goose-girl. I asked Mrs. Carstairs why this richly-grassed hilltop was so shunned. She replied, "Hard to believe. But there is a swath through the grass there that could have been the portion walked over by this Lilylight. A flock of domestic animals or fowl may be feeding on the hillside in apparent safety and contentment; yet if one of them crops a tuft from this particular swath, he suddenly falls dead. The grass and the soil have been analyzed by experts. Both seem to be harmless. But there it is. It would seem that the steps of Lilylight are mysteriously contaminated."

She paused a moment, looking thoughtful. Then she said, "A curious aftermath of tragedy. Perhaps deep, abiding grief poisons the body as well as the spirit."

The O'Rohan Blazonry

CASTLE BRAN, COUNTY MEATH, 1690

CASTLE BRAN is a dreary house now, and one feels that it has always been a dreary house. In its building no pattern was ever followed. The castle sprawls in a curiously jumbled sort of way. No one part of it, haphazardly attached as they all are, seems in any way related to its fellow. As I viewed the old pile from a distance, the group of buildings, huddled out of the rain under a few oak trees, looked like a deserted village. But Castle Bran isn't completely deserted.

The house has a vague, cloistered life of its own. An old gardener potters around the half-shattered hothouse. Now and again, if one is passing along the road to Trim and chances to look in at the gates, which are untended and usually swinging free, one sees either Mrs. O'Rohan or her very ancient father, or both, taking their constitutional along the unkempt terrace. Early hours are kept at Castle Bran. After nightfall there are seldom any lights in evidence. In this lone house nothing much happens to light up for.

Many persons will say "Oh, that old ruin?" when one asks about Castle Bran. But it isn't a ruin in the strictest sense, for one wing is lived in today—one of the long, narrow, high wings, which seems shunted off from the rest of the house. Then there is one big circular room that is used in the summer as a parlour because the thick stone walls make it cool. They also make it damp. The kind of damp one dies from. Plenty of O'Rohans have died from it. Yes, plenty of O'Rohans have died, as the full-to-overflowing crypt underneath this circular room will prove. Row upon row of moss-stained marble tombs are arranged in this crypt. They bear odd and ancient names: Countess Isabelle de Rohan, Died 1545; Sir Armond d'Estreville de Rohan, Died 1607; Michael Dargill O'Rohan, Died 1798.

The family has had a curious history. Curious, because the Norman family of D'Estreville, whence come the Irish O'Rohans, bears a name famed in martial exploits in France and England, yet little or nothing is known of the Irish branch who live at Castle Bran. They have always lived secretive as if inside the covers of a closed book. "They're shada'-like—aught nor either's known ave thim," an old man in the nearby village of Dunshaughlin once told me.

Succeeding generations of O'Rohans seem far more French than Irish in the secluded way in which they live, for even the male O'Rohans take no part in the village affairs, fox-hunting, racing, or the church. In the manner of the *ancien régime* of France they have a private chapel in one of the towers at Castle Bran. I unearthed documents, dry and uneventful, to show that the present O'Rohans were originally called De Rohan d'Estreville, and that the first member of the family, Sir Guy, came to Ireland with the Norman knights who followed in the train of Strongbow, Earl of Pembroke. Sir Guy is supposed to have lent his good right arm to the sacking of Wexford and Waterford. When the Danes were driven out of Ireland he decided to stay in this green and pleasant land. Where he actually settled before his descendants turned up on the banks of the Boyne Water, no one knows.

It is not clear just when the "de" was changed to "O'." But this fact of the change is interesting, because so long as the name remained De Rohan, the family prospered exceedingly. When it was changed to O'Rohan their fortunes immediately took a downward turn. For over three hundred years the Irish O'Rohans seem to have lived on the slim bounty of the Norman De Rohans. The Padraig of our story was educated in France and lived at the famous Chateau de Rohan near Dinard for five years. When he returned to Ireland in his twenty-fifth year he scarcely had time to unpack his luggage and settle into his quarters at the castle, before a trumpet rang out across the reaches of the River Boyne. With hundreds of other young Irishmen, Padraig O'Rohan joined the cause of James II. The historic Battle of the Boyne Water, presaging the eclipse of the Stuart cause, was fought within three miles of Castle Bran.

The story of the hound blazonry is the one claim to fame of gloomy, ramshackle Castle Bran.

The Battle of the Boyne Water was fought July 12, 1690. After the carnage of battle, the Irish dead lay untouched all day and far into the night. So many of the villagers and farmers had fled that part of the country that there was no one left to bury them. A few crafty characters crept from their hiding places to loot the corpses, but left the dead unburied, for a drenching downpour and cold winds soon drove them back into their sand-pit caves under the overhanging river bank.

Many bodies of Irishmen were covered only with a few handfuls of loose sod or branches of bracken. It did not take the rooks long to find and uncover these sketchily-buried cadavers. The birds pecked away at eye sockets and whatever exposed flesh they could reach. Savage dogs, starving, and running the river reaches in packs, roamed the countryside at will, feeding greedily on these carcasses. This feeding upon men's flesh made monsters of the ravenous dogs. They yowled and fought among themselves, making the night hideous, until the few people still in their houses along the river barred their doors against the prowlers. It became dangerous for a man to pass along the river bank unless armed or accompanied by two or three companions.

Among the Irish dead was Padraig O'Rohan of Castle Bran. Apparently Padraig had been on his way to his house after the battle, when weariness and his numerous wounds overcame him. He fell dying on the banks of the River Boyne almost directly across from the gate-lodge of Castle Bran.

At the castle there was a greyhound belonging to Padraig, who had brought him from France. Tancred was a special breed of Italian-French coursing hound, bred at the kennels of the Chateau de Rohan. This greyhound, soon after the clamour of battle ceased, loped up and down the river bank in search of his master. Perhaps because the heavy rains had deadened the scent, and the piled bracken hid the body from view, the hound failed to find Padraig. That night Tancred joined the pack of fierce dogs still ranging the river banks. For a few days the greyhound from the castle quested for food. Then, returning to his kennel, by chance he came across the body of his master. Tancred fought to save the corpse from the slavering fangs of the other dogs. He succeeded in driving the pack off, and from then on guarded the body of his master night and day. A terrible stretch of days ensued. Men returning to their homes gave the Boyne Water reaches a wide berth.

To satisfy his hunger the hound fed on other corpses, along with the other dogs. But he allowed no dog nor man to touch his master. When scores of corpses had been devoured along this stretch of river, the pack of wild dogs departed, but the greyhound Tancred remained behind on guard. A few days had elapsed when one night a soldier, recovering from wounds in a nearby country house, chanced on the river path. He nearly trod on the carrion of Padraig O'Rohan, which the greyhound had dragged into a thicket close to the river path. Tancred, awakened suddenly, sprang at the man, thinking he was about to disturb the body of his master. In self-defense, the soldier fired his pistol at the dog. As the man left the thicket he turned and saw the body of the loyal greyhound stretched beside what was left of the corpse of Padraig O'Rohan.

Next morning word was sent to The O'Rohan at Castle Bran that the body of his son Padraig had been found. The body was claimed and was buried in a tomb in the crypt under the floor of the summer sitting room in the circular keep.

For once in its long, socially uneventful history the heavy iron-latticed portals of forbidding Castle Bran were opened to admit mourners to the funeral of the eldest son of the House of O'Rohan. It is said that while there were a few relatives, distant connections of the family, for the most part the assembled persons were strangers who had grasped this opportunity to see the inside of a house that had always been a wonder and a mystery in the locality. The funeral was fully recorded by a young barrister who attended it and on reading his account of the ceremony I find it possible to evoke the scene quite clearly.

It appears that in the center of the Great Hall of Castle Bran was placed a carved and gilded catafalque resting on a bier draped in black velvet, heavily fringed in gold galloon, the tinsel threads dull and tarnished in keeping with the dust, decay, and evidences of neglect of the furnishings, which was greatly emphasized by the splendour of a new adjunct to the trapping, a pall of brilliant crimson velvet emblazoned with the gleaming image of an Italian greyhound that was embroidered life size in the center of the pall. The velvet was so folded that the blazoning rested across the lower limbs of the corpse of Padraig O'Rohan. The deceased was attired in full regimentals of a lieutenant in the army of King James II, and his face was hidden under a mask of silk skillfully painted to resemble as nearly as possible his features as he looked in life.

From the rafters of the groined ceiling hung twenty-four silk banners, one for each year of Padraig's life so untimely ripped from him. Each crimson banner displayed the coat-of-arms of the D'Estreville-O'Rohan family as it had always appeared when the ancient "flag of residence," draggled by the elements almost to the point of obliteration of its device, was flown from the battlements of the castle. All was in order as to the original devices of heraldry save one important item. In place of the device described in heraldic terms as "displayed between three Fleur-de-Lis Argent on a wreath of the colours Rouge-et-Or a Dolphin Sable," the figure of a "Hound Or Passant" had, to magnificent effect, usurped the black dolphin of the O'Rohans. A hound lying at rest, its front feet crossed in the watching posture of this breed of dog when on guard. I think, as I look at this blazoning today, how well this quiet hound bears out the family motto—*Franc ha Leal Eto Ge* (Free and Loyal art thou).

For many years persons within the house have told of hearing strange noises in the wall behind the tomb where the body of Padraig O'Rohan lies. It seemed to be the sound of a restless animal—like the restlessness of a dog worrying its bed, which sounded as if it were a nest made of dried leaves and bracken.

Then one night in the year 1815 workmen were erecting in the cellar of the keep a tomb to hold another O'Rohan killed in the wars. This one, Brandon O'Rohan, had been killed at the Battle of Waterloo, fighting in the army of the Iron Duke. The remains had just been brought to Castle Bran from France, sealed in a lead coffin. One workman said he noticed a cold rush of air and felt a sharp pain in his forearm. Looking towards the tomb wherein lay Padraig O'Rohan, the man saw a white, wraith-like hound, with bared fangs and blazing eyes. The hound was regarding the man viciously, one paw lifted as if ready to spring at him if he should come a step nearer. The workman dropped his tools and fled.

Some time later a cloudburst undermined one of the walls of the keep. This time The O'Rohan himself set about to help workmen repair the damage. Precisely the same thing happened that had occurred a few months before. The O'Rohan felt a sharp nip in the arm and a current of cold air swept across his face. There, on the lid of Padraig's tomb, crouched an angry hound. The O'Rohan threw his crowbar at the blazing-eyed apparition, which snarled and disappeared in the gloom. Almost immediately the men heard sounds of scratching in the wall: the sound of a rustling like an animal worrying his bed.

Many people tell of having seen a skeletal hound of a peculiar, luminous, yellow-white color, loping along the river bank at night. If the hound comes close to them they see his jaws are red with blood and his eyes burn redly in his head.

One dark, misty night, a farm boy riding a plow horse home from a neighbouring market fair chanced to pass the back gates of lonely Castle Bran. Just as he came abreast of the gates a hound came dashing out of the thick blanket of mist. He leapt at the haunches of the horse, as if he would devour him. The amazed and frightened boy beat at the dog with an ash stick he carried. The stick cut straight through the hound's yellowish-white body, as ephemeral as the mist itself. As the boy slipped from the horse's back to try and quiet the frantic animal, he saw the ghostly hound disappear into the river mist.

AGGIE-The PoST

Aggie the Post

THE ROADS AND COTEENS OF CONNEMARA, 1925

FOR CENTURIES it has been common usage in Ireland to identify a person who follows a given calling by his Christian name, to which is added, the like of a tail to a kite, a "flutter." For example, Michael Carmody of Ballyskillen who daily drives a small, two-wheel cart between Cork and Bantry, delivering letters and the larger parcels and ofttimes a crate of hysterically honking lag geese or a baby's perambulator, is known to all simply as Mike the Cart.

There is Mrs. Alantha Creevy, a portly, dignified woman of "forty-odd" years by her own admission—or so she was when I knew her, for she used to sniff and say, "I'm nearly ready to quit this life on the roads. I say I'm forty-odd. As the years pass over me thim 'odds' git odder and odder—an' me short in me breath." She bicycled about the remote hilly roads of Roscommon, Fermanagh and wild Leitrim, peddling highly coloured and perfumed toilet accessories made by a Dublin firm. The soaps in particular were moulded as eye-catchers in the shape of pink swans, poisonous purple tulips, rather obscene goats and innocent-eyed fleecy lambs. I have seen many instances which convinced me that these soaps were acquired to be used more often as decoration for a hearth mantelpiece or the center of a festive table than for laving the hands after a day's work in the bogs or the cow byres. Mrs. Creevy, the dispenser of pomades and beauty aids, was enthusiastically welcomed at remote farmsteads as Creevy the Soap.

And so it goes, up and down, out and around the length and breadth of the island. These people are as proud of their titles as a peer of the realm, for their titles indicate their widespread popular celebrity.

209

I have known many of these gentry, men and women, young and old, and still have among them several friends who, ranging the roads, deliver various articles to my door at Ballyskillen. For "stop press" news of the road, or "a flick ave gossip taken ferninst," I do not know their equals in lusty, wittily-recounted, highly-flavoured narrative of all that has to do with the daily round of the countryside. But when I add up the score I am persuaded that I must award the crossed palms for noteworthy performance to a remarkable woman who for fifty years daily walked the lonely roads of Connemara, delivering letters and parcels. She was known to the world as Aggie the Post.

The birth certificate of Aggie the Post, written in cramped handwriting by an ancient verger, bears the name Agnes Honoria Finbarrow. From the age of eight years old until the day soon after her twenty-first birthday when Agnes Finbarrow of Renvyle in the wild, rock-strewn wastes of Connemara was awarded the position of "mobile postmistress" of Ballynahinch, "for excellence of deportment, good nature and perseverance"—or so read the garda sergeant's report to the post office official from Dubin—Agnes Finbarrow had worked from seven o'clock in the morning until eight o'clock at night, as hard as any coal miner. Six days a week, first as "all girl," then errand clerk and finally saleslady, she had opened the shop at McGilpert's Sons, Drapers, Emporium for Findings. The shop label, perhaps obscure to the non-Irish, meant that pins, needles, reels of cotton and twisted silk thread, laces, linings and buckrams, in fact all and sundry articles needed by a tailor or seamstress, could be found at McGilpert's Emporium.

For fifty years following her elevation to postmistress, until the month of June after her seventy-first birthday, Aggie the Post covered roughly eight to ten miles a day in all possible vagaries of the chancy West of Ireland weathers. I once saw preserved in Renvyle post office a ledger, Aggie the Post's personal "in and out" book. It was her custom when starting out on her daily rounds to write in a vitally flowing hand, the sort of calligraphy one associates with celebrities autographing photographs for admirers, such phrases as "A beautifully fine day by God's grace now that I'm out in it"; or on her return at nightfall "I'm in, and my face scalded by sun hiding behind the mist, bad cess to it." In all her years of service there were only five days when Aggie missed paying her calls to outlying hamlets and the "hillround."

In appearance she was uncommonly tall and lean as a rake. Her immense vitality never played her false as age crept upon her. Her witty riposts are a legend of hilarity and the "rough edge of her tongue" on occasion would abash the most arrogant bully. Aggie had no vanity where her appearance was concerned. Her narrow, steel-blue eyes snapping, she would often say, "Me face is *not* me fortune. I tog meself out in what grandeur I can afford, and me wealth is me good nature." And so it was—every voice in the countryside vouched for it.

Her reference to "togs" needs amplifying here. Her mode of dress was original, to say the least. Summer and winter she wore elastic-sided Wellington boots, decidedly roomy as to toes but fitting her thin ankles like gloves. Boots like those are seen only in museums now. For winter and muddy roads she wore a pair of brown leather leggings. Incased in these, Aggie as she strode along the road appeared to be walking on stilts, so stiff-looking were her movements. Summer or winter, she always wore a short skirt about which the summing-up was "It's the like ave Joseph's coat, a regular raree show fer colours," so fiercely had raged among successive generations of children the controversy as to its original colour. Aggie's pride and joy was her impressive collection of blouses for summer and knitted cardigans for winter, stiff as armour plate from her having lined them with wadded waistcoats. "To repel the blasts across thim bogs," she would respond when, on a soft day of spring, some cottager would say to her, "Aggie, woman dear, ye'll be melted to a dab ave grease on the road. Would ye not lay aside yer bulky?" Her headgear was a deer-stalker cap, and it was looked to as a kind of barometer. If, on starting her "hillround," Aggie tied the flaps under her chin, it would be a blowy day when icy winter blasts blew damp and bleak from the uplands—"uneasy with wind and rain" as Aggie would write in her ledger. If she tied the flaps up on top of her head, the day would in all probability be fine. During July and August, when the fierceness of hot sun in a brazen heaven burns the sparse grass of Connemara fields, Aggie would proudly don her cool white linen old-fashioned sunbonnet which had a whalebone-ribbed awning that looked like the wings of an aeroplane. But even on the most melting day there flapped over her shoulders a long, loose brown cape of the kind that used to be called a "dolman."

This garment she wore in her official capacity, and it had sheltered Her Majesty's mailbag, as Aggie would tell you, from "many's the blather ave rain and the drip ave fog and the shrivel ave sun so strong it 'ud crack the skin ave me face that can take it." The miracle was that the cape could take an extraordinary stretching and bulging at the seams from overcrowded impedimenta. While Aggie set out on her morning rounds with the capacious mailbag and an assortment of parcels bulging under the folds of the dolman, she returned in late afternoon a far more rotund figure. As the mailbag gradually spilled its contents by wayside coteens and lonely farms, the dolman began to expand visibly all around Aggie's ramrod-spare figure, for its cleverly-arranged set of pockets never failed to fill to capacity en route. Besides parcels, Aggie collected all sorts of largess for her own use. The good wife at Kilytcarrow Farm, holding out a wedge of yellow Irish cheddar cheese or a rasher of home-cured bacon, would say, "Here, Post me dear, stow this away in yer pouch against the hunger from a long walk." Perhaps it would be the lady of the "great house" at Ballyconneely who would contribute a half-worn garment of tweed or poplin, or perhaps a cooked fowl or a brace of partridge. So Aggie gathered as she went.

It is told that one woman in Mamm's Cross whom Aggie cordially disliked for her brash ways and loud-mouthed blathering of dirty gossip—the mouth in question being a great maw for size in itself—one day rather sneeringly offered Aggie a brass lamp, its large round base badly scratched and dented from hard usage. "Here," the woman said, holding the battered article at arm's length, "here's a lamp to brighten the nights ave yer old age. Hee-hee-hee!"

Aggie the Post drew herself up to her six feet of rangy height. Her eyes flashed scorn. "I've no room fer it. But yerself has. There's twa places I could name where it 'ud fit ye. But just fer pleasantry, ram.it in yer gob to shut it up." She strode on her way. It is also recorded that from this day out, Aggie never delivered letter nor parcel to this woman's door again. She would engage a gossoon, or small boy, in the village at the price of a ha'penny piece a time, to take the woman whatever post was due her.

For many years Aggie the Post's official salary was eleven shillings weekly; in later years she was "upped" to fourteen. But she eked out a living and kept her invalid mother and crippled sister in comfort on the combined bounty of a generous parish and the farmers on the "hillround" who to a man and woman, save perhaps the blathermouth woman in Mamm's Cross, adored the "acres she walked over" at every step, as Aggie described her immense stride.

It is said that so unorthodox were Aggie's methods of performing her duties as she saw them, that to the rigid official mind her ways at times were an enigma. The village postmaster, a man of considerable age and soured on life in general, had his trials with her. Aggie used to wither him with her tongue when he threatened to give her the sack because, for example, she had acted as midwife in a desperate case that she came upon in a lonely farmhouse, to the peril of delivering any further mail that day. "Yer a cold piece ave trousers," she said. "Sure ye'd put a toad in the bed ave yer dyin' mother to hasten her end be fright."

In the early days of Aggie's incumbency, the farmers' wives used to shop contentedly in Clifden, Renvyle or Letterfrack on the weekly market days. Many of their purchases they would fetch home themselves in a gig or governess-cart. But progress brings changes, and one came that Aggie bitterly resented, though because of her touted good nature in all extremities she thought it better not to air her feelings publicly. The change was the outcome of the tendency of farm wives and ladies of the manors to shop in towns and have their millinery and such adornment sent home by post. Aggie the Post began having to handle as best she might hatboxes and other unwieldy cardboard parcels.

On one occasion which has become a classic in the region of Renvyle, no fewer than five new Easter bonnets arrived simultaneously at Renvyle post office, to be delivered on that Friday to their various owners. To add to Aggie's problem, the day was pouring wet and a fractious wind blew from off the bold Atlantic. Old Bannor the postmaster, knowing his Aggie, viewed the matter with some trepidation. He even went so far as to suggest that she allow a young boy on a bicycle to accompany her on her rounds and at least to carry the postbag. But Aggie bristled. "Don't fash yerself, Mister Bannor. I'm a servant ave the crown, though I'm a freeborn Irish woman and 'ull remain so. But I know me duty. The hats 'ull move with me, if I move at all." Slowly Aggie untied the strings of each hatbox. She took each bonnet out of its tissue wrappings and, holding the confection at arm's length, surveyed it appraisingly from every angle. At the first three she shook her head. As the fourth emerged from its wrappings she heaved a purely feminine sigh of pleasure. The hat was a poke bonnet of flaring yellow straw, its high crown wreathed with wild roses and clusters of pink clover. Green and white satin ribbon was arranged in loops and dangled in long streamers that tied under the chin. Aggie scrutinized the label. The hat was destined to adorn the head of Miss Oonagh Sparbridge, daughter of the leading barrister in Clifden.

The upshot of the matter was that each of the five ladies expectantly awaiting the arrival of Aggie the Post received her hat in time to wear it on Easter Sunday. Four of the hats were delivered in boxes. But the poke bonnet wreathed with wild roses and clover reposed on the top of Aggie's deer-stalker cap, the ribbon streamers tied under her pointed chin. Over her arm she carried the empty box. It is within reason to believe that Miss Oonagh was a shade startled to see

Aggie the Post approaching her house, as it were *cap-a-pie*. Perhaps she waxed irate and abusive at such impertinence. Somehow I believe that she was wonderfully entertained by the sight of gaunt Aggie, her face burnt brown as the crust on an oat-bannock and the frivolous bonnet perched on her head. In any case I am sure that Aggie would simply have said, "I delivered yer hat in good order. *How* I did it is another matter"—and gone on her way rejoicing.

Aggie's aversion to men was proverbial in the parish. In her younger days wooers were known to have sought her hand, but to no avail. "I've twa mouths to feed as it is," was her scathing remark to a notoriously lazy man. "What 'ud I be doin' with a third?" Year after year Aggie stuck to her freedom. I can well believe that in any event the four walls of a house and the confining life of a housewife would have proved stifling to her with her love of the open road and the wild, pure winds that blow over hill and moorland.

This theory was amply borne out when I learned, while paying a visit to a friend in Clifden, Connemara in 1927, that Aggie the Post did not survive by more than six months her removal from her office. She ignored her failing strength. She "came all over wroth an' screechin' abuse to all and either that 'ud mention it," as the new postmaster at Renvyle told me, when the government decided it was high time to install a more up-to-date rural postal service. The powers retired Aggie on a small pension. In her place they installed a smart young man on a bicycle. And then one day Aggie set out to walk the "hillround" once again, to call on her many friends. She had said every day of her retirement, "I miss 'em sore; I must go out one day to see if they miss me." But it was a day of fiercely-blowing wind, and it is suspected that in turning too quickly off the road to avoid a motor-carrier from one of the adjacent towns, Aggie slipped on loose shale and pitched down into a ravine. When the driver reached her, the heart of Aggie the Post had already fled to the wild free spaces and the "winds of Home."

Anyone, and he wishing to hear, could sit for hours in any pub or on the doorstep of countless farmsteads in the reaches of Connemara, and listen to tales of the shenanigans Aggie is purported to have indulged in during her rampageous life. As many are told about her active ghost.

One fragment of brisk, to-the-acid-point repartee is said to have taken place before a crowd of gawkers near the village of Letterfrack during the first year that Aggie the Post walked her rounds. It appears that the head forester on the demesne of Lord Balgawley had "flushed" a poacher who had raided the hutches where rabbits were bred. Apparently the poacher had hidden in the dense foliage of a beech tree growing close to the demesne wall that followed the curve of the highroad. Just as Aggie the Post came striding along, the hunted man made a break for it. He dropped from the branches of the beech tree and landed sprawling at Aggie's feet. Quick as a flash she took in the situation. She plumped her heavily-laden pouch onto the man's chest. Then, sitting astride his prostrate body, she proceeded to strip from the miserable poacher's legs a pair of brown leather leggings. As a crowd of road menders surrounded Aggie and her victim she called out, "I claim no reward from his lordship fer catchin' this disgrace ave the world, other than these leggin's. Sure an' all it's a class ave attire I've always craved, but the price is beyond me purse." She held one legging next to her leg. She let out a bellow of mirth. "Well be Saint Brigid-in-Flames, his legs is thinner than me own, so they'll be a perfect fit!" And so they were. She wore them almost daily for the rest of her life.

Then there was the time when a British visitor to Connemara had too much drink taken. For no other apparent reason than feeling his poteen too highly, the man accosted Aggie in the market square of Killadoon, that magical whitewash and gold-thatched village at the foot of Croagh Patrick, the Holy Mountain. The fellow proceeded to bait Aggie.

"So—yer the Post," the creature said. "What is this I hear that you are as well local midwife, marriage broker, saver of sinners, singer of lullabies to fretful babes and"—he paused, warming to his subject, guffawed loudly and added, "and *veterinary* surgeon." He was again convulsed with laughter. A few persons gathered to hear this bantering were ominously silent, waiting openmouthed for the blast that Aggie would surely hurl to singe the very whiskers off this buffoon. It came. Direct and wonderfully pat.

"I am," she said in a dulcet voice, "all ave thim things, and more." She lifted her chin, pointed as that of a dog fox, and said, the dulcet tone of voice now whetted with a cutting edge: "And there's one of me accomplishments I'd like this livin' minute to practice on yerself. A *purge* ave oil ave balsam. Fer from the minchin' look ave yer whey-white visage, and the walk ave ye like a horse wid the springhalt, I'd wager me blackthorn shillelagh here"—she brandished the stick aloft threateningly—"yer heir to all the diseases known to the Royal College ave Veterinary Surgeons." Aggie spat a sizable gob at the man's feet, in the immemorial gesture of contempt peculiar to Irish tinkers, and turning on her heel strode away about her business.

Another story of Aggie while still alive is this rare weirdy bit. In the exact center of the market place of the remote village of Partry, "hidden be nature and kept so be ourselves" the natives smilingly tell you, there is a huge circular stone set flush with the cobbles: in effect a kind of pagan altar. A great iron horseshoe that would seem to have been forged for a horse of giant breed is imbedded in the stone and is surrounded by concentric rings of stone setts. It is said to mark the exact spot where witches were burned in 1697. It is almost certain that this is the spot where witches were exhibited, according to custom, after being put to death. The body of a witch (and her evil spirit or familiar) was held to be indestructible until buried at a crossroads and pinned down with a stake driven through the heart. The imbedded horseshoe, symbolic of the Horse of Annar, protection against the powers of evil in pagan Gaelic lore, was a potent bringer of good luck. But the luck would last only so long as no human hand touched the metal of the shoe.

About the year 1900 there lived in Partry a certain Paddy Gormon who delighted in playing practical jokes. One night while he was on a spree a crony dared him to remove the horseshoe from the round stone. Paddy is said to have laughed the dare off for the moment. But in the dead of night he returned to the market place, removed the imbedded relic and hid it—not without some trepidation, it may be imagined, in a region so superstitious as the West of Ireland. When Paddy awakened sobered, he would have returned the horseshoe—but alas, he could not remember where he had cached it. Oddly enough, the evil released by his deed did not appear to affect the culprit Gormon. Instead, Partry, a village of perhaps eight hundred souls, was visited with a plague of suicides by hanging among the weavers of woolen cloth. Hangings were reported at every turn, until the magistrates were at their wits' end. At last the panic-stricken Paddy Gormon shipped out to sea and was never heard from more.

One day while pursuing her rounds, Aggie the Post felt unaccountably tired. Her head swam from the intense heat of a brassy sun beating down, and herself in the open roads. Spying a stone culvert, Aggie thought to lave her face with cool spring water from the Partry Mountains. As she leant down to scoop up water in her cupped hands, lo and behold, there lay the big iron horseshoe at the bottom of the spring. She took it to one of the magistrates. The shoe was immediately fixed again, extra firmly, in its original position. The epidemic of suicides promptly came to an end. Aggie the Post forthwith found herself a local heroine. She was feted by the town council and was told that the councilmen would be happy to gratify whatever wish she might express. To everyone's surprise, Aggie's wish, though unique, was modest. She asked only for fishing tackle and a day off from her duties. She said that when she had bent down to the stream to cup up water in her hands, she had seen "a grand, big monster ave a trout, lingerin' haphazard-like, cryin' out fer me hook." So Aggie received the finest fishing gear that money could buy. Her holiday was one of the five days during all her tenure of office that she did not appear in her dolman ready to traipse her "hillround." Local history reports that Aggie caught her "monster ave a trout" and a half dozen more besides, all of impressive size and weight. The particular spot at the culvert became popular with anglers and to this day is known as Aggie's Dip.

Besides the tales of Aggie's living exploits there are many stories of her ghostly hauntings. These vary as much as the shadings of her character. One tale is that of a harassed mother who had to nurse a sick husband in the house and equally sick livestock in the byres. The woman was frantic, trying to be in two places at once. She put her baby in a cradle out of doors under a thorn apple tree so that, inside or out, she might keep an eye on the infant. But flies bothered the child. While his mother was in the cow byre he started to scream his lungs out. Coming out of the byre, the mother was at first terrified to see the tall figure of a woman bending over the baby, who had gone quiet. It was then, hearing the soft musical voice crooning a lullaby, that the baby's mother recognized the figure as that of Aggie the Post who had often delighted, while on her rounds, to sing restless infants to sleep with the softly-cadenced lullabies of the West Country.

Another time, a shepherd far out on the hills fell and broke his leg. His agony was heightened by the fact that his sheep strayed far afield. Cry out as he might, the shepherd was too far from the highroad to attract attention. Finally, in extreme pain, he started to crawl towards a gate giving onto a bohireen where he knew there was a farmhouse. But the agony of dragging his broken leg overcame him. He fainted. When he came to, his sheep were all lying in a circle about him, and beside him sat the cloaked figure of Aggie the Post. The shepherd thought he was delirious at the least.

Before long he became aware of shouting coming from the direction of the highroad. Soon three of his neighbours pushed up the slope on which he lay. In the excitement of being found, the shepherd had forgotten the woman. Later he wondered if he had or had *not* seen her. When he inquired as to how the men had known of his accident and where to find him, one of them said:

"It was Aggie the Post—er her ghost, I mean. She appeared in the byre-yard of Tomas here, and touched him on the arm."

The man Tomas nodded. "And a damn cold touch it was—I'd not want it again. But I see now it was in a good cause."

Aggie's ghost had motioned in the direction of the hillside where the shepherd lay. Tomas had called out to the other two men he had met on the road, to come with him.

When the story was told, the four men looked around for Aggie the Good Samaritan. But there was no trace—she had gone off on her eternal "hillround."

Kilfaddon's Reach
and the Dark O'Foyles

DUNQUIN, COUNTY KERRY

SHADDONCARRIG is marked on only one map of Ireland that I have ever seen. If the name of this small village, a straggle of ancient stone, thatch and shale-roofed coteens, is in any way recorded elsewhere I have never come across it. The map is actually an old painted parchment scroll; the calligraphy employed to indicate the name and state of the baronies, as the demesnes of chieftains were identified in early usage, is primitive in the extreme, but on the whole the parchment chart is immensely decorative.

The map hangs in a house near Dunquin. A broody class of house, its high, narrow, deeply-embrasured windows stare off and away across the inherently choppy, chancy Bay of Dingle to the violet-misted Blasket Islands. The house is called Kilfaddon's Reach. When first I visited the place ten years or more past, it belonged to the last surviving member of the Kilfaddon family. Countrymen hereabouts refer to the place simply as "that auld Reach house." In appearance it is an unpretentious, albeit spacious building, the characteristic whitewashed stone farm manor of the locality. An outside stairway hugging one wall is traced by a spidery black iron handrail. This motif imparts a faintly Spanish air to the house, a style frequently encountered along the western coast of Ireland, stemming from the late Middle Ages when Spanish Town was built in Galway Old City by survivors from the Spanish Armada wrecked on its stormy shore.

Facing a long interrupted "reach" of Dingle Bay, vegetation is sparse. A tree or scrub of bog oak is a rarity. Only crazily-piled rocks, worn to a perilous slipperiness from centuries of sand-scrubbing by the long Atlantic rollers, mark the spot where anciently rose Shaddoncarrig Castle, only a gutted hulk now, yet still somehow maintaining a kind of frowning grandeur in its stubborn survival against time and the relentless winds.

To the medieval mind of the Kerry man Shaddoncarrig Tower is a heartening symbol of power. It does not matter that not a vestige of the "palace," as a King of Kerry's house was called, nor the "college" (to practice the art of learning) remains. Shaddoncarrig is a palace of the mind. One day when I was out sketching along the Dingle shore, I met a tall countrywoman, big in herself, and she walking the Old Coaching Road from Slea to Tralee. During a conversation concerning direction, she gave a flick to the end of her shawl, gesturing towards a ruined keep. "That's Shaddoncarrig—great hearts and the memories ave grand deeds er buried there. 'Twas there the Kilfaddons once ruled the Kingdom ave Kerry."

There is an everlasting jubilation about the dwellers within its boundaries. It is still the Kingdom of Kerry to them. They are a proud, free people; their songs fly out of their throats and away into the upper air, the like of the larks that, all along the western coast, accompany as a sort of celestial chorus the wild swans of Coole, forever winging aloft.

But it was a near thing, this present freedom, for if the Dark O'Foyles had had their way the whole of Kerry might have been lost by constant warring between the tribal chiefs from the north and their ancient enemy, the Norman British. Except for mountains and water, the ancient grandeur of the land entire might have been today only a "palace of the mind."

In 1262, the walled town of Shaddoncarrig was put to the ordeal of fire and the sword by the Bloody Blakes of Menlo. With the treacherous help of their cronies in deceit, the Dark O'Foyles, the Blakes managed to launch a surprise attack at a breach in the wall facing the western plain. It was the aftermath of this carnage that started the downfall of the proud and powerful Kilfaddons. In essence the curtain of this story rises, as on a theatre piece, to reveal the influence exercised by a member of the O'Foyle family over a son of the Kilfaddon. From that day out, the O'Foyles became the black nemesis of the Tribe Kilfaddon.

Everything about the Dark O'Foyles, as they have always been called, was dark. The deeds engendered in their minds for vengeance and for usurping land and power were as murky as the dark pitfalls of a subterranean cave, and as chancy. The O'Foyle breed were, history tells us, "of a black handsomeness, the like of wild and crag-bound eagles. The men were powerful and untamed. The women were a race apart, so cunningly fashioned to tempt, they were. In the thick coils of their peat-black hair, the eyes of men were caught."

The first of this devil's brood to enter the picture is a dark daughter, Drogheda O'Foyle of storied, pagan-wild beauty. During the unfolding of this tale of passion and revenge, it signifies that it is the O'Foyle women who dominate and destroy the more effete Kilfaddon men.

The first time I saw the parchment map of Kerry and Connaught which shows the exact location of the walled fortress town of Shaddoncarrig, I was impressed by the beauty of its flowingly-painted design, as well as its remarkable state of preservation. There it hung upon a dining-room wall in a remote house on the mist-ridden shores of Dunquin. Seacoast houses in Ireland are notoriously mist-ridden—an "ancient damping" the old ones say—and this piece of old, yellowed parchment was not even preserved behind glass. Yet, I noticed, its colours were rich and unfaded, and the minute monkish lettering in sepia might have been wrought yesterday. I looked closely at the date, which was painted with a great flourish in one corner. 1396. The razing of Shaddoncarrig had taken place half a century before the monk who fashioned this scroll started to paint its history. But he was still close enough to the sound and fury of the rape of this great "Kingdom place," as he refers to it on the map, to be very conscious of its historical importance.

As I traced many of the old names—the tribal "acres," the "baronies" which have disappeared from later maps—I noticed that just at the point where the name Shaddoncarrig appeared, there was a spot of what looked very much like dried blood: not a blot or carelessly-blurred spatter, but a deliberate, bloody fingerprint placed as a seal would be. The whorls of russet-brown all but obscured the name of the town. Then my eyes traced further along the coast of Galway Bay to Spiddal. There was a fingerprint again, but this time it was a black smudge.

I turned to my host, Roden Kilfaddon, to question him. He was smiling broadly. "I have been waiting for you to discover the markings made hundreds of years ago by old Nevin O'Foyle on his deathbed," he said. "They are of major import to my family, because they mark the start of the insidious campaign against us. Nevin O'Foyle, the son of Shamas O'Foyle who betrayed our town of Shaddoncarrig to the Blakes, was mortally wounded by my ancestor Bray Kilfaddon. The old informer (all O'Foyles were, it appears, legendary informers) had himself brought dying to his house at Spiddal Rock. His wounds overcame him, but as he lay weltering in his own malevolent blood, he called for a rolled map to be brought to him. Ironically, this very map had belonged to the Kilfaddons and been stolen by some O'Foyle in an earlier sacking of Shaddoncarrig. The old man called his sons and daughters about his couch and pointed to the spot where the seat of Kilfaddon power had stood. He told his dark brood that they must never allow the Kilfaddons to regain their hold of the spot to which he pointed."

I looked closely at the fingerprint, and said, "The blood running down Nevin's finger underscored his point, with a vengeance."

Tracing the coast line westward, Roden continued, "The old informer must have dipped his finger in a pot of soot, which I believe was used in those days to smear on armour so that the sun would not strike rays of light from off the metal and reveal a company of warriors to the enemy."

"So," I said, "in soot mixed with blood Old Nevin jabbed again at the map."

"Yes," answered Kilfaddon. "This time it was to indicate the place to build a stronghold to shelter the rising O'Foyles. However, this dark-visaged gentry never rose out of the muck of treachery and deceit and fawning servility to the Blakes." He paused. "Of a surety, the Kilfaddons sank as well. But just into a kind of decent oblivion."

Over a good tea, with oaten bannocks and rashers of curling Limerick bacon, we discussed some of the events which had taken place after Old Nevin had bloodied the map as Death rode him down. It appears that, as far as can be traced from various histories, memoirs and the like, Nevin O'Foyle banked heavily on the female allure of his buxom, raven-haired daughters, and their daughters who would come after them, to enslave the light-blooded Kilfaddons. This scheming worked, apparently. We would say today, the old man "played his hunch."

It is a well-known fact that three or four times in different generations, more orderly members of the Kilfaddon family tried to have the map of Connaught cleaned of its blood and soot. But, as Roden Kilfaddon said, "Old Nevin, looking up from the bowels of Hell, shakes his head; that's not the way he wants it.

KILFADDON'S REACH AND THE DARK O'FOYLES · 223

With forethought and devious purpose he placed those spots on the parchment for keeps."

I agreed that those smudges of his thumbprint are inviolate reminders. Even if his family has not prospered through the years, neither have his sworn enemies, the hated Kilfaddons. No amount of attempted cleaning or rubbing at those spots will erase them.

The present owner of Reach House says that many times in the years he has lived here he has been disturbed in the night by the sound of crackling coming from the dining room. It is as if someone were handling the parchment map, spreading and smoothing it over their knees or on a table.

Once, about the year 1910, Roden's father listened to an enthusiastic antiquarian from Dublin who wished to take the map back with him to show at a meeting of the Trinity College Cartography Society. Mr. Kilfaddon granted his wish, provided that after the map was shown, one more try would be made to clean the spots. If successful, it might succeed in laying the increasingly restless ghost of Old Nevin. The Dublin professor thought it pure sacrilege to deface so ancient and rare a document, but he was forced to agree to the terms. He need not have worried. In Dublin the map was cleaned with a certain acid and white chalk. When it came back, spotless to all appearances, it was hung in its accustomed place over the fireplace in the dining room of Reach House. During the night everyone in the house, five different persons in all, heard great commotion in the dark dining room. On instant investigation the doors and windows were found impossible to open. In the morning the room was as it always appeared at breakfast time, with one exception: The two ancient spots—one the red-brown of dried blood, the other black as soot—had reappeared upon the old map of Kerry.

The actual ramifications of the affair O'Foyle-Kilfaddon, as it waxed and waned down the years, are, except for a few vivid incidents, nearly impossible to trace. But enough data exists to prove the terrific impact which the Dark O'Foyles, especially the women of the tribe, made upon the aristocratic, cultured, but physically weaker Kilfaddons.

It is recorded that hardly a living soul escaped from the catastrophe that overwhelmed Shaddoncarrig in 1262, when it was reduced to a mass of flame-riven, smoking stones in the "Blake Massacre." Three of the ill-starred Kilfaddons managed to escape, by doffing their armour and swimming to a dense woodland on the farther banks of Dingle Cove. From there the two Kilfaddon brothers, Larn and Moylan, and the latter's son, a boy of twenty, fled across bogs westward and established a claim for land. This was granted them, at a heavy price, by the O'Duvenays of Upper Galway.

At a place called Annaghdown on the shore of Lough Corrib, these men built a castle. A soaring, gaunt tower, it was never more than a fortified keep. Its ruins can be seen today. They are a triumph of masonry, the dry-laid stone construction being still in such good repair that, though the roof has caved in, the heavy stone window-bracings are intact and the winding stone stairway leading upwards along the interior walls is undamaged. With a little care and imagination, Kilfaddon's keep could be made livable today.

The long view of the keep as you approach it from the valley road is superbly rewarding. The massive retaining wall, which was never wholly completed, incorporates white-veined purple quartz slabs five feet long. It was Gannor, the young son of Moylan Kilfaddon, who built the castle on the lough, and it was himself who was trapped by the dark beauty Drogheda O'Foyle "of the swan-white breast and the sloe-black eyes deep as sin," as an old bard song describes her. Gannor ran away from his house and married her and it is said they begat a brood of children "all of the raven black ilk."

Again, old chronicles tell that Meradagh, daughter of Drogheda and Gannor, was accused of sorcery, and was later burned by a mob from Cong who were incensed to such wildness that they bound her with fishing nets and flung her onto a pyre composed of her own household gear. Many cases of violence accredited to the O'Foyles are gory to the hilt. They stopped at nothing and feared no man born of woman. Each and every member of the tribe was a law unto himself. It was a day of high rejoicing among their ranks when they managed to get a Kilfaddon in their grasp. No matter what the dealings, it was always the Dark O'Foyles who dominated the issue.

Accounts in great variety of the behaviour of the O'Foyle women, acknowledged beauties all, have come down the generations. There is the story of one Oonagh O'Foyle, a granddaughter of Nevin, tales of whose stupendous beauty and amorous accomplishments were set to music by the bards—to their eternal prospering, for never had they been so luxuriously received by kings and chieftains throughout the length and breadth of Ireland as when they entertained their noble audiences with rhymed bardry extolling the O'Foyle women. Then there were the twin beauties, Brigid and Briony O'Foyle, who early on rose from the squalor of brothels huddling along the Mallarany quays to queen it in Restoration London as a duo to be hired for the night—"jeweled and perfumed and painted in fashion," according to Samuel Pepys—by the young bloods intimate with Charles II when his pleasure-mad court reached its zenith of sophisticated debauchery. The ultimate fate of the sisters is clouded over. It is documented that Brigid was "whipped away" to Paris by an infatuated French vistor to London, who "kept her as his chattel until her beauty waned." The veil of oblivion obscures her end. The more opulent Briony joined the players of Covent Garden for a time. She then appeared in Dublin, still ravishing to behold, and walked the "purlieus of Ashton Quay as a common prostitute." Perhaps she is one of the throng of ephemeral shades—lovely ladies clad in satin, taffeta and lace, moving with the extreme lassitude of their calling—that myself and others that I know have seen, as night descends over Dublin, hovering in the bosky shadows of Phoenix Park and St. Stephen's Green.

In 1710, Creedy O'Foyle and his wild pack of largely illegitimate brats lived in an ancient coteen near Barna, not far from where his ancestor, Old Nevin, had placed the sooty mark on the map of Connaught. Creedy was guilty, along with a passel of other sins, of having murdered his brother and run off with the widow, who was by birth a Kilfaddon. One of Creedy's sons became the notorious thief and pickpocket, Packy O'Foyle. He was of wild, eagle-like handsomeness, proverbially charming to women, who swooned for his advances. He had a meteoric career which set agog the European capitals, the licentious world of his time, because of the adroitness and bravado with which he plied his trade. His selection of victims was fastidious, his wit barbed, and his anger malevolent.

Once in Dublin he returned the Lord Lieutenant's purse with a filthily-worded note drawing a parallel between his lordship's emptiness of purse and head and his minute male organ "happily hidden from view under satins and laces." When, during an electrical storm, Packy was about to be guillotined in Paris for robbing and murdering a marquis' young daughter whom he had induced to run off with him, a sudden bolt of lightning killed his executioner. In the ensuing confusion the nimble Packy escaped. In his later years he became the god of thieves and criminals of every sort from Dublin to Rome.

In Dublin he presided over the most remarkable caravansary that ever flourished—and flourish as a gilded stew it did. It was called St. Patrick's Purgatory, a thieves' kitchen of deepest dye. Packy's succession of trollops acted as hostesses for him. At that period, roughly 1750 to 1795, Georgian Dublin swarmed with every known kind of impostor, criminal and beggar. At night, when these miscreants had thrown off the strictures of the day, the habiliments of woe and of beggarly infirmity concocted in every conceivable deceitful malformation by which to cadge a penny, the diabolical orgies at St. Patrick's Purgatory commenced.

All night the fiddles whined and drunken voices yelled their lungs out. Packy distributed handbills, some of which are preserved, inviting gentry of the highest standing to visit his nightly routs and to be sure to bring a full purse. It is said that he once auctioned off Pandora, his daughter by a mistress called Hell-Hag, to the dissolute, foppish Lord Arvagh, who claimed Pandora by outbidding all other rakehells. Pandora left the shebang with him. The next noonday he roused blearily to find his Henrietta Street house ransacked, but his prize Pandora innocently asleep at his side. Packy's daughter by Pandora, Letitia, married Ashlin Kilfaddon in 1765. That is the last marriage between O'Foyles and Kilfaddons that history has recorded.

There have, however, been a number of more or less scandalous "attachments" and reported ghostly visitations by sundry rapscallion O'Foyles galore, since then. One day in 1909, when Mrs. Miles Kilfaddon was living at Reach House, a dark, disheveled woman, far gone in drink taken, staggered across the paddock in front of the porch. From an upstairs window Mrs. Kilfaddon watched the woman's stumbling approach. She called a servant and together they met the woman on the stone terrace in front of the house, before she could in her wildness of mood effect an entrance, which seemed to be her intention. The woman stopped in front of the two persons on the terrace and surveyed them drunkenly. One of her eyes had at some time been gouged completely from its socket, and the black pirate's patch which was supposed to cover it had slipped around under the woman's chin. She beat the air with black-gloved fists, demanding to be let inside the house, crying out that Julius Kilfaddon was her husband, and if she had her rights she, Mrs. Julius—not Mrs. Miles—would be mistress here.

A farmer who was in a nearby field was summoned. After an altercation ending in a volley of vile invective, he led the woman away. It was learned later that before Julius Kilfaddon, a notoriously objectionable second cousin of Miles, had been shipped off to Canada by his father two years before, he had lived at Spiddal with one of the lowest of the O'Foyle women. When the self-styled Mrs. Julius Kilfaddon sobered up in the Tralee jail, she told a strange story of being haunted by a figure of an old man in black armour who came and stood over her at night. She said that on one occasion she followed him through the door as he had beckoned her to do many times before. The dark, bent figure, which walked with a halting gait as if sorely wounded, led her to a long, whitewashed coteen half hidden by a hedge of gnarled bog oak near Barna on the Sea Wall Road.

It was just on daybreak, she said, when they arrived at the coteen. The ghostly old man had pointed to a map hanging on a wall of the big room facing the sea. It was just breaking light. The ghost, she said, appeared to be nearly demented with anxiety lest she not understand what he was trying to tell her. Finally he had waved his arms wildly and pushed her away with such force that she had fallen on the dirt floor. Then he vanished out the open door into the shadows of false dawn. Soon after this the woman had learned that Julius Kilfaddon was a cousin to Mrs. Miles Kilfaddon's husband, who had been dead for three years. In a drunken mood all sorts of visions of claiming Kilfaddon property by lies and stealth had clogged her mind. So she had gone to Reach House because Julius had once told her it belonged to him.

When two of the Tralee garda went with the O'Foyle woman to the small house whither she had followed the ghost of Old Nevin O'Foyle, they found, hanging on the wall, a map traced on heavy linen. It was a replica, though of much later date surely, of the painted parchment map hanging above the dining-room fireplace at Reach House. There was just one difference, of mysterious import. On the stained *linen* map of Shaddoncarrig there were no fingerprints. But there was, scarcely discernible in one corner of the map, a scrawled signature—"Patrick O'Foyle, Adventurer of the World." It is known along the Sea Wall Road that in his younger days Packy, that will-o'-the-wisp blackguard, was often seen flitting about the roads and pubeens of this region.

I surmise that the marks so carefully placed on the ancient parchment by wily Old Nevin may have been secretly intended to mark the position of buried treasure, possibly Kilfaddon gold, stashed away by The O'Foyle, who was notoriously a prince of looters. Frequently caches of gold loot of mysterious origin are discovered, particularly in the West of Ireland. In the period in which Old Nevin lived, minted coin of purest gold was wafer-thin—coins such as may be seen today in the National Gallery in Dublin, so fragile that they could be "debased" or trimmed by pressure of a fingernail. You can see there, too, all sorts of golden plastrons, lanullas, wrist and upper-arm bracelets, and the wide jewel-set circlet crowns, insubstantial as lily petals, worn by the legion petty kings of ancient Ireland. Old Nevin must have had a store of such treasure. But relentless Death mowed him down before he could dispose of his loot, or make known his hideaway to whomsoever of his breed he wished to be his heir. I believe his nocturnal appearances at the Reach are for the purpose of scanning his marked map to refresh his memory as to the location of the buried treasure. To some extent this idea is borne out by tales told by carters, men of the roads, and fishermen, both native and visitors, enthusiastic anglers from all over who annually come to villages that edge the Kerry shores. Nevin O'Foyle's ghost seems to be extraordinarily restless, indefatigable in his searching.

Recently in the bar of the Friendly Angler at Dunquin I listened to a native fisherman named Tandy. I asked him what he knew of the legendary O'Foyle-Kilfaddon saga. A few mugs of porter taken and he became voluble. He expatiated on the theme.

"Arragh, it's all a grand class ave pother in these parts. There's still a few ave thim foreign black O'Foyle breed about the land, though the dark blood ave thim has thinned. The men are a spindly lot ave creatures, though the women rage and rut around continual. As fer Auld Nevin now. I do be out on the bay an' its fringes at all times ave a day's breadth. Many's the night, dark er shiny it makes no matter, that I've seen the tall, limpin' figger, bent over all crooked the like ave a priest's crozier, ave that audacious auld reprobate Nevin O'Foyle out ave ancient days."

I asked Tandy, "You're convinced it *is* The O'Foyle, are you?"

"Ach—it's himself all right. I've seen him prowlin' too many times to doubt it." With his blackthorn cudgel, the sort of protective weapon carried hereabouts by men of the night, Tandy prodded the sanded floor as if searching for something. "Surely, it's a great class ave wonder at all. I see the auld fella' night after night, always the same—moilin' an' broilin' wid rage." Illogically he added, "Arragh, the poor auld gander's liable to do himself an injury."

Tandy rose from his bench, stretched the longest pair of arms I've ever seen on mortal man, and opined that he must get back to his fishing lines. I wondered how a ghost manages to "do himself an injury."

"The next time you encounter the ghost of O'Foyle," I said, "give him Hail and Farewell for me. Himself and the accumulated O'Foyle shenanigans have for years highly entertained me."

The Twelve Dead Queens

KINVARA CASTLE, CONNAUGHT, 1400

THE TRUE GAEL is a proud man, and a silent one. He rarely speaks to strangers, and then only in the Gaelic tongue. One meets him mostly these days in the "back and beyond" counties of Roscommon, Leitrim, Fermanagh and in remote parts of Tipperary. There are some men who hide away in the dark Glens of Antrim. A few gentry, rather sarcastically called "distillery bhoyos," even live in caves high up in the fastnesses of the brooding Slieve Aughty Mountains. There are poachers hiding out by day in the forests of dwarf oak and rusty bracken along the winding Kilcrow River.

Mountainy men usually wander down, in late summer, to the fishing villages of Connaught, County Clare, Kerry and Galway. More often than not these rangy men stride along on their lone. Proud Kings of Ireland they look, with shuttered eyes in weather-darkened, sombre faces. They wear wide-brimmed hats of dark tweed, hand-quilted in a pattern of stars by their inarticulate womenfolk.

There is a legend among the Mountainy men that he who always walks under the stars will live a long life, and take great joy of it. So, to insure this boon, in the hot sun of midday and in days of driving rain, you will always see a Mountainy man "under the stars" of his hat. But on nights of bright star-shine he always walks the paths, treading lightly as do all forest creatures, with his head lifted high and his eyes on the stars.

The reason for a Mountainy man's yearly visit to a fishing village along the Sea Wall Road is not a sociable one; for the most part the Gael on his lone still

231

remains wary, withdrawn from his fellow men. It is the need for provisions that draws him to the lowlands—fresh fish from the bountiful Atlantic to salt and dry for winter food, tobacco and tea for "herself." As these men barter with the fishermen, they appear monuments of diffidence. For hours, or as long as the sale of the morning's catch lasts, they will walk up and down the strand, appraising the quality and size of each fish hung over the seaweed-rimed baskets. Finally the bartering starts in earnest, rapidly gaining momentum. The haggling is always grim. Sometimes there is a fight ending in bloodshed. Finally, his purchase made and a sack full of fish slung over his shoulder, the Mountainy man or the man from "back and away in Roscommon" will hurry along up the beach a little way, find a secluded spot and proceed to build himself a driftwood fire among the piled stones.

From a small leather pouch hanging at his belt, the man will take handfuls of dried peat-moss and toss it on the fire. Clouds of aromatic smoke rise in blue circles in the still autumn air. All is now ready for the fish-smoking. First the fish are split up the belly and flattened out, then skewered on long forked iron pins, brought along for just this purpose—three fish to a pin. The iron rod is stuck upright between two large stones. The pin is then bent to hang over the fire, for the fish must simmer in their own juice over smoking embers.

Sometimes it takes a day and a night to prepare a batch of fish in this manner. The fish must be tender and juicy, not tough and blackened. The white flesh must turn from pale yellow to pink, with brown frills at the edges. The ultimate taste must be easy in the mouth, and must leave a lingering memory after.

Through the long hours of watching to see that the azure peat-smoke is thick, and the fire not too hot, the men ruminate and forever ponder. I once asked a young fisherman, whom I met walking along the beach near Ballyvaughn, what he imagined these men from the remote mountain fastnesses were thinking about. He switched a small cobeen pipe, in size and colour the like of a walnut, from one side of his mouth to the other.

"If the *saints* asked me, I'd not know," he said. "I'll wager ye this though, they do be wonderin' how to shift the weight of their sins to another's back. They're a chancy lot, at best. The sound of their great hobnails on the stones is like the chorus of all the anvils of deceit."

That simile, I thought, was very apt—and the young fisherman was probably right, for he had had dealings with Mountainy men. I have only looked at them from afar, arrested by their arrogance, their air of belonging to a legendary race. It was while I was sketching the traditional fish-smoking on the sands of Kinvara Headland a few days later, that this same fisherman Phelim told me the strangely haunting story of the Twelve Dead Queens, a mysterious company of stately women who for centuries have claimed Kinvara Keep for their own. By day these women take the forms of twelve white swans, drifting and preening snowy feathers on the smooth waters of a lagoon which laps the walls of the old castle on three sides. At night they take their places in the ruined banquet hall of the keep, as gorgeously-bedecked queens from beyond the Western World.

I had gone to stay at Ballyferriter a few days before coming to the small fishing village of Kinvara. While I was there a friend had told me a little of the story of the Twelve Dead Queens, but my knowledge was blurred and sketchy. I knew that if I went to a native of Kinvara or Liscannor I would hear not only a more detailed narrative but one told in the rich, evocative speech of Connaught.

Knowing that my friend Phelim the fisherman would not come in until sundown with his day's haul of fish, I walked up a little hill near the cottage where I was staying; from there I had a sweeping view of the sea. A group of people were gathering carragheen moss, an occupation practiced in this locality during the long, raking tides of early spring and autumn. These tides dig deep into the weed thatch on the breast of Neptune, casting upon the curving beaches of the western coast a silver-green harvest of health-restoring moss. The harvest is gathered in joyfully. The people along the shore call it "God's gift," for it is theirs for the taking.

From where I lay among the sand-grasses I could see Mac Dara's Island, a floating emerald-rimed rock off the Connemara coast. I thought of the story I had heard of predatory Mac Dara, and his rape of Gorunna, the wife of Callan ni Paddan who owned all the headland called *Feakle Callaigh* (The Witch's Tooth) off the Kerry coast.

The thick mists that blew over me, with a swish of rain quickly followed by sunshine, were familiar to this stretch of seacoast. This was the same kind of enveloping mist that had befuddled Mac Dara many centuries ago, causing him to fall from the Witch's Tooth straight into the sea, as he fled from Gorunna's rage-demented husband. The plum-brown, serrated rock on which his body was washed up is known as Mac Dara's Island and for all but a few brilliant days in autumn it is shrouded, as if in a pall to shield Mac Dara's memory, in impenetrable mist.

Presently I saw the fishing boats coming in, so I walked down to the shore. The group of people I had watched combing the rocks for carragheen approached. They all seemed a singularly happy, carefree lot, swinging the baskets piled high with the dripping bronze sea-moss; themselves in the clothes they had worn in the sea, sopping wet and rimed with glistening salt.

After Phelim had left the counting of his day's catch to a younger brother, we went into a small pub near the sea wall. Over a warming glass of mulled porter he told me this tale.

"Ye see that big, auld tower now?" he said, pointing out beyond the low arched door. "Sometimes called Slaney's Keep, it's an auld, ancient place, once upon a time lived in be a chief of the Tribe Slaney. The auld ones along this line ave coast say the O'Cullen fought Brian Gillfinnen fer fifty years to hold it; then, at the end, death and famine routed the O'Cullen out of it. That one may be the like of many tales, told twice the length at each telling, and ten times believed. I'd not know that. Anyhow, along in the year 1400 the strangest of all shenanigans took place, as I'll prove to ye this livin' minute."

Phelim took a long drink from his mug and continued. "I bedded down one night in the shada' of the keep wall. In the way of it it 'ud be midsummer and warm. The castle had long stood empty and unguarded. I was wakened early be the flames of sunrise an' the inchin' dawn waves lickin' me feet. I ate me mite ave breakfast, and was about to collect me fishin' gear, when I was startled be the sound of timber bumpin' against a rock, away out at the mouth of the little inlet that runs in from the bay. Runnin' down to the shaly beach, I saw a longboat in all grandeur with a painted prow the like ave what we call King Ballan ave Connaught's barge. It was floatin' silently across the water towards me.

"The boat had a wild, weird look, for it was daubed all over with raw red paint in strange signs and devices. Gently as ye please, guided be no human hand, it sailed along the narrow lagoon and stopped right in front ave meself. The sights I saw set me awry, be the Holy. I started to hoist away out ave that. Then I stopped me leppin' and looked again.

"Laid out in three rows in the bottom ave the boat were the bodies ave twelve dead women. They'd been big, handsome, healthy women in life be the rosy look they had in death. They'd red on their cheeks, and a smile hung at the corners ave their mouths. Each one wore a red dress, and they'd great green capes, all. The hoods of these capes were thrown back from their white faces.

Gold rings were on their fingers and copper chains hung all about thim. Arragh, it was all that gorgeous. A jeweled lanulla, as big as a gull's egg, pinned the cloak ave each and ivery one ave 'em, on the shoulder." Phelim's long brown fingers fluttered in demonstration of the pinning of the antique brooch called a lanulla.

"Propped up in the stern ave the boat was an old fella, a class ave bard or fiddler. The harp restin' against his knee was new and shiny-bright with gold. Gold, ha! gold was the least ave it. They all wore gold, as free as foam on the wave; even the old fiddler had great gold hoops in his ears. I've niver ranged far from Kinvara's strand, but these dead women had the look ave great strangers about 'em, and a great air of power and riches behind 'em. Queens all, ivery one. No doubt ave that. Queens from out the Western World."

I saw Phelim looking into his empty mug, so I signaled for more drink. He smiled. "Well, I hope ye'll credit me when I tell ye that be this time I was in a high lather, not knowin' what to do. If I told anyone along the roads, the Lord Constable would hear ave it, and maybe drape me with the sin of murder —twelve murders, and an extra one fer the old bard. So, as I loped out and away from there, I looked back at the swaying barge and a great quiet over all."

I realized the telling of this legend would take time, so I suggested we have some food. Phelim nodded and continued. "For a long time before all this happened the wild swans flew over from Coole every night, but divil a stop did they iver make on this lagoon, but flew straight to their nestin' place on the little Lough of Cutra near Derrybrien. Then one day not long after I'm seein' the Twelve Dead Queens in the lagoon at Kinvara Keep, the wild swans appeared in great numbers. Farmers, fishermen and men of the roads saw swans nestin' for the first time in memory on that stretch ave lough we call Kinvara Water. Women from the village, wadin' in the lagoon to catch crayfish among thim ribby rocks, were after tellin' tales ave seein' twelve stately white swans glidin' round and round on the breast ave the inlet."

I looked up. Cold ham and green salad and a Kerry-gold cheese were set before us. There was silence for a while after we started eating. Then in his soft voice Phelim went on. "So I looked for meself. An auld, moulting swan, a dirty gray in colour, nearer black than not, dozed among the reeds. But the twelve white swans seemed to heed 'im, fer I noticed they niver sailed far away.

"Then the hooley happened. One night in early summer I was comin' home to me coteen, nigh on midnight it was, in the village ave Kinvara. I passed the castle. Glancin' at the tower I was clutched with a class ave curiosity to see what caused the flickerin' light behind the empty winda's ave the Great Hall ave Kinvara Keep. As far as I knew, the castle had been blind with neglect fer many years past. Even as a small boy I'd collected gulls' eggs in the stone crannies ave the Great Hall. I crept up to the gate, that hung wide on its hinges, made ave tough ox-hide, the sort that only lasted as long as ye drenched 'em continual wid fish oil.

"Ochone, the sight I saw takin' place within the Hall was a great scandal at all." Here Phelim pushed back his chair and, being a born actor, prepared to enact the scene. "A sound ave windy harp-music came from behind the empty winda's. It was soft, but clear in the still night. Hoistin' meself up on the gate-wall, the better to see all that was goin' on, within I saw twelve high-polished women, big and bright in themselves as a full moon over Aran, dressed in red gowns and hung round wid jewels—idintical to the queens I had seen laid out in their death in the bottom ave the painted barge. All ave thim were high in their spirits. They nodded and smirked at one another as they drank from golden goblets. Crouched in a shadowy corner sat an old harper; he plucked softly on a gold harp and sang a rune that was the tale ave great deeds in a far place.

"If ye ask me did I believe me eyes, I'd say I did and I didn't. All night I lay shiverin' and in doubt. The next day I took me neighbour Sully to have a look at the same winda' that I had looked through the night before. All we saw was a mess ave cluttered stones fallen from the roof, all dirtied up be gulls' droppin's. Dead rooks and piles ave dried seaweed littered the floor. No banquet ave grand queens there, surely." Phelim sat down and took a swallow of whisky.

"Then as I turned away from the winda' and started fer the gate, I saw twelve white swans sailin' proudly, long white necks curved the like ave the letter S, in a single line on the water ave the lagoon. Sully and I stood gawpin' like a pair ave gaums on the bank as the swans sailed past. As sure as I'm me own man the swans nodded their heads at us and clattered their hard, yella' beaks. A hissin' sound came from an angry gray swan sittin' on a nest ave twigs among the reeds. The auld bard I didn't doubt, resentin' our young ardour.

"Well, there, me friend, ye have it all," said Phelim.

After Phelim had gone down to the small stone breakwater to receive the tally of his catch, I strolled out to the Sea Wall Road and looked off and away through the lingering twilight to where Kinvara Keep loomed dun-gray and brooding. Quite apart from the enthralling legend which hangs about its lichened walls, the keep is a stately ruin, appropriately massive. The stonework reared like some pagan monolith, with a low-hanging cloud, undulant as a banner, appearing to rest on the broken battlements. A stormy sunset sweeping the horizon burned behind the tower.

It was almost as if the stage had been set for Cathleen ni Houlihan to parade and lament her eternal woes. Soon, I thought, it will be night and the twelve white swans will rise from the dark lagoon, shake the water from their pale breasts and disappear among the reeds. I ruminated on the transformation scene that is said to take place—a banquet in the castle to presage a world crisis. After a time, I thought, in single file, twelve women—handsome, proud, big in themselves, glorious in red, purple, green and tawny silks—will walk up the path leading to the hanging gate of Kinvara Keep. An old bard will lead them, and he playing lightly on a muted harp. Jewels will flash and wink and rich, pagan colours will smoulder in the starlight, for there is great grandeur athwart the keep at the prophetic banquet held by the Twelve Queens "from out the Western World."

Little Miss Costello's Shop

BELLAVARY, COUNTY MAYO, 1890

BELLAVARY, lying in the center of misty County Mayo, prides itself today on being as wide-awake a village as one will find over the length and breadth of Ireland. On Tuesdays the countrymen bring to market produce of many kinds, fruits and vegetables fresh from outlying gardens. On Saturdays farmers assemble in a roped-off space between St. Kevin's Cross and Mrs. O'Marra Riordon's public house, to buy and sell cattle on the hoof, driven into town singly or in droves. Carts are piled high with wicker and willow-withe crates, crowded with yawking poultry and long-necked lag geese. The town council rather pompously calls this noisy gathering the Saturday Livestock Fair. Between fairs Bellavary pursues an uneventful way of life, its quiet tenor stirred but once a day by a demon motorbus from Ballina. The bus roars through the High Street, scattering mud, dust, children and geese impartially, until toothless Grandma Riordon (the Rosie Creevy one will meet in this story) leans out the window which is her vantage point in her daughter-in-law's public house, waving her stick and screeching, "Look at that divil's velocipede rock now, going at that outrageous pace! Sure, all in it are headed straight for destruction and Saint Peter's Gate."

Yes—there have been great changes in Bellavary since Miss Laura Costello's day. Only Grandma Riordon remembers—for it was many years ago—when a tiny, shy woman appeared one day from off the Mallarany mail coach, a horse-drawn vehicle in those days. A stranger in a quiet town, the woman was christened "Little Miss Costello" and so she was affectionately called by her neighbours during the years she lived among them.

In 1890, the year Miss Costello arrived in Bellavary, it was a sprawling, drowsy, tree-shaded village of pink-washed houses. In a dense grove of ash trees, surrounded by a wall, there stood one tall gray house known as Gun Hill. It was inhabited by a retired military man, an eccentric old gentleman, General Kintoura by name. Of himself he said wryly, "I am financially reduced by the wars and disgusted by bigotry, so I vegetate in this forgotten hole." The only other house anywhere near Gun Hill was a few hundred yards further out of town—a small cottage, long empty but at this time to let. It was called the Beehive. As for Bellavary itself, a few small shops fronted along what was then called the Green Walk, presently the more modern High Street.

St. Kevin's Church and the Royal Hibernian Hall were the two buildings of any size or importance in the village. The Royal Hibernian was in great demand. In its Oratory were held town council meetings and those fiery political harangues that are indigenous to all Irish villages. The oval ballroom accommodated all manner of functions, from the long-discussed wedding reception of Patricia Heffernon, whose slightly fuddled groom arrived sporting a mourning "weeper" on his arm instead of a white-moiré wedding sash, to the festivities of the annual hunt ball.

Mail coaches from the seaport towns of Mallarany and Castlebar clattered through Bellavary twice weekly. While bowlegged, cape-coated grooms changed coach horses at Riordon's Hotel, passengers getting down to stretch their legs often visited Miss Costello's Curiosity Shop. One way and another, she enjoyed a small but pleasant patronage.

At first the people of Bellavary wondered a bit about Miss Costello. She had arrived unheralded. She never spoke of herself or what she had done before she appeared in their midst. Her family, if she had any, was never mentioned. How did she live? they asked each other. Surely the small amounts she asked for her odd little curios, by which she set such store, couldn't keep her housed and fed. Someone suggested "a small annuity, perhaps." If this was so, she must collect it while on one of the short trips she took to places of which she never spoke. These trips, she said, were made to replenish her stock. Perhaps she was a kinswoman to the rich Costellos of Galway, a family of Spanish origin. That she came of good family, all agreed. The tone of her musical voice, her quiet manners, her delicate bones, all spoke of high breeding.

In the spring of 1890, a few weeks before Miss Costello arrived, a "To Let" sign had been put up in the dust-streaked window of the small shop squeezed in between "MOULTON-Drapers" and the old stone shop, "PLUNKET BROS.

Saddlers." Two days after the advent of Miss Laura Costello, activity sprang to life within the walls of the shop. Windows long opaque with grime shone from vigorous scrubbing with soap and water. Befrilled white mull curtains were hung from newly-painted window sashes. The villagers looked wonderingly at the sign which Johnny Killogue painted and hung between the two bow windows. In large black-and-gold letters on a dove-gray ground one read:

CURIOSITY SHOP
Curios from the Wide World
MISS COSTELLO

The first morning Miss Costello appeared at her new shop was a bright, sunny one. She was well but plainly dressed in a gown of lavender-and-brown striped chambray fashionably draped with a modest bustle. She wore a brown taffeta shoulder cape and a small brown bonnet. Her hands, which were particularly noticed by young Rosie Creevy, who missed little in this world, were "that little, arragh they'd be the like of a wax doll's." Entering the shop, Rosie smiled a wide welcome to Miss Costello. "Good day to ye, ma'am. Could I help ye at all?"

Miss Costello smiled back. "Thank you, you may, since you are so kind. You are Rosie Creevy, yes?" The two smiles parried and lodged. Then and there was born a great friendship which lasted through many years.

The day on which Miss Costello and Rosie Creevy met for the first time was a day of whirlwind activity. A carter from Mallarany arrived about noon. Piled high on his cart were corded boxes and hampers. These contained Miss Costello's remarkable collection of "curiosities."

These nostalgic objects might not have been remarkable in a metropolitan city, where sophisticated tastes see many such, but to the inhabitants of Bellavary, who saw little but utilitarian objects in the daily round, these brightly-coloured trifles distilled a quality of magic when they were spread out in the windows of Miss Costello's shop. To Rosie, it was as if she held the rainbow in her hands. Big, rawboned, red, peasant hands they were, but oddly gentle when handling these curios from far places. It was a great joke, enjoyed hugely by Rosie, the difference between her hands and the tiny, white, blue-veined hands of her adored Miss Costello. Rosie would hold her hands, outstretched, beside Miss Costello's. Rocking back and forth she would wax hysterical. Great gusts of laughter would sweep the little shop. "Sure, I'm a great gaum beside ye, entirely. I'd say we two 'ud not be made ave the same class of clay."

For a while Miss Costello lived at Riordon's Hotel. One day she moved into Beehive Cottage, out on the Ardnaree Road, past General Kintoura's house. On a clear day one could see the Lough of Conn from a rise behind the cottage. Miss Costello always said, when strangers in her shop inquired where she lived, "I've a cottage overlooking the Lough of Conn. I love the water." Then her eyes would seem to veil over and her voice would take on a wistful note. "I was born near the sea."

Perhaps that accounted for some of the visitors who came to her shop, rather mysterious seafaring men with bundles or small parcels, usually protected by waterproof wrappings.

One day Mathew Malloy, a neighbor of Miss Costello's, came into her shop. He talked for a while, then, curiosity getting the better of manners, he asked, "How is it that so many men the like of sailors and sea captains find their way to your shop? Bellavary's such an out-of-way, inland village, too."

Quietly she replied, "Mallarany, that port on Clew Bay, is only twenty miles away." She continued to look at the man. "You know that as well as I do. Besides, the men you see coming here are all friends of mine. They bring me curios to sell. Regard." She held up a pair of peacock-blue embroidered Chinese slippers.

The years passed. Sometimes Miss Costello's shop was rich in curios from the wide world. Then there would be months on end when the small-paned bow windows showed blank, with nothing behind them save a few sun-faded silk boxes and an old carved-ivory elephant tusk, to be used perhaps for a paperweight. Rosie Creevy said it had the evil eye. "It's carved from the divil's tooth, if ye ask me." The first time Rosie saw it and picked it up, it slipped from her fingers and fell on her bare foot. She let out a yowl. "Arragh, ye'll never sell it, it's accursed, the blaugho." (A Gaelic term for an amulet of evil portent.) It had been brought to the shop by a Lascar sailor off a ship from India.

When Rosie was nineteen, Miss Costello went away during the summer on one of her trips and left Rosie in charge of her shop. This particular trip lasted longer than usual. When she did return, it seemed she was more frail, a shade more bent in the shoulders than when she went away. After all, Rosie knew that Miss Costello was only in the late forties. Her sandy-red hair showed not a thread of gray. But her eyes were clear and bright, and she had brought back a wealth of curios. Box after box was unpacked by Rosie, who waxed rapturous at all she saw. Miss Costello said she had been in Paris and Belgium. From Paris she had brought Rosie a present. Laughing as she presented it to the nineteen-year-old girl, Miss Costello said, "You will think this a strange gift, my dear: a walking stick. But besides being handsome, it has value. One day you may have need of it. The top, as you see, is a silver dolphin. Press this catch and the fish opens its mouth. I believe Madame de Montespan kept snuff in it."

Rosie was seldom seen without this stick from then out. For years she used it more or less as a drum major wields a baton. The silver dolphin was filled with reeking violet scent. As an old woman she waved it to punctuate frantic diatribes at "thim demon busses."

When Miss Costello had at last unpacked her purchases from the Continental trip, a ravishing display of curiosities was spread out in her windows. There were fans of painted silk and paper from France and Spain; two exquisite Spanish lace mantillas, one black, one white; a French music box with dancing figurines on top which revolved in a stately dance when it played a waltz tune; parasols of violet and yellow with pinked and fringed taffeta flounces and carved ebony handles; and a fantastic sailor doll in blue, white and gold, with yellow floss curls. There was a barbary pirate doll with ferocious eyebrows and sweeping mustachios embroidered in black silk on his scowling ocher face, and eyes of green spangles which glittered wickedly in the candlelight. There were books of delicately-painted watercolours showing views of famous Belgian chateaux. There were silver bangles, and old rose-paste slipper buckles. According to Rosie, the most wonderful of all was an Arab headdress from Biskra, fashioned of gold rosettes and tufts of shimmering kingfisher feathers.

"I love loot," Miss Costello told an enthusiastic customer, her fingers touching lightly her treasures. "Loot from the seven seas. The simple people of Bellavary wonder about me, as I expected they would. I often catch the eye of Barrister Connolly; I know he is cogitating, 'Little Laura Costello—quiet as a brown hen—I wonder what she's really up to?'" She laughed. "The joke of it is—*nothing*. I am like a child, or a magpie. I collect toys. Bright, curious toys."

During the year, shortly after the turn of the century, marked in Irish history as the "birth of the troubles," there was a skirmish in Galway Port between Irish sailors of Sinn Fein sympathies and a rabble-rouser from the Clonbeen shipyards who had not yet made up his mind which side his sympathies lay on. His drunken, fiery words started a shindig that caused a deal of blood-letting before the riot was put down by the constabulary. During the fight a young fanatic of the republican army escaped into the hills. Later he was captured in the woods behind Beehive Cottage. The rebel might have been found anywhere within miles. It happened to be close to Miss Costello's house. For a few days constabulary patrols sat at Miss Costello's gate. She smiled at them, that winning smile of hers. She served them bannocks and pots of hot tea. Quietly the guards slipped away and for a while no more was heard of skulking rebels.

Then in Mallarany there was a brawl in a waterfront pub. A sailor was knifed by a fugitive from British patrols. He was a part-time sailor; mostly he signed on for short channel trips. His name was Denis Lannery. In his pocket was found a slip of paper on which was written, in the inevitable purple ink used in France, this address:

Curiosity Shop
Bellavary
County Mayo

Buys and Sells

Miss Costello

When questioned by the British garrison police, the man Lannery, who was dying from loss of blood, told this story. He had been given a small parcel when his ship left Le Havre. A young Frenchman had given it to him, along with the written address to which he was to deliver it. More than that he did not know. He had never seen nor heard of Miss Costello. When the parcel was opened it was found to contain a tambourine such as is used by Spanish gypsy dancers in Granada. Painted with great skill on the tightly-stretched pigskin covering was a lurid bullfight scene, showing a lithe matador performing a veronica. The clatters in the rim of the tambourine were thin silver disks, delicately etched.

When Miss Costello was shown this tambourine, she shrugged her childlike shoulders. "I know nothing about it," she said. "Just one more sailor in need of a little immediate cash. They come to me from all over, because I am known to buy any curiosities they have to sell." For a time after this she was discreetly watched by the Mallarany garda. Denis Lannery died of his knife wounds and for a year or more all was quiet in Bellavary.

Miss Costello made her annual trip to the Continent. She brought back many rare curios. There were not so many customers as in former years. She knew that her shop was overstocked, but she still continued to collect odd pieces. Now and again a sailor would appear, transact a little business, and depart. Usually the sailors came on foot and left the same way. The drivers of mail coaches did not like to take sailors as fares. They were trouble-breeders—the coachmen did not trust them.

A few years before this rebel bruhaha occurred, Rosie Creevy had married Rory Riordon, who owned the hotel—he "chose her from many," he proudly said. A fine match for strapping Rosie, all of Bellavary agreed. She continued to visit her friend Miss Costello every day, with each year another little Riordon clinging to her skirts. Time passed unnoticed in Bellavary.

That is, until 1916 when all hell broke loose. The first sign of trouble in Bellavary occurred one night when an unknown man fired two shots through two different windows. First he took a shot at Little Miss Costello who came to an upper bedroom window of the Beehive in answer to a pebble thrown against a pane of glass. The shot missed her. How wide of the mark we will never know, for she closed the window, returned to bed and never mentioned the incident to anyone. Then a shadow slipped stealthily along General Kintoura's high wall. The shot fired through an open window at Gun Hill killed disgruntled old General Kintoura in a split second. It was Johnny Killogue, next morning, who told of seeing the killer's shadow, of hearing two shots fired a few moments apart, and of catching a glimpse of a crouching skelterer escaping across the lough in a curragh.

The day after the inexplicable assassination of General Kintoura, Miss Costello appeared at her shop as usual, dressed in the soft lilac dress she had worn to Mass two days before on Easter Sunday. For a while she sat behind her desk. Later she built a small fire in the grate, for if one were out of the sun the air retained a winter chill. Besides, she had decided that morning, when she arose after so disturbed a night, to clean out her desk, which was crammed with papers and old letters. She sat over the blaze all afternoon, burning them down to the last scrap.

At teatime Rosie Riordon came in to tell her of the disastrous riots that had taken place in Dublin yesterday. Many people had been killed. Rosie shook her head. "On Easter Monda' too—Holy Mother!" There was great damage by fire in O'Connell Street, she continued. Merrion Square had been swept by gunfire until there wasn't a pane of glass left in the houses.

After Rosie left the shop, Miss Costello brewed herself a pot of strong red tea.

She had just finished her second cup when Barrister Connolly came in with more news. He said it was thought the Irish patriots could hold out indefinitely. Miss Costello listened quietly. As Connolly was leaving, she said, "Has anything been heard of Sir Roger Casement?"

Quick as a flash, Patrick Connolly turned: "What do you know of Casement? As a matter of fact, he has been captured in a small town on the Kerry coast. I repeat, what do you know of Casement, that you are so interested?"

Connolly was startled. Miss Costello's small, frail body seemed to cave in before his eyes; she turned deathly pale, then as quickly rallied. As if all strength was drained from her limbs, Laura Costello rose slowly from her chair. Supporting herself with one hand on the edge of the table in front of her, she lifted her chin and in a firm voice replied, "I have every reason to show interest. Sir Roger Casement and I were once betrothed. Many years ago." She paused, her eyes looking off and away through the window. "Family differences—you know. But . . ." There was a long pause as if the clutches of memory were proving too strong for her, then Miss Costello said in a scarcely audible voice, "Such was our love for one another that in the sight of God and Holy Mother, Roger Casement and I were husband and wife."

Half an hour later a note was delivered to Rosie Riordon, who at the time was busy hemming the white-net veil to be worn by her daughter Kathleen at her First Communion. Written in Miss Costello's small, elegant hand, it was a terrifying message:

"Rosie, my dear girl, I have just learned that a very close friend of mine, Sir Roger Casement, has been captured by the British somewhere on the Kerry coast. They will shoot him, of course—we all knew that was the penalty of capture. My work is done. One day Ireland will be free. Be sure of that, Rosie, as you hope for Heaven. Keep the children away from my shop, and stay away yourself. God keep you always. Laura Costello Casement."

Like a streak of lightning, Rosie, for all her two-hundred-odd pounds, was out of her room and down the stairs at the double. Just as she gained the street door a terrible concussion of sound, a blast of fury, rocked the hotel on its foundations. Flying fragments of lath and plaster from the curiosity shop deluged the pavement. Rosie shot across the street thinking only of one thing: Miss Costello was somewhere in that shambles.

When the dust and smoke had somewhat cleared, Rosie found Miss Costello lying in the roofless back room of the shop. She was horribly blackened by burned powder and as Rosie tried to lift her, her arms swung limply at her sides. But she was still alive. Rosie took Miss Costello's head in her lap. "Mother of God, why did ye do it, Miss Costello dear?" Remembering the words of the note, "Keep the children away from my shop," she knew this explosion had been deliberate.

Opening her eyes a little, Miss Costello smiled. "It is the only way, Rosie. I couldn't face Roger's death. Hand grenades—I hid them for him—in the back—shop." Her head sank to her chest. "I'll come back, Rosie——I'll come back—— wait for me here."

Rosie held her very close, gently rocking back and forth, keening—the keening of deep grief—for Miss Costello was dead.

A very modern building was put up on the spot once occupied by Miss Costello's Curiosity Shop. The greatest sufferer in the explosion was PLUNKET BROS. Saddlers. The wall next Miss Costello's shop had caved in. The old building was torn down. The new building, which I saw recently, is quite the most imposing in Bellavary. Since Miss Costello's death there have been three or four tenants in this new shop on the ground floor. On one pretext or another, all of them have soon packed up their stock in trade and sought other pastures.

One man opened an ironmongery. He was the first shopkeeper to tenant the new building. His wife, who served behind the counter, said the place gave her the creeps. When asked to explain, she became angry and said she couldn't put a name to it. "Just creeps; it's as if somebody was always watching me, disapproving too; whoever or whatever *it* is seems always in corners, watching."

Customers said the same thing: someone furtively watching. After a time many persons shunned the shop. In a few months the husband of the woman with the "creeps" died from the effects of a fall down the stone steps of the areaway. "Steep they was," he said. "Always I was careful. This night, I felt somebody put a hand in the small of me back and give me a good push. I know of course there was nobody there, but . . . ." The statement hung in mid-air. After his lingering death, his wife left Bellavary.

The next tenant was a draper, a man named Paukey. He bought out old Joshua Moulton and combined the two shops. Again many of Paukey's customers complained of the silent watcher. One day Rosie took her eldest daughter into Paukey's shop to pick out dress-lengths of summer muslin. As she stood at the counter, she told her husband later, Rosie had felt a hand, almost a child's hand it seemed, on her shoulder. A soft whisper of a voice in her ear murmured, "Rosie

—Rosie Creevy." The daughter *heard* nothing, but she said she felt a cold rush of air past her face, and she thought someone was watching her.

Paukey told how one night when he was closing the shop late, he heard what sounded like coins clinking one against another. Peering into the darkness, he saw a small, rather bent woman in a lilac-coloured dress, counting what seemed to be gold sovereigns. At least he said they winked like gold in the light from the one gas jet. When he went over to the desk, no one was there.

Then there was the episode of the bangles. A woman came into Paukey's shop one day. She stooped and picked up a curious silver bangle from the floor. She handed it to Paukey, thinking someone had lost it off a bracelet. He put it aside until someone should inquire about a lost bangle. Later that same day another customer picked up a silver bangle from the counter. Then for days almost every person who entered the shop picked up one of these bangles. Some even found two or three. Finally Paukey went to Mrs. Riordon with his handful of silver bangles. As Rosie took them in her hand she caught her breath and turned stark white. "No, it's not possible," she said. "These bangles were on a long chain brought back from France by Miss Costello when I was a young girl workin' in her shop. I remember she told me she bought it from a sailor in a place called Tunis. But she sold the chain to a traveler woman long ago."

Then there was the episode of the fan. The shop had another new tenant by this time, a greengrocer named Corry. It had been vacated by Paukey soon after the affair of the bangles. He left Bellavary muttering that he could not stand the unseen watcher in the shadowy corners. "Ochone," he said, "that shada' has me nerves up the mast wid the dread." Sean Corry had heard tales aplenty about strange happenings in this shop and the furtive presence who disapproved of newcomers. He resolved to live it down and listen to no nonsense.

One night as Corry was closing shop, he saw a woman with a small parcel in her hand standing just inside the street door. He had just locked this door from the inside. The key was still in the lock. The woman was dressed in the fashion of a former time; she wore a brown bonnet and cape over a striped dress. As he watched, fascinated, his visitor walked over to the counter. She put down her parcel, which was long and narrow. Pointing a childishly small hand towards it, she whispered, "For Rosie." She turned and disappeared into the room Corry used for storage, behind the shop.

When Mrs. Riordon opened the parcel she found a silk fan. The white silk background was nearly covered with pink and crimson roses painted in florid

Victorian style in watercolour. For a while Rosie Riordon held the fan outspread in her ample lap, remembering. A small grandchild came bounding into the room. Spying the brightly-coloured fan he exclaimed, "Granda, what is that? Roses?"

His grandmother nodded, smiled absently. She furled the fan, got up from her chair and went over to stare out of the window at the modern shopfront of "Sean Corry—Greengrocer."

Absently opening and closing the Victorian fan, Rosie murmured to herself, "No matter whose name is painted on the swinging sign above the door, nor what articles are sold within, it will always be Little Miss Costello's Curiosity Shop."

The Thicket of Gold

SHANGANAGH CASTLE, COUNTY DOWN, 1200

THE PAGAN GAEL, in the early days of Irish history, had a passion for giving an identifying name to every manifestation of nature that came within his sight. All over the island today, one finds evidence of this orgy of creating landmarks out of the most undistinguished hillocks of turf. But, by the Irish power of simile, plus imagination, the names sound like music to the ear and lie pleasantly on the tongue when they are pronounced. Place names resound in Irish song and legend down the centuries. In the ninth and tenth centuries, for example, the chief of a powerful tribe would designate every outcrop of rock, every clump of trees and bushes, every bog and rivulet of water, so that they might be used as landmarks. If he was so fortunate as to have a mountain rising heavenwards from somewhere inside the boundaries of his landhold, so much the better.

In County Down we find that The O'Slane, once of Shanganagh Castle, used his imagination to fine effect. He distributed names with a prodigal hand. If you walk the roads of County Down and have for a traveling companion, as I did, a "woman of the roads," it will prove to be one of the greatest treats of your life. No people on earth can match the Irish tinker or vagrant man or woman "of the roads" in their richness of vocabulary, their full-bodied pith and humour, as well as their intimate knowledge of Gaelic history and an astonishing grasp of present events.

I once walked for the length of an afternoon in late June through the valley of the River Lagan in County Down. As I had passed through the village of Ballynahinch I felt a halt on me, a risen thirst. Sitting at the door of a pub which crouches

251

in the shadow of the old ruined castle of the O'Doons was a tinker woman, swathed in a collection of gray and green shawls. She looked as ancient as the castle rock itself. In spite of the dust stains of travel, she had a pleasant, wide-eyed look about her face which instantly won me. After we had each drunk a mug of the tangy local cider, I asked if she was walking to Lurgan, about ten miles up the valley. "I am, yer honour, and beyond," she said. With the superbly simple courtesy of her race, the woman added, "It'd be the great honour, sir, to share the road with ye. Shall we crack a word or two as we range along?" So we set off.

A little way out of the village, the woman motioned to a mound of turf, faced with lichened stones, which rose on the left of the road. In Gaelic she said *"Tagha-shinny* (The House of the Fox)." On the other side of the road was an upland pasture, its sloping shoulders taut against the sky. *"Clooneenagh* (The Lone Meadow)." A young girl sat on a milestone; beside her slept a baby wrapped in a shawl. The girl, I noticed, was cramming milkweed-down into a ticking of finest hand-woven linen. My companion said, *"Labasheela* (The Bed of Silk)."

As the sun was setting in a pageant of brilliant orange and crimson banners, denoting a hot day the morn, we descended a hill. Laid out before us was as extraordinary a study in contrasts as I have ever seen. A stone pack-horse bridge, so hung with moss and ivy that it betrayed its great age, spanned the narrow, treacherously deep River Lagan. On one side of the river was a dark, brooding thicket of dwarf bog oak. Eerily misshapen trees huddled together, their branches snarled, the like of a gypsy woman's hair—*Scartnamacagh* (The Thicket of Beggars). On the other bank of the stream was a carpet of pink and crimson bog mallow—*Canavaun* (The Flowering Bog). Behind this vivid mass rose a clump of tall, wide-spreading golden beech trees. Yellow-green now in midsummer, they would be like molten gold in late September. Here lay *Scartanore* (The Thicket of Gold), as the tinker woman so aptly put it "Auld, ancient acres" with a vengeance.

The story one is told of why the patch of woods on one side of the River Lagan is dreary and bare-branched, while on the opposite side it is heavy-leaved and burnished gold, is an ancient legend which, sung by the bards, comes down the centuries by word of mouth. Shamelessly embroidered here and there, the original tale is pieced together from a few old documents, mostly in "house books" which were kept intact by the members of ancient families, some of whom still live in the Ballynahinch and Lurgan districts. One can depend on nothing in the nature of authoritative history prior to the early part of the fifth century. We must take upon trust all that is told by the bard or monk historians who flourished as the chief chroniclers of the time between 800 and 1000 A.D.

This is the story as I heard it.

A boy called Patricius was a Christian Gaul, born at Boulogne about 400 A.D. His father was a burgess of that seaport, and a man of wealth. When Nial of the Nine Hostages invaded Gaul, Patricius was taken captive, so at the age of sixteen he landed in Ireland a slave. He is later heard of for a while as tending his master's cattle at Armoy in County Antrim. Six years later he escaped in the dead of night, boarded a ship, and, after a stormy passage, landed on the coast of his native land. While the storm in the Channel raged, Patricius said he was visited by strange dreams, visitations of a shining sexless figure, doubtless an archangel, who told him to return to the land where he had endured captivity and to convert the inhabitants to Christianity. He then took orders at the Galician Church.

He landed first in County Wicklow, about 445 A.D. Proceeding to Strangford Lough in County Down, he preached at every crossroad and collected many converts. St. Patrick, as he was now called, proceeded to Meath, where he met rebuff from King Leoghare, the son of his old enemy Nial. King Leoghare forbade his followers to listen to the preachings of the former slave, on pain of death.

At that time, a monk called Driomas wrote a legend which was circulated, either openly or by stealth, throughout Ireland. He said that St. Patrick upset a meeting of High Kings one night, when they were gathered for conclave at Tara. St. Patrick built a monstrous fire on a neighbouring hill. The great company of warriors at Tara saw the blaze and rushed out to fight the fire. On a round rock, away from the drifting smoke, St. Patrick preached. Over half of the men who had come to fight the fire were converted by the miraculous tongue of the inspired saint.

Seeing how well this ruse had worked, St. Patrick continued this practice of lighting fires on hills and at wooded crossroads. When men came to put the fires out, they remained to pray.

Once, however, St. Patrick's plan did not work. When he came to the valley of the Lagan he started a fire on one side which burned brightly, and to the astonishment of all, hundreds of beggars who had hidden themselves and their ill-gotten loot in the dense thicket were badly burned, many mortally. All the beggars who could crawled to the feet of St. Patrick, and in his supreme moment he healed them by touching their burns. From that spot, with an army of converts at his heels, St. Patrick crossed the bridge to the other side of the river. Here he applied the torch to the beech wood. But the thicket would not burn, although the countryside was very dry from a long drought. It was a druids' burying ground, and in the center were three stone buildings where Cormac Ulphad taught the arts of War, Literature, and Jurisprudence. Druid gold was hoarded here, and while no flame nor smoke appeared, the whole wood glowed in a haze of gold.

By this time, interest in the doctrine of St. Patrick was so far-reaching that the chiefs of tribes received him at their fortresses. They bade their people respect and follow his teaching. When a messenger was sent by Brehon Donahy of Castle Clew, requesting his presence, St. Patrick left the region of the blackened "Thicket of the Beggars" and the burnished "Thicket of Gold" and marched in triumph towards Connaught.

In 1161, a family of O'Banner-Roe built a massive, square "treasure house" of stone with walls twelve feet thick, near the village of Rathfrilland. This family is said to have lived in the treasure house and worked night and day with pack horses transferring gold from the druids' hoard in the Thicket of Gold, on the bank of the River Lagan, twenty miles away to the massive vaults in the building one may presently visit. Apparently this family of O'Banner-Roe did not remain long in the vicinity, once their job was done. Before they left the valley, a towering castle was under construction on a hill overlooking the two thickets and the treasure house. When this four-towered fortress was completed ten years later, The O'Slane took possession of the castle by sudden surprise attack, as well as the treasure house and all the druid loot it contained. The O'Slane, "a great red monster of a man," married a daughter of Shamas O'Banner-Roe. Mailha O'Banner-Roe bore him five sons and five daughters, and by her avarice and treachery provoked the hideous family curse.

One night after the Battle of Clontarf, in 1014, a far-spent man and horse rode into the court before the Keep of Shanganagh Castle. The man was a feared and famous warrior, Humphrey de Borgo. He was wounded near to death, and hunted. To add stature to his misfortunes, a price was on his head. At first, when his wounds were treated by Mailha O'Slane, he thought she was a friend and that he had found sanctuary, for he was hard pressed by his enemy, Conn Decies. De Borgo wanted only time to recover his strength, then he would board a ship for France. He made his mistake when he told the grasping Mailha O'Slane that there was a price on his head. It was a big price, in gold, and she was a covetous woman. Gold was her god. She had no other.

As soon as De Borgo was asleep, Mailha sent a messenger into the highroads to search for The Decies' men-at-arms and acquaint them of the whereabouts of the man they were pursuing. The Decies was found encamped near the Mound of Clontarf, and was given treacherous Mailha's message. He immediately rode to Shanganagh Castle and forthwith took De Borgo prisoner. The Decies paid Mailha the forfeit. With this she was well pleased, for the weight of the leathern bag of gold was a great wonder, surely. As the betrayed man was being led in chains past the devious and now scornful woman, he cursed her and her children after her. In a passion of rage, Mailha spit in the face of De Borgo, who lunged at her. A man-at-arms, fearing De Borgo would do his mistress a hurt, raised his spear. Humphrey de Borgo fell upon its point and opened one of his wounds. As he lay dying in a spreading pool of his own blood, he repeated his curse: "May your tongue, so faithless to a friend, shrivel in your mouth, Mailha O'Slane. May you never speak again."

The O'Slane fortunes, while high in gold and worldly power, declined with the years. Constant border wars drained O'Slane of his men, and four of his sons were killed in battle. Mailha was prey to ill health from the day she spat in the face of Humphrey de Borgo, causing a rise of fury which resulted in his death. As if touched by the breath of an Asian plague, Mailha's face bloated and her skin grew dark. Great sores serrated her mouth and throat. As time passed she could not talk nor utter a sound save a raven croak. Her days were a misery and a torment, and a terrible hunger was ever with her, for to eat a mouthful of food was an agony like swallowing living flame.

The one son left to The O'Slane and Mailha was Roe, the youngest. A grand, tall boy, big in himself, with the strength of ten, his flaming hair swept his broad shoulders. His eyes were bluer than the Lough of Erne. The very sight of the massive young Roe made Mailha tremble with her great love for him.

A day came, a drear day of battle horns and arms piled in the Hall of Shanganagh. It meant more war, and only this one son, Roe, left to carry the wild-boar banner of O'Slane on the hill of battle. The days dragged. Mailha O'Slane sat by the window in her bower. Though she could not speak, she could weep and moan with longing. Lone she sat, lone she braided her hands. Watching the mountain road, lone, she waited.

One gray dawn, when all about the silent castle bog and bracken lay dank under mist, the sound of a horseman riding hard pounded on the cobbled court in front of Shanganagh Keep. Mailha ran to the head of the staircase which led down from her bower to the Hall. A mud-stained gallowglass stood at the foot of the stairway looking up at her. In his hands he carried a bloody bundle, something tied up in a tabard like that worn by Roe over his armour. Slowly Mailha walked down the stone steps. When she reached the bottom, the young soldier told her that her lord, The O'Slane, lay dead within the enemy lines. His squires could not reach his corpse until later. The battle was going against the O'Slane host.

Haltingly, the man gave Mailha the bundle. Walking over to a table in the center of the Hall the dazed woman laid the wet, red-stained tabard upon it. She opened the folds. Had Mailha been able to utter a sound she would have shrieked at what she beheld lying before her. But it had been a long time since any sound at all had issued from her withered lips. Among the folds of cloth, soaked in blood, lay the big right hand, the sword-wielding hand, of her son Roe, Roe the strong, the beautiful Roe, the "heart's heart" of her. Mailha knew instantly it was his hand, for on the middle finger she had slipped, the morning of his departure, the bronze-gold ring bearing a carved boar, the tribal device of the House of O'Slane.

"Lady O'Slane," the young gallowglass said, "Roe is dead, his body flung into the morass of the bog."

As he turned from the awful stillness of the grieving woman to take himself away out of that, he noticed that her eyes stared blankly ahead, unseeing, as do blind eyes, and that tears streamed down her cheeks in such case as to partially wash away the blood from the severed hand. By the fitful light of a flaming cresset set into an iron ring on the stone wall, he saw that Mailha, as if sunk in a trance of memory, was gently stroking the ring upon the finger of her son. But what the gallowglass did not see, as he stooped to pass through the low arched door into the courtyard, was Mailha O'Slane sink slowly to her knees, clutch at the hand on the table, then fall prone to lie her length, dead upon the stones of the chamber floor.

Shanganagh Castle has had many vicissitudes in the ensuing years. Various families, none, it would appear, for long tenure, have lived there, first within the great, bleak keep built by Mory O'Slane, who was always called "The O'Slane," then in the late-Renaissance house built in the shadow of the keep which still stands. Mory and Roe and all the other long-dead tribe O'Slane seem to rest quietly in their graves; but not speechless, distracted Mailha. Many persons, through the years, have seen this woman, weighed down with the sins of treachery and avarice, walk through the vaulted passages and down the stairs of the old keep. She has even been seen on occasion at the present Shanganagh Castle. The manifestation seldom varies. The figure of Mailha O'Slane, so garbed in medieval robe and mantle as to resemble a habited nun, walks slowly along the passages. Her head is swathed in a wimple. Her face is distorted in an agony of grief. Her lips gape and writhe as if she were about to utter a shriek. No sound comes. She has never in all her visitations been heard to articulate even a whisper. In her arms, almost as if it were a child that she is cradling, there is a ragged cloth resembling a short cape. It is matted with dried blood, and lying in its folds is a pallid white hand, a male hand, big-veined, the long, strong fingers bent as if clutching the haft of a sword. On one of the fingers is a bronze-gold ring of massive antique workmanship. Eyes staring straight ahead, the grief-wrung ghost of Mailha O'Slane walks haltingly through the empty wind-swept chamber of Shanganagh Keep, her fingers ever restless, stroking, stroking the golden boar ring on the hand of Roe.

The Sorceress
"Horror upon Horror Piled"

RATHA CASTLE, COUNTY TYRONE, 900

MANY A POET has written and many a bard has sung that the dark hills and undulating bronze-green bogs of County Tyrone cradle more ghosts and ghostly legends than any other "clutch of acres" in Holy Ireland. This may well be so, for during the many years I have devoted to ghost-tracking I have come upon dozens of tales of long-dead but not forgotten creatures who restlessly prowl the springy turf of Tyrone. Creatures like the beautiful saintly Lady Branig of Tower Branig Castle, whose poignant story I have told in my book *James Reynolds' Ireland*.

I have found the entire gamut of human vagaries, frailties and just pure un-adulterated horror, in the story of Glana O'Herlihy, called in her time the Sorceress of the Red Death. Her sobriquet may have root in the fact that this demoniac woman always appeared in blood-red garments. It is recounted that even her armour, for she was warrior queen of impressive stature as well as witch, was forged from bronze linked chains and plates—"all red bronze she shone on the Hill of Ratha; her gleaming shamed the setting sun."

I have found in old chronicles in the library of the Hill of Cashel that Glana was by the ancient Gaelic historians "confused extremely" with Circe and/or Medea. The Circe legend is as old as time itself. William Butler Yeats traced twenty-two different nationality versions.

The O'Herlihy family of Dunfanaghy in western Ireland claim that the ninth-century sorceress Glana of Ratha Tower was an ancestor who changed her habitation at will. She could, they maintain, transport her fortress tower as easily

259

as she changed her shape. The magic fortress of Glana, cresting the stark Hill of Ratha, was guarded by a revolving phallic plinth. No one could enter the castle until the plinth was still. The ramp leading to the center courtyard was spiral— a pattern symbolizing ever-recurring death and rebirth. Glana could avail herself of all and sundry shapes at instant will. Yeats wrote, "In one span of twenty-four hours Glana changed from sow to mare, vixen, bitch, she-ass, loathsome hag, viper, bed-worm, she-wolf, mermaid, rodent, horned toad, tigress and she-bear."

Glana O'Herlihy pillaged the countryside far and wide. No castle fortress— and at that early time in Ireland most defenses were great circular mounds, of roughhewn stone covered with turf, which surrounded stone living quarters— could withstand her assaults, for she "hit below the belt" with a vengeance, employing all sorts of magical tricks to gain her ends.

She had a passion for hunting, and her quarry were as often human beings as beasts of the wild. It is said she went about accompanied by a pack of massive, brutally savage hunting dogs of a breed no one had ever seen before that time, and never since. A thick-bodied, long-legged kind of mastiff with the rip-point fangs of a wild boar. No growl, no bark, the Ratha hounds were mute. Doubtless a breed of canine destroyer of her own magical creation. Glana made these hounds the ministers of the most inhuman cruelty. Not only did she employ them to execute her revenge upon her enemies, but she made the glens and bogs of the island from sea to sea her hunting ground, and the country people her game. But it appears that, sorceress though she was, there were times when a greater power than hers took a tormenting situation in hand.

On one occasion Glana set her hounds to worry a boy of twelve years old, whose sole offense was being the son of a swineherd who had driven his porkers across the path of Glana's retinue riding to Dungannon. The man was forthwith brought down by savaging hounds. They tore the miserable herdsman to pieces and then Glana set them upon the boy. It was regarded as a miracle, and is still talked about in the countryside as if it had happened yesterday, that the hounds refused to touch the child. Glana finally unleashed her two most ferocious dogs which she habitually kept on leash at her side, but with no greater success. Some of the hounds slunk away from the cowering boy, while the two last unleashed crept to him on their bellies and licked his hands.

Another instance is cited when Glana won her quarry in a most horrific manner. One day she and some of her ladies were bathing in a secluded pool. Two young farmers came upon them unawares. Not recognizing the tyrant

Glana in her naked state, the two youths hurled obscene remarks and invitations at her and her ladies. Leaping from the water, Glana seized a dagger from her girdle which hung across the limb of a tree beside the pool. With her own hand she cut the throat of each fellow, and seizing the gaping wound drank the gush of hot blood.

The episode of the murder of the two farmers is said to be re-enacted at a lonely pond of brackish water called Derg Pool. First appears the figure of a heroically-built naked woman, her flesh gleaming lividly in the night. Persons who have seen this apparition say that the woman leaps out of the pool, brandishing a kind of short sword, a dagger of ancient design. She makes motions as if slashing at an opponent, and her face suddenly becomes spattered with gouts of blood. Then, as if drenched in a bath of blood, the ghost of Glana O'Herlihy fades from view.

Down the years there have been recorded dire occurrences at Derg Pool. At least a dozen murders have been committed there and never once has the murderer been caught. Always the story is the same. The victim is usually a strongly-built young man of farm stock whose body will be found with his throat cut, on a morning after the full of the moon, by a poacher or a carter or drover driving cattle to the market town of Castlederg situate a few miles from the pool along this frequented highway. The body is always naked, whatever clothes the man may have worn are never found, and the peculiar lividness and shrunken appearance of the flesh is due to the fact that, in vampire case, all blood has been sucked from the body—tooth marks are found at the edges of the slashed throat.

There are countless tales of the sorceress powers of Glana. An entertaining one is that of her upsetting the plans of her daughter Aesia, who, it would seem, could no longer stomach her mother's depredations and had secretly made arrangements with some malcontent gallowglasses in Glana's employ to procure horses for herself and her tirewoman. This was successfully accomplished. At the mid of night Aesia and her tirewoman met the men-at-arms, about ten in number, in a small wood at the foot of Ratha Hill. As the escaping party thought themselves unobserved, they mounted and set off at a gallop across country, for what destination chroniclers do not say. But devious Aesia had not reckoned on the magical powers of her mother. No sooner were they mounted and away than the Lady Aesia and her escort were attacked from the air by swarms of nauseous-smelling creatures, half bat and half horned viper. The poisonous stings maddened the horses to such fury that the riders were thrown to the ground where many lay stung to death. It is said that Glana appeared to her hysterical daughter, revealed in a mass of red flames, and foully upbraided her for her treachery. By all accounts Glana later forgave Aesia, for the latter appears in history as the queen of Ranal, King of Kerry, and a prolific queen she was, for if all documents are to be believed, she bore her lord thirty children, all of them sons.

The theme of Glana appearing in flames persists throughout the references one turns up about this stupendous woman, particularly when going about her sorceries. Her battle banners, too, were flaming red. It may, of course, be because of her predilection for the colour red for her garments, and at the early times in which she purports to have lived great circular-cut mantles and capes were customary wear. Thus yards of red wool or damask beating in the wind would greatly resemble flames.

The time that I saw the ghost of Glana O'Herlihy was between the two World Wars, about 1935. I had been ranging the Nine Glens of Antrim and was driving to my house in County Kildare by way of the Lough of Neagh and Dungannon. It was a bleak night, I remember; the darkness was stygian and the wind blowing across the lough strong and perishing cold. I stopped for petrol at the small village of Arboe Cross. There was a kind of hush athwart the place, a furtive look of fear, or so it seemed to me, in the eyes of the petrol-pump attendant and a few loiterers grouped around the door of a nearby coteen. I asked if anything was seriously amiss in the village or on the highroad I would be traveling.

"There is. There's murder about," the man answered me shortly.

I noticed that he seemed disinclined to talk further, but I wanted to know more. From his covert answers to my questioning I learned that a young farmer who farmed his little hold a mile or so down the road had been found lying beside a gate on his place with his throat cut. The body was naked and his bauneen homespun garments nowhere to be found. And only the night before, the attendant told me, himself had seen the ghost of Red Glana "all wrapped in flames" standing on a knoll beside the lane along which he was bicycling to his home. I could see he had the wind up, perhaps wondering if he were marked to be the' sorceress' next victim.

I drove on, pondering many things. Tales out of the mist of time—magic and sudden death. Rounding a bend in the road I had to move at a crawl, for the road narrowed to the width of a lane and even my headlights in no way dispelled the gloom of this black night. Off to my right I suddenly saw what at first I thought was a brush fire or perhaps a tinker's camp and he cooking his supper over a fire of sticks. But the flames moved towards me as a pillar of red light. It was the figure of a tall woman, a veritable giantess, huge of thigh and breast. Her head and chin were swathed in a wimple of some gleaming red material. All about her limbs a great cloak of coarse red sacking writhed, as if a live thing, in the wind that had reached nearly tempest volume. I stopped the car, turned off my headlights, and just waited. She was now only a few yards from me. The curiously red-gold eyes set in dark caverns in a bony face seemed to blaze balefully, hot red, as was everything about the woman. What interested me most was that this ghost seemed wholly undecided as to what she was going to do. She turned this way and that, started forward, then moved backward. Then, as easily as a leaf wrested from a branch by the wind whirls away into the air, so did Glana O'Herlihy float on clouds of red mist off and away into the night.

For a long time I sat and watched what from a distance looked like a floating ball of fire. Then all was inky blackness and I was alone in a remote Tyrone glen.

Veiled Lady
in the Shuttered House

DUNBARRA HOUSE, COUNTY TIPPERARY

JUST WHEN I developed more than a passing interest in Dunbarra House I cannot remember. I do remember driving along the Clonmel road where it forks at Lannerary Tower and strikes across rolling grazing land to the noisy little market town of Cabinteely. Perhaps it was the suddenness with which the house was projected on my consciousness as I made a quick turn in the road and came upon it. This was the first time I had driven along this road since a destructive electrical storm had swept across the region. Rain, driven with tremendous force by a wind of hurricane proportions, had blasted many fine old trees. Landmark trees were gone, sheds and outbuildings of farms blown down. Scenes of destruction loomed large all about the landscape. Four or five great oak and sycamore trees in the savanna surrounding the gate-lodge of Dunbarra lay in a heap of tangled roots and branches. For the first time since its erection the bone-white walls of the many-windowed house stood starkly revealed. These foundered trees, with their dense summer foliage, had effectively screened the house from the eyes of passers-by who traveled this fairly frequented road. I had long known, of course, that there was a large house behind the semicircular screen of trees, for in bare-branch winter it stood still retired but partially revealed. The strange, altogether tragic history of the house I remembered having heard about numerous times. No

265

matter that the house was named Dunbarra, people in the neighbourhood always referred to the place as "poor Mrs. Kintullagh's house."

Five generations of the family Kintullagh had lived at Dunbarra House in succession. Amos Kintullagh started building it in 1724. He never lived to see it completed. His profligate son, Riorden Kintullagh, put the finishing touches to the house in 1793. Riorden had lived here scarcely a year when he came within an ace of losing it. In a moment of sheer brainstorm he bet his entire fortune on a horse running in the Punchestown races. The horse lost the race by yards. The news traveled quickly, and in the ensuing avalanche of creditors Riorden was all but overwhelmed. In the nick of time a rich Miss Canby from Cork appeared on his horizon. Still believing in his luck he made one more desperate cast as a sop to Fortune, in this instance personified by Miss Canby. In this chancy cast he won.

It would seem Letitia Canby tamed Riorden. Perhaps she yanked the purse strings so tight she choked his initiative. In any case Riorden Kintullagh and his rich wife, after saving the house for the family, disappear as participants in the saga. The next Kintullagh to make an imprint on the sands of time is *"The* Mrs. Kintullagh."

When I used to pass Dunbarra in the winter, the big, rather austere house always appeared to be closely shuttered. I assumed it was untenanted. The day I saw Dunbarra in a sense unmasked after the big storm, it seemed I had come face to face with the secluded house for the first time. Strangest of all was the fact that instead of the monotony of row upon row of windows tightly shuttered in solid, dark-green planks, every window was open free to the light. Each pane of glass winked pleasantly in the late-afternoon sun.

When I duly arrived for tea at my friends' house outside Cabinteely I asked if they knew whether Dunbarra House had a new tenant at last, and, if so, who it was. There were three persons in the room besides myself. Each turned and looked searchingly at me, then each flicked a glance of surprise at the others. My hostess set her cup down carefully on the table. "Why do you ask that? what makes you think Dunbarra has a new tenant?" Taken point-blank, I related as best I could how in the past hour I had driven along the road skirting the demesne wall of Dunbarra. Because the erstwhile screen of trees lay on the ground I had, for the first time, got a really good look at the house. I said, "Today was the first time all the shutters were wide open. The house looked lived-in. Even inviting."

One of the women, a Mrs. Haverly, laughed shortly. "Don't think for a minute that opened shutters necessarily mean a new tenant. Probably a caretaker airing the house, and God knows it needs it. *She*'ll walk the rooms tonight, closing the shutters, every damned last one of them."

"She?" I said. "Who will close the shutters?"

Mrs. Haverly answered, "Mrs. Kintullagh, of course."

"But," I said, "I have heard she has been dead for over thirty years."

Mrs. Haverly smiled witheringly. "What does *that* matter? Mrs. Kintullagh will *still* close the shutters."

In 1880 Danvers Kintullagh, grandson of Riorden Kintullagh, inherited Dunbarra House in the lovely County Tipperary, "The County Tip" the Irish call it with great affection and appreciation of its fertility. The best grazing for thoroughbred horses in all Ireland is to be found along the many rippling watercourses of Tipperary. Danvers was twenty-three years old when his father, heavily involved in an illicit love affair with a married English adventuress, died in a shooting accident in a Dublin club. Whether by accident or design was never proven. A doctor, and the press, said "Death by misadventure." The verdict rested exactly—there.

Danvers' tastes, unlike those of a number of his ancestors and his father in particular, were relatively quiet. His great fondness for his horses and dogs was equalled only by his love for Dunbarra and the country surrounding it. Many said that Danvers Kintullagh, despite his dark good looks and friendliness, would remain a bachelor all his life. Danvers always smiled when he heard this and said "Perhaps."

When he was thirty, Danvers went to Rome and then Vienna to ride his hunters in the two horse shows he liked best on the Continent, at the Borghese Gardens in Rome, and at Semmering in Austria.

In Vienna he met a young woman the like of whom he had never seen before. What captivated him most was her unusual background. Her mother was Irish, an O'Hanrahan from County Wicklow, while her father was Austrian, with large estates near Melk on the Danube. Danvers took a good look at Fräulein von Kürthallan; he asked her to waltz, which she did, divinely. He took another good look, and asked her to marry him.

It was not quite as easy as all that, in the long run. The hand of Rhoda von Kürthallan was far from unsought. In a short time, however, she successfully coped with a number of over-persistent suitors and retired to the seclusion of the family *schloss* at Melk to spend a quiet summer. A scant three months after Rhoda and Danvers first waltzed together at the Cavalry Club in Vienna, they were married.

The tenantry on the Dunbarra demesne were loud and strong in their approval of the new Mrs. Kintullagh. She was tall and golden-fair. She would work wonders, they prophesied, in that big, grim barracks of a house. Rhoda threw wide its doors and its many windows. Brilliant lights were placed in the chandeliers of the high-ceiled rooms. The magnificent carved swags, featuring game, fruits, and flowers, which framed the huge portrait of Amos Kintullagh in the drawing room, when properly lit showed for the first time the bewildering detail of carving. It was this carving, when it arrived from London in Riorden's day, that had caused old Mrs. Gillfoyle, the housekeeper, to tell a visitor, "It cost the master a fortune, I'll have ye know. I've heard him tell it was made by a man named Crinkling Gibbons, in London." In the grand days of Edwardian entertaining, Dunbarra House held its own with any Great House in Ireland. Long a bachelor den, it had needed only a woman's magic hand to bring out its erstwhile rich and spacious grace of living.

Life moved along serenely enough at Dunbarra House for the first ten or twelve years of Rhoda and Danvers Kintullagh's marriage. During the last decade of the nineteenth century, the social scene in Dublin and among the big country houses scattered through the Irish counties was brilliant. Big parties were given at Dunbarra, dancing parties mostly. Hunt balls always closed the winter season, and early in August when long twilights lasted until eleven o'clock, on the night before the opening of the classic Dublin Horse Show, Rhoda and Danvers always gave a garden party on the wide lawns which spread about the house. Gaily-striped marquees were set up under the sycamores in the savanna near the entrance gates. Besides friends of Rhoda and Danvers, the tenantry was invited and regularly showed up in full force, as well as the local fire department from Ballyragget. Fortunes were told by a woman from the Gypsy Claddagh, outside Galway. Gala was the word for these affairs.

Shortly before one of these garden parties—I believe the year was 1894—two of the housemaids had to be hurriedly replaced. One of the girls was leaving to marry a young farmer from Armagh. The other girl had decided to try her fortune in America. There was a great scurrying around to comb all farms and villages in the vicinity, in the hope of rounding up two girls sufficiently well trained in the ways of a big house to be able to serve on short notice. One was eventually found, a girl from Cabinteely. Brand, the butler, was ready to give up the search, which he was conducting personally, because no girl could be found to take the other vacant place.

Brand was heartened when, two days before the party, a neighbour, Mrs. Lynch, drove over to Dunbarra for lunch. She said she knew of a woman who had once worked for her but was not in service now because she had gone to live with a widowed sister-in-law on a farm back and beyond Tullaroan. "One thing I must tell you," she said to Rhoda, "the woman Rom is a dour, dark-visaged creature, silent as the grave, but I found her a good worker and, as far as I know, honest."

Brand sent for the woman, who arrived as evening was settling over Dunbarra House. As Mrs. Lynch had said, the woman was the dark, Spanish type usually tagged as "from Galway," and so she told Brand she was. She listened quietly with lowered eyes while Brand talked to her, and he felt her to be alien, of another race. After he had told her the duties expected of her and the wages she would receive, he asked her full name. The woman looked up, startled. Harshly she answered, "My name is . . . Kata . . . er . . . Katherine Rom."

Later that night, as Brand lay wakeful on his bed, planning the thousand-and-one details of the coming party, he suddenly sat bolt upright. Rom, the woman had said. "My name is Kata . . . Katherine Rom." Rom meant a gypsy, short for Romany. Kata had a dark sound. The woman was a gypsy. So—he did not like this turn of events at all.

Brand kept a careful watch on Katherine Rom after the day of the garden party. She stayed on and he was glad of her services. She did her work well and kept completely to herself. He could find no fault with her and she in turn seemed quite content at Dunbarra. The rest of the staff looked a little askance at Katherine. They all shied away oddly from using the "foreign" Kata during the first days. But soon she was accepted below stairs, not as one of themselves perhaps, but as a necessary part of the household. Months passed; everything seemed serene. Brand decided he needed a holiday. Soon he left for a month's visit to a seaside resort in Wales.

Then a change came over Katherine Rom. Instead of going about her work quietly, as had been her manner, she lazed, doing little if any work. For hours she would stand motionless in front of the big window on the landing of the front-hall stairs—hands folded across her breasts, eyes hooded, her mouth drawn down at the corners into a thin, colourless line. On looking closely one would see it was a bitter face, a terribly bitter face.

Katherine took to prowling in dark corridors. When it was her duty to light the evening lamps, they went unlit. One night Danvers Kintullagh bumped into her in the darkness of the upper corridor. He spoke sharply, telling her to light the lamps instantly, before someone fumbling in the dark had an accident. As he walked towards the stair well he heard Katherine muttering. It sounded like imprecations in a strange tongue. He turned, angrily demanding to know what she meant by such impertinence—the corridor was empty.

Danvers decided then and there to dismiss this sullen woman from Dunbarra; there was too much devious gypsy in her to suit his taste. She had had a devilish gleam—almost, he thought, of madness—in her eyes just now when he had reprimanded her about the unlit lamps. Well—he shrugged. Tomorrow she would go.

Early next morning, McKillvy, his head stable groom, came breathless into the morning room where Danvers was at breakfast. McKillvy bore the disquieting news that Tamaranda, one of the finest brood mares at the Dunbarra Stud, was coughing her life out and far gone with chills. As Danvers hurried into the hall to get his coat he saw, standing flattened against the wall, the woman he had meant to dismiss. Again he thought, she must go—but later, later. Tamaranda is more important now. But as he passed the woman something compelled him to look at her. She was regarding him with half-closed eyes from which gleamed a terrible hatred. Passion twitched at the corners of her mouth.

About twelve o'clock that morning Rhoda Kintullagh decided to go for a walk, the day being cool and fine. As she passed a door on the stair landing, she thought she heard a woman weeping. She tried the door of a small room off the landing, a room that had been built originally as a kind of minstrel gallery to accommodate a small orchestra. It was never used now, for the ventilation was poor. A few fishing rods, a croquet set, and the like of sporting odds and ends were stored there. Rhoda shook the door, but, oddly, it was locked from the inside. As she stood wondering what to do, the door was flung open and a wild, disheveled figure ran out, cut past Rhoda and raced down the stairs and out the front door. So Katherine Rom, her mind in a torment of pent-up passion, fled Dunbarra House.

For a number of years nothing more was seen or heard of her. Her clothes were put in the small trunk she had brought to Dunbarra, and it corded and set aside along with an envelope containing her wages due. After a few months, when she did not return nor send anyone to fetch her property, it was sent to the Claddagh, to Katherine's sister-in-law, who in turn said she knew nothing, nor had in years known anything, of her sister's whereabouts.

One night at dinner Danvers remarked that gypsies had set out an encampment near the Ballycooley Bridge at the southern end of his demesne. "Of course I may be wrong," he said, "but I'd lay any odds that I saw the woman Rom, who used to work for us. I stopped to look at a piebald nag one of the boys was feeding; suddenly this woman appeared, gave me the rough side of her tongue in Romany for no reason, and disappeared into one of the caravans."

Two days after this episode Danvers Kintullagh was supported home by McKillvy, late in the afternoon. As they had been crossing a small ravine near the stud farm, the footbridge had given way under their combined weight. McKillvy had saved himself by catching hold of a tree root. Danvers had fallen into the deep, rock-edged stream. He had hit his head on a rock and McKillvy said he feared there might be a slight concussion. What McKillvy did not mention at this time was that he had made a discovery as he had climbed out of the stream: somebody had recently roughly hacked through the supports of the hanging bridge. But it was not from a concussion that Danvers Kintullagh died, a week later. It was from pleurisy contracted when he fell into the icy waters of the spring freshet.

The funeral of Danvers Kintullagh was set for Saturday, allowing three days for relatives to arrive from as far away as London. During this time Rhoda kept to her room. So shattering was the suddenness of this disaster that time, for her, stood still. The morning of the funeral, her friend Mrs. Lynch went up to the darkened room to help Rhoda dress for the drive to the church. Danvers was to lie in one of the stone alcoves reserved for dead Kintullaghs of Dunbarra House at Shanahoe Church, a few miles from Ballyragget. A long cold drive over bad roads faced the widow. Progress would be slow; she must dress warmly. At the last minute before going downstairs, she put on a long black cape with a high collar, a garment so enveloping that it swept the ground. A heavy mourning veil she held in her hand. All was ready, so Mrs. Lynch went ahead to attend to some last details.

As Rhoda passed the door of the bedroom that had been Danvers', she stopped. She put her hand on the knob, and stood for a few moments thinking.

Then, brushing a hand across her eyes as if trying to banish memory forever, she pulled the long black veil over her face and slowly descended the stairs.

It was a dark raw day of fitful light and shadow. Lamps had not been lighted in the lower hall, for the entire household was driving to the church. As Rhoda stepped onto the landing midway of the stairs, she heard a sharp rustling of heavy skirts. Looking around, she was startled and amazed to see, emerging from the little room on the landing, Katherine Rom, who in a flash stood in front of her, barring the way. The woman was bareheaded and her clothes were stained and torn by thorns; some of the spiky branches trailed from her skirt. In her hands she carried a copper tub such as the maids used to bring hot water to the bedrooms. The tub was full of water, boiling hot, for clouds of steam rose in the air. With a screech incarnate of fury, the gypsy hurled the water full at Rhoda. For a moment, clutching wildly at her seared face, Rhoda stood, a pillar of hissing steam. Then, all strength deserting her, she fell to the floor insensible.

Indescribable confusion reigned; some of the people gathered in the hall below, who had witnessed the whole terrible attack, rushed into the back of the house to catch the gypsy. Others lifted Rhoda from the soaked landing where she had dropped. She was carried up to her room and laid upon the bed. A doctor was called from Tullaroan close by. Katherine Rom was caught in the cellar of Dunbarra, where she fought savagely, fantastically full of strength. Raving against her captors, the woman was carted off to Ballyragget, mad, as only those who for generations have lived on the borderline of dementia as many gypsies do, can be deranged.

The doctor, after examining Rhoda Kintullagh, said that with long and guarded nursing and expert surgical skill, there was more than an even chance she would survive. Her face would be frightfully scarred. So deep were the burns that great patches of seared and shriveled flesh came off when the heavy crepe mourning veil was unwound. To this diagnosis the doctor added that if it had not been for the thick, all-enveloping cloak which Rhoda at the moment of departure had hung across her shoulders, she would have been so horribly burned about the body that she would have died immediately, from shock if not from the actual burns.

Long months dragged by, in a stilled Dunbarra that resembled a hospital. Doctors and nurses from Dublin came and went, up and down the stairway, in and out of the hushed bedroom where Rhoda lay, inert in unconsciousness or tossing in agony. Then came the day when slowly, surely, mending of grafted tissues commenced in earnest. It took a year for Rhoda to recover sufficiently to spend a few hours a day on the sunny terrace at the back of the house with her constant friend Margaret Lynch close at hand. Later in the summer they went to Glengariff on lovely Bantry Bay. It was quiet there in the small Rose Hotel. Rhoda insisted on seclusion, for she must learn to support seclusion. Life she would live behind a thick, swathed veil. They stayed at Glengariff until the world-famous Bantry roses were beginning to fade. Then, of a sudden, a deep melancholy seemed to prostrate Rhoda. She wanted to return home immediately. "I have plans," she told Margaret Lynch, "plans for Dunbarra and for myself."

The first evening that Mrs. Kintullagh was again in residence at Dunbarra House she called Brand into the study. She sat in a wide, deep Italian chair, in front of the open window that looked out across the demesne towards the river meadows. As always these days, she was dressed in a long-sleeved, high-collared gown. Her head and face were swathed in a heavy silk veil of pale rose-colour. She told Brand she wished him to reduce the present staff. She left it to his discretion which ones were to go. From now out, for as long as she lived, life at Dunbarra would be so altered as to seem to many to be nonexistent. She would entertain no guests save Mrs. Lynch. She wished all the rooms on the lower floor of the house put in holland sheets. The morning room on the second floor and her bedroom would be all she required. If he wished to look for other employment, she would give him the highest of references. Brand told Mrs. Kintullagh everything would be done as she wished. For himself, he would remain at Dunbarra.

After Brand had left the room, Mrs. Kintullagh did a strange thing. She walked over to the fireplace at one end of the room. Above the mantle hung a full-length portrait of herself, painted in Vienna by Präler, soon after her marriage. Against a background of richly-hanging folds of ruby damask, she stood in a court gown of amber velvet. The lines of her body were long and flowing. Her highbred face was spirited, her eyes seemed alight. Under the high-dressed gold hair, the eyes looked straight at you with an expression of unforgettable magic. The veiled woman looked long at the picture. Then she walked over to a mirror hanging on the opposite wall. Carefully, for the scars on her face were still tender to the touch, she unwound the veil that concealed her face. Standing close to the mirror, she studied her reflection. For a space of minutes Rhoda stood rigid, her eyes searching every plane of her ruined face. Anyone listening might have heards sobs of anguish, though barely audible. Rewinding the veil about her face, Mrs. Kintullagh walked out of the room.

That evening, from window to window went Mrs. Kintullagh. She walked slowly through each room, closing and locking from the inside every shutter in Dunbarra House. Only in the servants' wing did she leave the windows wide to the evening light.

For sixteen years the shutters at Dunbarra House were never opened. Sometimes a tall woman was seen walking on the path beside the river, or along the driveway leading to Dunbarra from the gate-lodge. The woman never walked beyond the savanna of oaks and sycamores. She was always heavily veiled. In winter she wore a long cloak and was darkly veiled. In summer she was always dressed in white, with a sweeping sun hat veiled in light colours, the rose, violet or primrose-yellow of her favourite flowers. As far as is known, no one ever looked upon the face of Mrs. Kintullagh after she veiled it from the world and closed the shutters of her house against the chance of prying eyes. She died after seventeen years of seclusion. An eminent doctor in Dublin, discussing her extraordinary life, said, "Self-immurement, through terrifying shyness against meeting one's fellow men, can have few parallels to the case of Rhoda Kintullagh."

Brand and his wife lived at Dunbarra for a few months after Mrs. Kintullagh's death. Then they went to work for Mrs. Lynch at Castle Banner, as butler and housekeeper. An old man named Shamas Cartoe was placed at Dunbarra as caretaker. His young niece came in from a farm down the river and cooked for him at odd hours. It was this girl, Forbie Keogh, who was the first person to see the returned ghost of heavily-veiled Mrs. Kintullagh. Forbie was returning home late at night, after having spent the evening with her uncle Shamas at Dunbarra. She told of meeting a strange woman whom she never remembered having seen before, walking along the river path. As Forbie told it later, she had stood aside to let the woman pass, because she seemed to be in a great hurry to reach Dunbarra. As Forbie greeted her with the customary "Good night to ye, me lady, and God's rest," the woman passed out of sight among the trees overhanging the river bank. What impressed Forbie most were two things. The woman did not return her greeting, nor seem to notice her at all. Forbie thought it was odd that on such a sultry night the lady should be so heavily veiled.

The heir to the Dunbarra demesne, which comprised some two thousand acres of arable farms and park land immediately surrounding the house, was one James Kintullagh, a first cousin of Danvers. As James came seldom to Ireland, preferring his flat in Paris to the life of an Irish country squire, it was concluded he would sell Dunbarra as soon as possible. But when the place was put up for sale there were few bidders. Those who did come and have a look at the big white house never once came through with an offer. Dunbarra's history was too well known. Walking through the rooms left one with a feeling of discomfort. One prospective buyer remarked, "The house, inside and out, seems to exude a quality of creeping dread."

The firm of Lane, Canning, Canning, and Burke, Ltd., in Dame Street, Dublin, were executors of the estate. Someone suggested to Mr. Lane that it might be a good idea to remove the shutters from Dunbarra. It had become increasingly difficult to keep them open. Every shutter, except those in the servants' wing, had been clamped back against the wall of the house with strong iron hooks. Time and again old Shamas would laboriously open the shutters in the afternoon. Next morning every one would be closed and locked.

One night two of the garda from Tullaroan were to set to watch the house, just to make sure no prowler was playing tricks with the shutters. As so often happens to night watchers, one man slept soundly through most of the night. The other man, along about two o'clock in the morning, dozed off. He told later of being awakened suddenly by the irritating sound of a rasping hinge. He looked up at the front of the house. The shutters of one tall window in the library were slowly closing.

Standing, half-obscured, in the window of the dark room was a woman in white. Her arms reached out the window, each hand grasped a panel, and seemingly with no effort at all closed the heavy, stoutly-clamped shutters. The garda heard the lock click. Then all was silence. The astounded man leapt to his feet and looked up and down the towering façade of Dunbarra House. Each and every one of its many windows was blankly shuttered.

The house remained closed for many years. Mrs. Lynch employed a competent overseer, Daughtery Moylan, who worked the farms, and one might say the demesne prospered. But no one other than old Shamas, who, with years crowding, was "all but a push from the brink ave Purgatory" as his niece Forbie put it, would sleep a night under the roof of Dunbarra House.

Every few years a bid would be put in for the house. The executors would have the shutters opened, the high, beautifully-proportioned rooms would be aired and a few of the best pieces of furniture pulled out from under the holland sheets. But no amount of dressing-up ever captured the desired signature of a buyer, or even a tenant on let. Perhaps because of farm boys having too widely reported seeing Mrs. Kintullagh hurrying along the river path in the direction of Dunbarra, and of her rasping the shutters closed, Forbie gave the path a wide berth when going home late at night. It may well be that Mrs. Kintullagh fears that if she loiters she may be late to close the shutters at her house. For, with occasional prospective tenants "to view," she often finds them open when she arrives. That displeases her. She must hurry, for it is a long way for a woman to walk to and from Dunbarra House and the alcoved Church of St. Barnabas at Shanahoe near Ballyragget.